Scott Foresman - Addison Wesley

Daily Cumulative Review Masters

Grade 5

Scott Foresman - Addison Wesley

Editorial Offices: Glenview, Illinois • New York, New York
Sales Offices: Reading, Massachusetts • Duluth, Georgia • Glenview, Illinois
Carrollton, Texas • Menlo Park, California

http://www.sf.aw.com

Overview

Daily Cumulative Review Masters provide a continuous review of skills and concepts from Scott Foresman - Addison Wesley MATH. A Daily Review master is provided for each lesson in the Student Edition.

The first section of each master reviews a key objective from the previous lesson. The second section of each master reviews material covered two lessons prior to the current lesson. The third section provides a Mixed Review of problems from previous lessons or chapters. Lesson references are provided with each exercise in Mixed Review.

Daily Review Masters for Chapter 1 review key concepts from the previous year as well as from Chapter 1.

The *Daily Cumulative Review* format helps students solidify and retain math skills learned throughout the school year.

ISBN 0-201-36906-0

Printed in the United States of America

1 2 3 4 5 6 7 8 9 10 – PO – 03 02 01 00 99 98

Contents

Chapter 7: Fractions and Mixed Numbers

Chapter 8: Fraction Operations and Customary Linear Measurement

Chapter 9: Fractions and Multiplication

Chapter 10: Length, Perimeter, and Area

Chapter 11: Measurement

Chapter 12: Ratio, Percent, and Probability

Name ______________________________

Daily Cumulative Review

Mixed Review *(From Last Year)*

Write the word name for each number.

1. 380,109

____

2. 8,705,042

____

Estimate each sum or difference. Round to the nearest hundred.

3. 639 + 279 ________

4. 191 + 568 ________

5. 412 − 219 ________

Find each product.

6. 7×5

7. 9×2

8. 6×8

9. 4×0

10. 3×8

Classify each angle as right, acute, or obtuse.

11. ________________ **12.** ________________ **13.** ________________

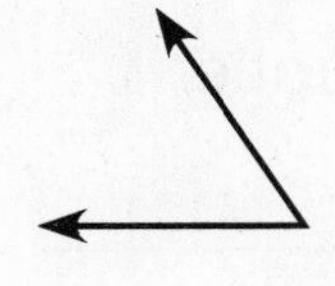

14. Thea and Chris went to the pool at 2:05 P.M. and and left at 4:28 P.M. How long were they there? ________________

15. Shaquille has 56 basketball cards in his collection. His sister Lindsey has 47 cards in her collection. How many cards do they have in all? ________________

Name ______________________________

Daily Cumulative Review

Use the graph to answer 1–3. *(Lesson 1-1)*

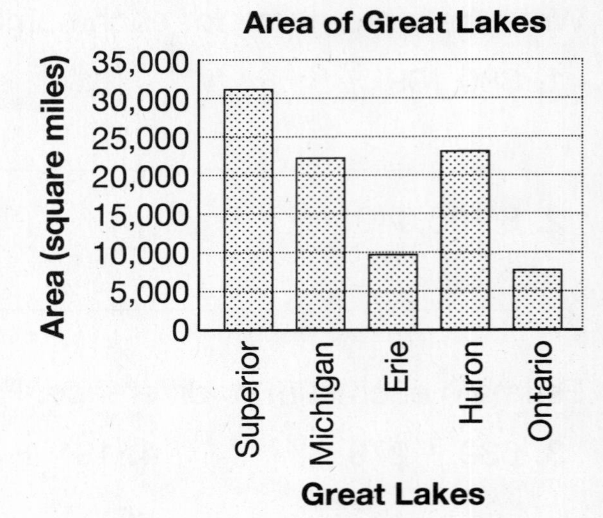

1. Which is the largest of the Great Lakes?

____

2. Which lake has an area of about 10,000 square miles?

____

3. About how many square miles is Lake Huron?

____

Mixed Review *(From Last Year)*

Compare. Write >, <, or =.

4. 735 ◯ 537 **5.** 29,803 ◯ 29,820 **6.** 5,213 ◯ 5,212

Find each sum or difference.

7. $\begin{array}{r} 83 \\ -\ 26 \\ \hline \end{array}$ **8.** $\begin{array}{r} 31 \\ +\ 47 \\ \hline \end{array}$ **9.** $\begin{array}{r} 56 \\ +\ 29 \\ \hline \end{array}$ **10.** $\begin{array}{r} 45 \\ -\ 37 \\ \hline \end{array}$

Find each quotient.

11. 14 ÷ 7 ________ **12.** 32 ÷ 8 ________ **13.** 45 ÷ 9 ________

Write a fraction for each part of the rug.

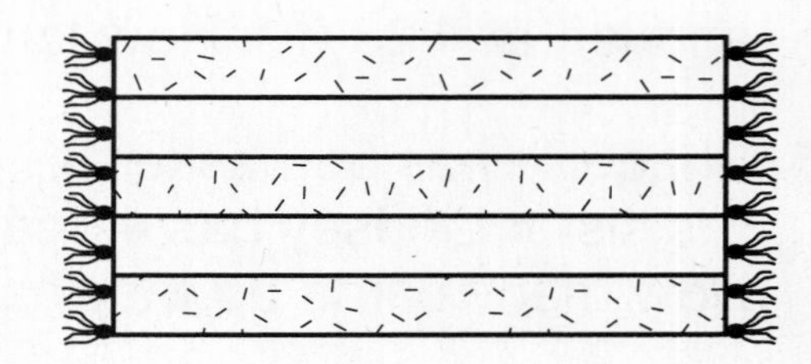

14. The part with a design. ____________

15. The plain part. ____________

16. A triangle has sides that are 36 feet, 25 feet, and 47 feet long. What is the perimeter of the triangle? ____________

Name ____________________

Daily Cumulative Review

Use the line graph to answer 1–3. *(Lesson 1-2)*

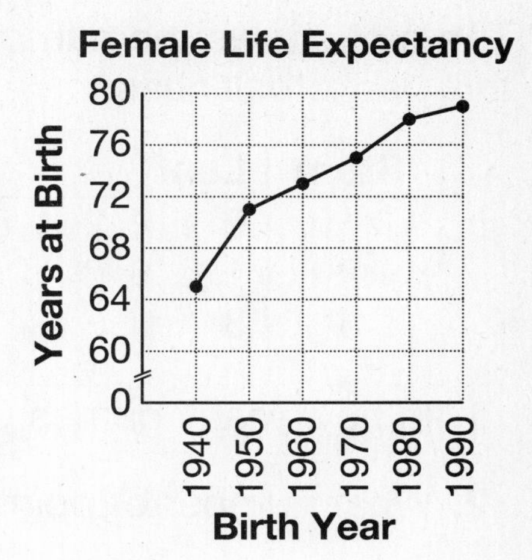

1. How many years can a female born in 1970 expect to live?

____

2. Between which two years was the increase in life expectancy the greatest?

____

3. Write the coordinates that represent the life expectancy of a girl born in 1990.

____

Use the pictograph to answer 4–6. *(Lesson 1-1)*

4. Which two eggs have the same incubation time?

____

5. Which egg will hatch in the fewest number of days? ____________

6. What is the incubation time for a chicken egg? ____________

Egg Incubation Time

Chicken	🥚🥚🥚🥚🥚🥚🥚
Goose	🥚🥚🥚🥚🥚🥚🥚🥚🥚🥚
Turkey	🥚🥚🥚🥚🥚🥚🥚🥚🥚½
Duck	🥚🥚🥚🥚🥚🥚🥚🥚🥚🥚
Pigeon	🥚🥚🥚🥚🥚🥚

🥚 = 3 days

Mixed Review *(From Last Year)*

7. $\$8.47 - 2.51$

8. $\$3.78 + 5.95$

9. $\$56.07 + 12.49$

10. $\$82.05 - 36.19$

Compare. Write >, < or =.

11. $\frac{1}{3} \bigcirc \frac{1}{6}$ **12.** $\frac{4}{5} \bigcirc \frac{2}{5}$ **13.** $\frac{3}{10} \bigcirc \frac{1}{2}$

14. A Walk-A-Thon course is 2,846 yards long. How many feet is it?

____

Name ______________________________

Daily Review
1-4

Daily Cumulative Review

Use the stem-and-leaf plot to answer 1–3. *(Lesson 1-3)*

The plot shows the number of points Jeri scored in games this basketball season.

Stem	Leaf
1	0 1 2 2 4 8 8 8 9
2	1 6 6 8
3	3

1. In how many games did Jeri score more than 20 points? ________

2. What number of points did Jeri score most often? ________

3. Jeri scored in every game she played. How many games did she play?

____

Use the line graph to answer 4–6. *(Lesson 1-2)*

The graph shows average tuition and required fees for full-time students for in-state 4-year colleges and universities in the United States.

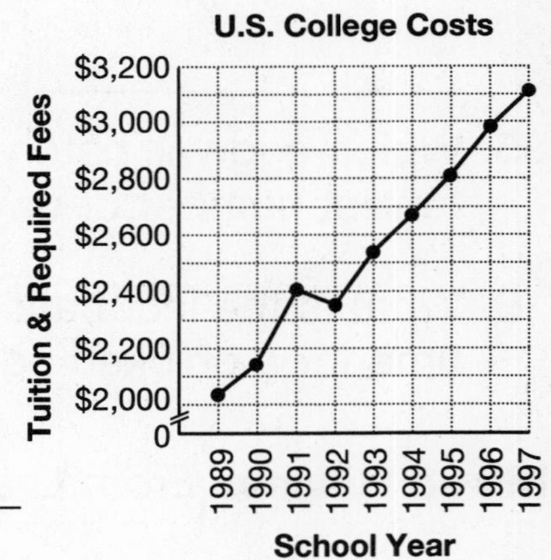

4. What has happened to tuition and required fees since 1992?

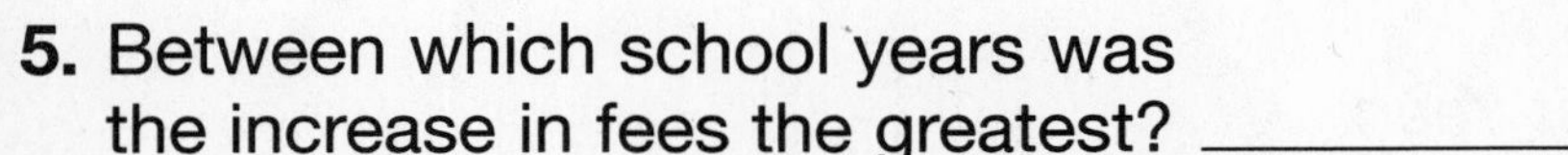

5. Between which school years was the increase in fees the greatest? ________

6. Between which years did tuition and required fees decrease? ________

Mixed Review

7. 3×20 ________ *(Gr. 4)*

8. 6×40 ________ *(Gr. 4)*

9. 8×60 ________ *(Gr. 4)*

10. *(Gr. 4)* Tina's dog had 6 puppies. Two of them had brown fur. What fraction of the puppies had brown fur? Write the fraction in simplest form. ________

Name ______________________

Daily Review 1-5

Daily Cumulative Review

Use the line plot to answer 1 and 2. *(Lesson 1-4)*

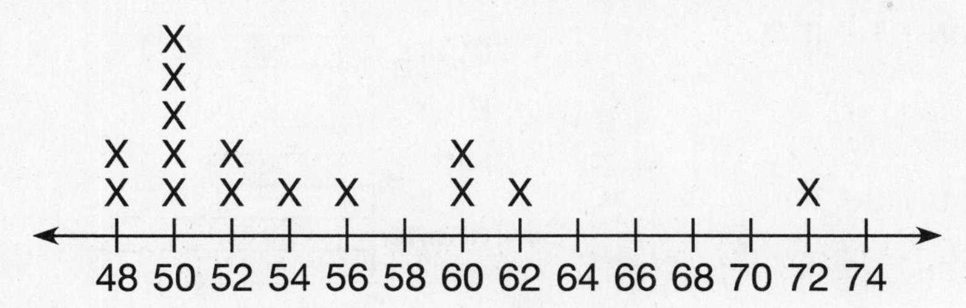

1. For the above data, give the:

a. range __________ **b.** mode __________ **c.** median __________

2. Are about half of the tallest buildings 52 stories or taller? Explain.

____

Use the stem-and-leaf plot to answer 3–5. *(Lesson 1-3)*

3. What was the difference in the smallest number of newspapers brought in for recycling and the greatest number?

____

4. What number of newspapers was recycled most often?

____

Number of Newspapers Brought for Recycling

Stem	Leaf
0	5 6 7 7 9
1	0 2 2 5 5 5
2	1 3

5. How many different bundles of newspapers were recycled? ______

Mixed Review

6. *(Gr. 4)* $\frac{1}{6} + \frac{2}{3}$ __________ **7.** *(Gr. 4)* $\frac{3}{5} - \frac{3}{10}$ __________ **8.** *(Gr. 4)* $\frac{3}{8} + \frac{1}{4}$ __________

9. *(Gr. 4)* Shari spends $\frac{1}{3}$ of her time sleeping and $\frac{1}{4}$ of her time in school. Does she spend more time sleeping or in school? __________

Name ______________________________

Daily Review 1-6

Daily Cumulative Review

Use the data in the bar graph to answer 1–2. *(Lesson 1-5)*

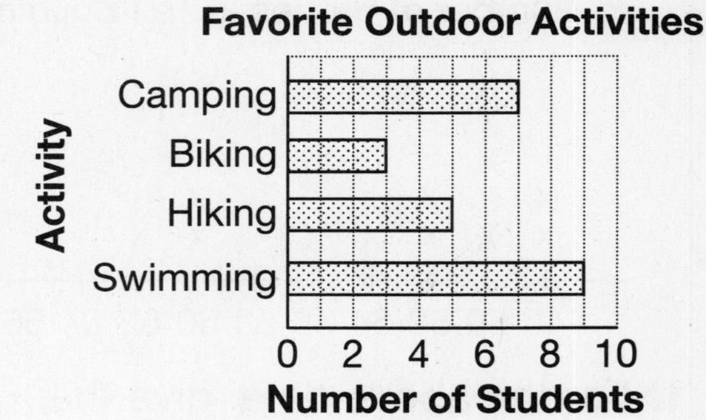

1. How many more students preferred swimming over hiking?

____

2. What operation did you use to solve the problem?

____

Find the range, median, and mode for each set of numbers in 3–4. *(Lesson 1-4)*

3. 10, 15, 10, 12, 11

a. range ________ **b.** median ________ **c.** mode ________

4. 22, 13, 20, 25, 20, 31

a. range ________ **b.** median ________ **c.** mode ________

Mixed Review

5. $4.7 + 0.16 =$ ________ *(Gr. 4)*

6. $6.4 - 3.16 =$ ________ *(Gr. 4)*

7. Order the decimals from least to greatest. 11.25, 11.2, 11.5, 11.05 *(Gr. 4)*

____

Use the line graph to answer **8–9**.

8. What was the foreign-born population trend from 1910 to 1970? *(1-2)*

____

9. What was the trend from 1970 to 1990? *(1-2)*

____

Name ______________________________

Daily Review 1-7

Daily Cumulative Review

Write the operation needed for each problem. Then solve each problem. *(Lesson 1-6)*

1. A dinner for two at the Chicken King costs $6.98. If Jim and Maria split expenses evenly, how much will each pay? ______________ ________

2. In five hours, the temperature fell from 45 degrees Fahrenheit to only 20 degrees Fahrenheit. How much did the temperature fall? ______________ ________

3. A theater sold 150 tickets at $4 each. How much did the theater receive? ______________ ________

Use any strategy to answer 4–5. *(Lesson 1-5)*

4. Rebekah had $90 in her account before she deposited $15 more. How much money is in her account now? ________

5. There are 3 feet in a yard. The I-610 Ship Channel Bridge in Houston is 210 yards long. How many feet is this? ________

Mixed Review

Use the line graph to answer **6–7**.

6. *(1-2)* During which month did the club have the most money?

____

7. *(1-2)* How much money was in the club treasury in April?

____

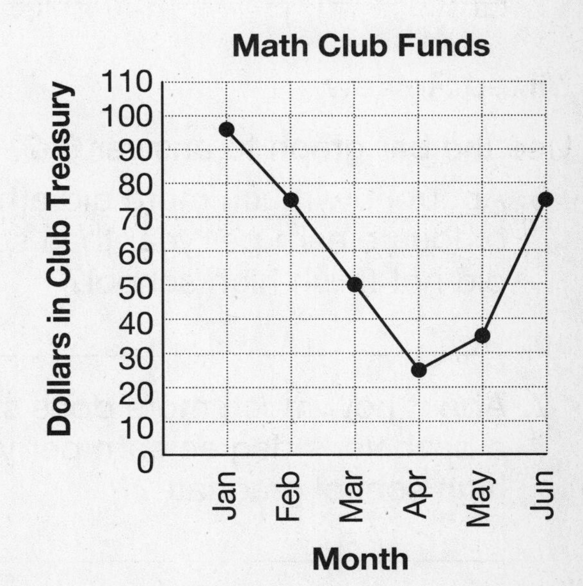

Name ______________________________

Daily Review 1-8

Daily Cumulative Review

Find the rule for each table. Give the rule using words and a variable.
(Lesson 1-7)

1.

A	B
0	0
1	3
4	12
6	18

____

____

2.

A	B
1	0
5	4
9	8
13	12

____

____

3.

A	B
1	6
4	9
8	13
10	15

____

____

Choose the operation for each problem. Then solve each problem.
(Lesson 1-6)

4. Rika has finished all but 2 of her math problems. Her teacher had assigned 15 problems. How many problems has she completed?

______________________ ______________

5. Shawn earned $3.75 an hour working for a neighbor. How much did he earn in 4 hours?

______________________ ______________

Mixed Review

Use the bar graph to answer **6–7**.

6. *(1-1)* About how much more did a high school graduate earn per year than someone who did not finish high school?

____

7. *(1-1)* About how much more does someone with a bachelor's degree earn per year than a high school graduate?

____

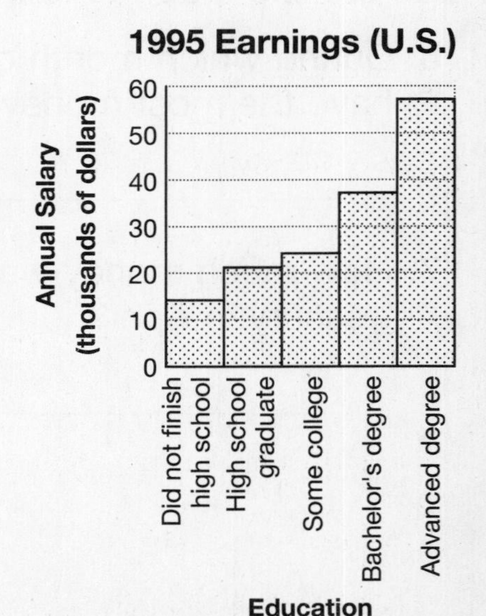

Name ____________________

Daily Review 1-9

Daily Cumulative Review

Choose a scale and make a bar graph of the data in the table.
(Lesson 1-8)

Normal Annual Precipitation to Nearest Inch			
Barrow, AK	5	Houston, TX	46
Phoenix, AZ	8	Duluth, MN	30

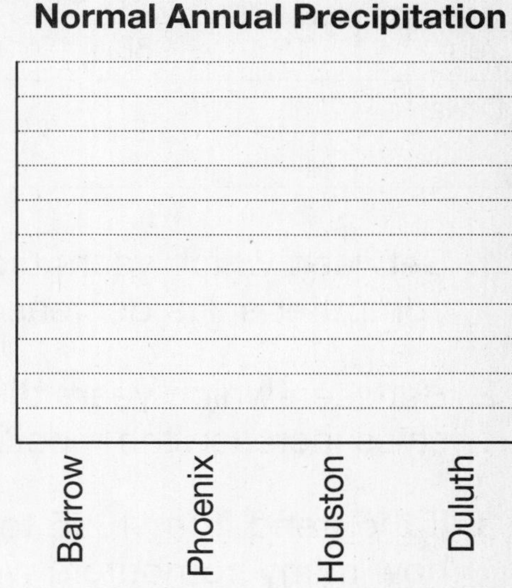

1. What scale did you use?

____

2. What is the range of the data?

____

Find the rule for each table. Give the rule using words and a variable.
(Lesson 1-7)

3.

A	B
15	3
20	4
25	5
30	6

____

____

4.

A	B
6	4
9	7
12	10
15	13

____

____

5.

A	B
3	7
7	11
11	15
15	19

____

____

Mixed Review

The stem-and-leaf plot shows the minutes Kim spent practicing her flute each day.

Use the plot to answer **6–7**.

Stem	Leaf
2	5 5 7
3	0 0 2 5
3	5

6. *(1-3)* What is the least amount of time Kim practiced? ____________

7. *(1-3)* How many days did she practice? ____________

Name ____________________

Daily Cumulative Review

Use this table to make a line graph. *(Lesson 1-9)*

United States Computer Sales

Year	1987	1988	1989	1990	1991	1992	1993	1994	1995	1996
Dollars (Millions)	3.1	3.5	3.9	4.0	3.9	4.9	5.9	6.7	8.4	9.4

1. Between which years did computer sales decrease? ____________

2. Between which years did sales increase the most? ____________

3. If the trend from 1995 to 1996 continued, how many computers were sold in 1997?

____

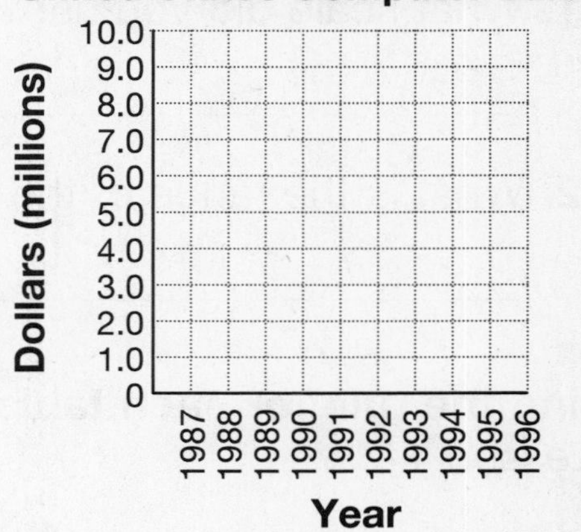

Use the graph to answer 4–5. *(Lesson 1-8)*

4. What is the scale on the graph?

____

5. What would make the graph easier to read?

____

____

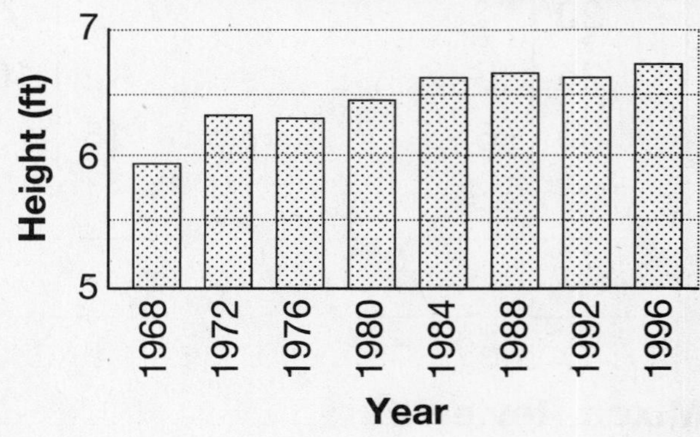

Mixed Review

6. Use the line plot to give the
(1-4)

a. range ________

b. mode ________

c. median ________

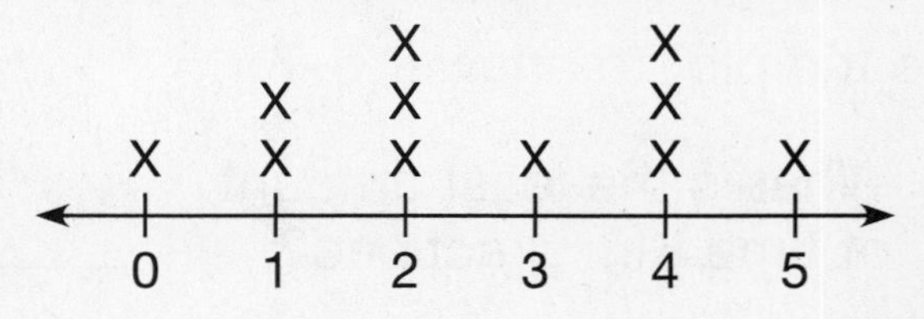

Name ____________________

Daily Review
1-11

Daily Cumulative Review

Make a stem-and-leaf plot for the height data. *(Lesson 1-10)*

Heights of Vollyball Team Members (inches)				
57	59	64	61	59
59	60	58	57	62
60	65	59	61	59

Stem	Leaf

1. What is the most common height on the volleyball team? ________

2. What is the median height on the team? ________

Use the table to answer 3–4. (Hint: Make a line graph.) *(Lesson 1-9)*

Number of Teams in the NBA			
Year	Teams	Year	Teams
1960	8	1980	22
1970	14	1990	27

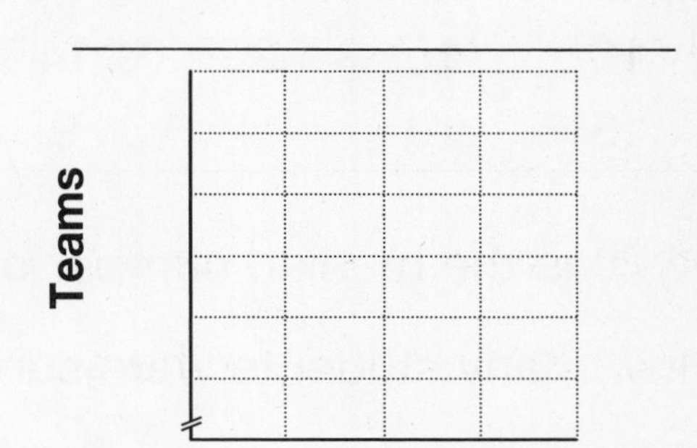

3. How many teams were in the NBA in 1970? ________

4. What trend does the data show? ________

Mixed Review

5. *(1-7)* Complete the table. Write its rule using a variable.

A	5	10	15	20	25	30
B	7	12	17			

Rule: ________

6. *(1-5)* Marc bought 3 gallons of gasoline for his lawn mower. The gas cost $1.09 per gallon. How much did Marc pay for the gasoline?

____

Name ________________________________

Daily Review 2-1

Daily Cumulative Review

Use any strategy to solve each problem. *(Lesson 1-11)*

1. At a clearance sale, shorts cost $9 each and shirts cost $15 each. How many shorts and shirts did Julie buy if she spent $63?

____

2. Angela has 35 cents in dimes and nickels. She has more nickels than dimes. How many nickels and dimes does she have?

____

Make a stem-and-leaf plot for the distance data. *(Lesson 1-10)*

3.

Miles to School			
6	9	5	15
12	15	20	14
15	10	4	9

Stem	Leaf

4. What is the median number of miles? ____________

5. How many students were surveyed? ____________

Mixed Review

6. *(1-5)* Lee and his sister bought a computer game for $89. His sister paid $46. How much did Lee pay? ____________

Use the bar graph to answer **7–9**.

7. *(1-1)* How many people lived in Los Angeles County in 1996? ____________

8. *(1-1)* How many people lived in Orange County, CA, in 1996? ____________

9. *(1-1)* About how many more people lived in Cook County than in Harris County in 1996?

____

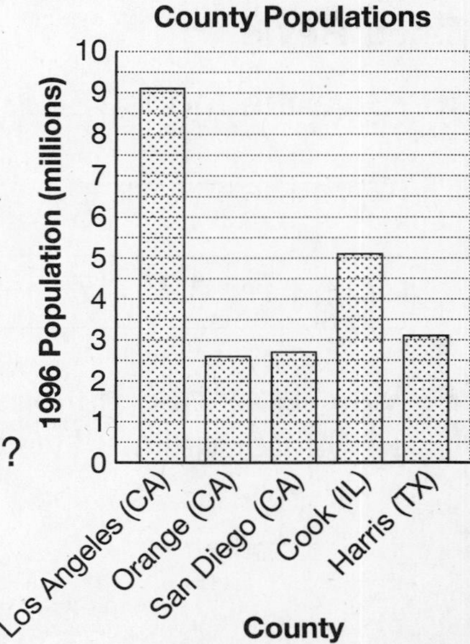

Name ______________________

Daily Review 2-2

Daily Cumulative Review

Use patterns to answer 1–2. *(Lesson 2-1)*

1. If a textbook has 500 pages, how many pages are in:

a. 10 textbooks? ________ **b.** 20 textbooks? ________

c. 200 textbooks? ________ **d.** 2,000 textbooks? ________

2. If you had one million dollars in $100 bills, how many $100 bills would you have? ________

Use logical reasoning to solve. *(Lesson 1-11)*

3. Connor, Emily, Caroline, and Andy are Mrs. Martin's children. Emily is the oldest daughter and Caroline is the youngest child. The names of her two youngest children start with the same letter of the alphabet. Her oldest child is not a girl. In what order were Mrs. Martin's children born?

____

Mixed Review

4. Write the rule using a variable: a number less 5.6 ________
(1-7)

Use the line plot to answer **5–8**.

Service Calls Per Day

Day	0	1	2	3	4	5	6	7	8
Marks		X		XX		XXX	X		XX

Day

5. Give the range. ________
(1-4)

6. Give the mode. ________
(1-4)

7. Give the median. ________
(1-4)

8. How many days had fewer than 5 service calls? ________
(1-4)

9. Jeffrey earns $90 each week for mowing lawns. How much will he earn for mowing in 3 weeks? ________
(1-6)

Name ______________________________

Daily Cumulative Review

Write each number in word form. *(Lesson 2-2)*

1. 2,030,005 ______________________________

2. 87,000,540 ______________________________

Use a calculator to answer 3 and 4. *(Lesson 2-1)*

3. 1 mile = 5,280 feet. About how many miles would be in one million feet? ____________

4. If Mr. Miser hid $1,000 in his mattress every month of his daughter's life, how old would she be when the mattress contained one million dollars? ____________

Mixed Review

Use the line graph to answer **5** and **6**.

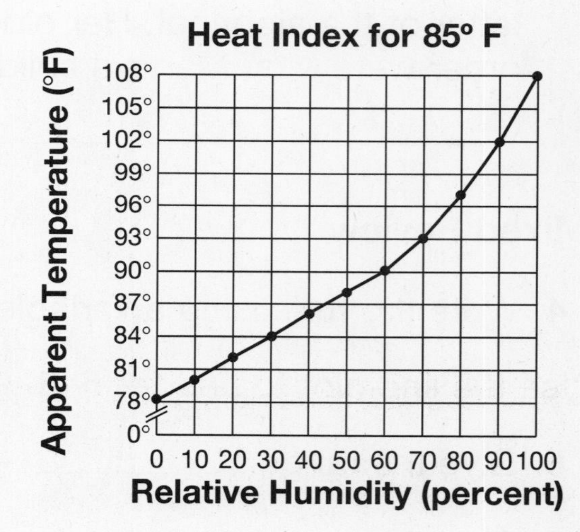

5. *(1-2)* If the relative humidity is 60%, how hot does 85°F feel?

____

6. *(1-2)* What is the relative humidity if the air temperature is 85°F but it feels like 93°F?

____

Use the bar graph to answer **7** and **8**.

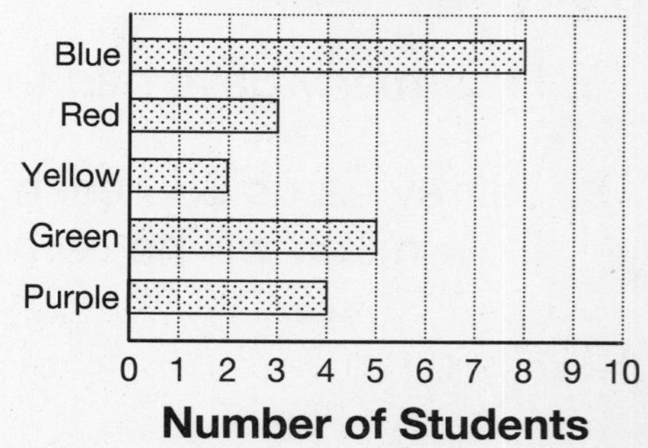

7. *(1-5)* How many students preferred blue or green? ____________

8. *(1-5)* After the survey, 6 students changed their favorite color. How many did not? ____________

Name ______________________

Daily Review
2-4

Daily Cumulative Review

Write each number using exponents. *(Lesson 2-3)*

1. 10,000 ________

2. 10,000,000 ________

3. 10 × 10 × 10 × 10 × 10 ________

4. 10 × 10 × 10 ________

Write each number in standard form. *(Lesson 2-2)*

5. Ten million, three hundred five thousand, six ________

6. Five hundred thirty million, forty-five thousand, two hundred

____

7. 60,000,000 + 50,000 + 300 + 70 ________

Mixed Review

8. *(1-11)* Robbie, Jetta, Anna, and Kara are best friends. In a spelling bee, they won the top 4 prizes. Jetta did not win fourth prize. Anna placed just above Jetta. Kara placed just under Robbi. In what order, from first to fourth, did the four friends place?

____

Use the stem-and-leaf plot to answer each question.

Minutes of Long Distance Calls

Stem	Leaf
0	5 6 6 6
1	0 0 2 7
2	1 4 8
3	3

9. *(1-3)* How many long distance calls were made?

____

10. *(1-3)* What was the median length of the calls?

____

11. *(1-3)* What was the range of the length of the calls?

____

12. *(1-3)* Rose made the longest call. How long did she talk?

____

Name ______________________________

Daily Cumulative Review

Write each number in standard form. *(Lesson 2-4)*

1. Six hundred fifty billion, seven million ______________

2. Ten billion, five hundred thousand, thirty ______________

3. Three billion, three hundred thousand, two ______________

Insert the missing exponent. *(Lesson 2-3)*

4. $10^{\square} = 100$

5. $10^{\square} = 10{,}000{,}000$

6. $10^{\square} = 1{,}000{,}000{,}000$

7. $10^{\square} = 10{,}000$

Mixed Review

8. Make a line graph. Use the data in the table.
(1-9)

Attendance at the Spring Festival	
1996	250
1997	325
1998	275

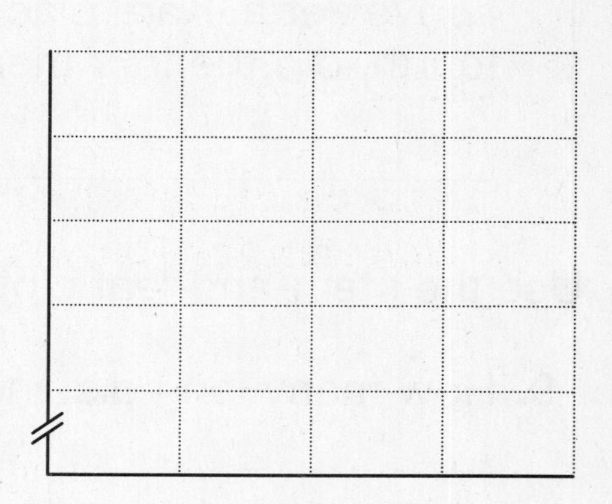

9. Complete the table. Write its rule using a variable.
(1-7)

A	2	6	8	10	16	18
B	1	3	4			

Rule: ______________

Name ____________________

Daily Cumulative Review

Write >, <, or = to complete. *(Lesson 2-5)*

1. 647,900 ◯ 674,200

2. 10,510 ◯ 10,501

3. Twelve thousand ◯ 1,200

4. 85,678 ◯ sixty thousand

5. Four million, one hundred ◯ 4,000,100

Complete. *(Lesson 2-4)*

6. 260,030,515 = two hundred sixty __________, thirty __________,

five __________ fifteen

7. 800,080,008 = eight __________, eighty __________, eight

8. How many 1,000s in 500,000? __________

9. How many 100s in 80,000? __________

Mixed Review

10. *(1-8)* Choose a scale and make a horizontal bar graph of the data in the table.

Source of Reference Material for Reports	
Encyclopedia	18
Dictionary	8
Internet	4
Magazine	12

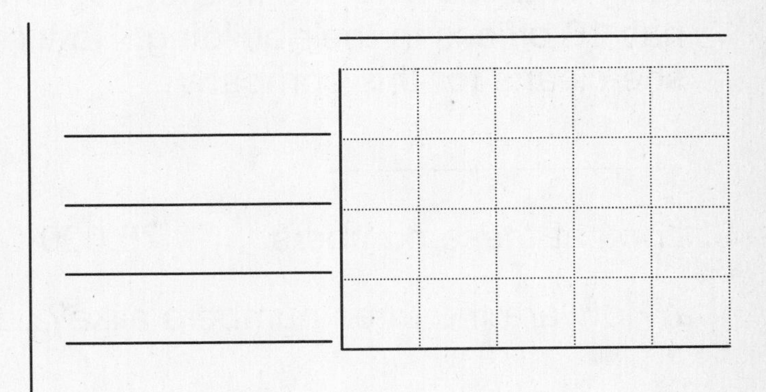

11. *(2-1)* What is the value in dollars of 500,000 dimes? __________

12. *(2-3)* Complete. __________ × 100 = 650,000

Name ______________________

Daily Review
2-7

Daily Cumulative Review

Round to the nearest hundred thousand. *(Lesson 2-6)*

1. 6,452,371 ____________ **2.** 479,200 ____________

3. 57,200 ____________ **4.** 39,749,098 ____________

Order the numbers from least to greatest. *(Lesson 2-5)*

5. 734,261 743,425 697,998 699,035

____

6. 1,643,000 1,570,000 2,090,117 2,087,200

____

Mixed Review

7. *(1-11)* A store owner anticipates needing 2 salespeople for every 5 aisles of merchandise during a sale. There are 20 aisles in the store. How many sales people should he schedule to work during the sale?

____

8. *(1-5)* Mary charges $6 per office for vacuuming and dusting. A company has 16 offices in their building. How much does Mary earn each time she cleans for this company?

____

9. *(2-2)* Look at these numbers. 76,000 4,006,000 506,000

a. How are the three numbers alike? ____________

____

b. How are the three numbers different? ____________

____

c. Write each number in word form. ____________

____

Name ______________________

Daily Review
2-8

Daily Cumulative Review

Write each decimal shown. *(Lesson 2-7)*

1. ______________

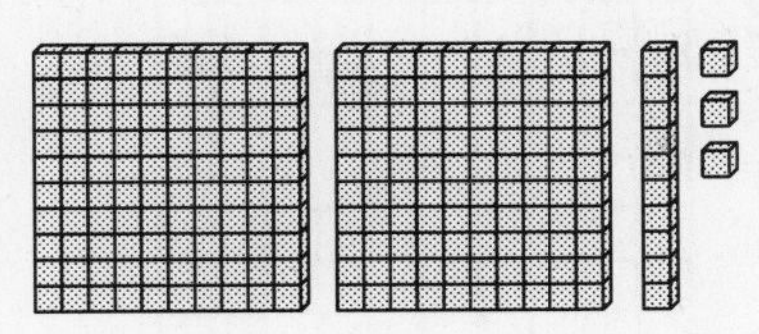

2. ______________

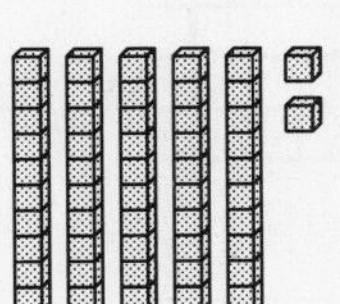

Use the table to answer 3 and 4. *(Lesson 2-6)*

3. Which airport had passenger arrivals and departures closest to 40,000,000?

____

4. Which two airports had the same number of passenger arrivals and departures if rounded to the nearest 100,000?

____

Traffic at U.S. Airports, 1996	
Airport	**Passenger Arrivals and Departures**
Chicago-O'Hare	69,133,189
Atlanta	63,344,730
Dallas/Ft. Worth	58,034,503
Los Angeles	57,974,559
San Francisco	39,247,308
Miami	33,504,579

Mixed Review

5. How many 10,000s make 1,000,000?
(2-3)

____

6. Find the range, mode, and median for 18, 19, 16, 10, 19.
(1-4)

range: __________ mode: __________ median: __________

7. David had 34 stuffed animals. He needed more space in his room so he gave Gayle 19 of them. How many stuffed animals does David have now? ______________
(1-6)

Name ______________________

Daily Review 2-9

Daily Cumulative Review

Write two decimals that name each shaded part. *(Lesson 2-8)*

1. 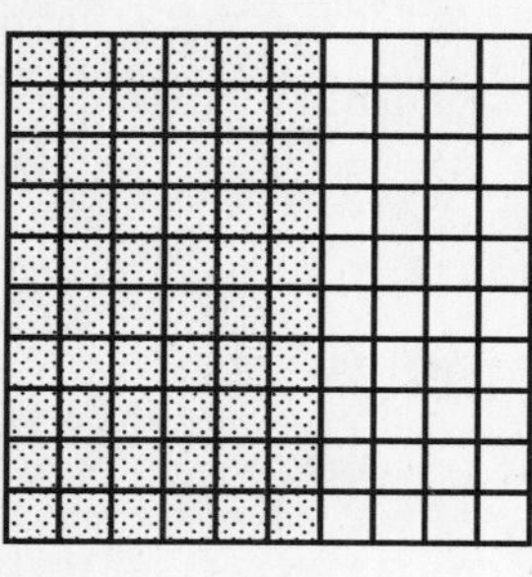
______

2. 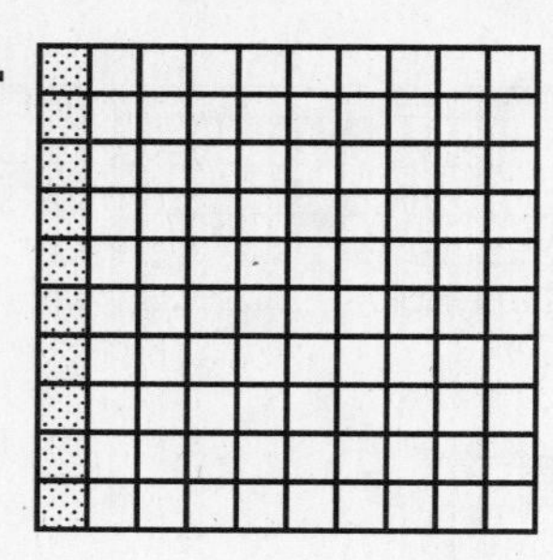
______

3. 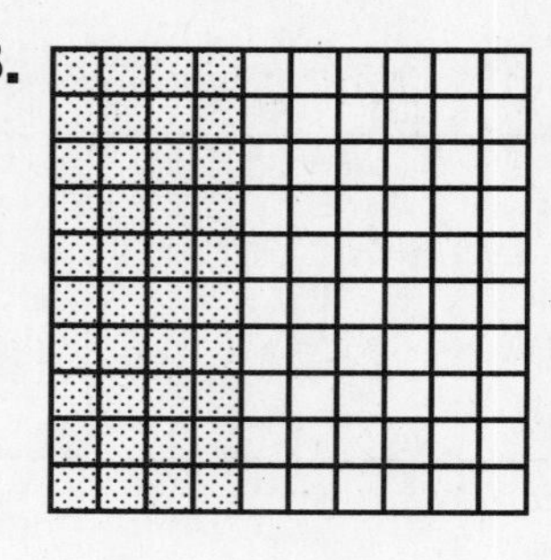
______

Write each number in decimal form. *(Lesson 2-7)*

4. 5 hundredths ______ **5.** 6 tenths ______ **6.** 7 ______

7. one and forty hundredths ______

Mixed Review

Write the place-value position for each digit of 10,793,258,000.

8. 2 ______ *(2-4)* **9.** 9 ______ *(2-4)*

10. 8 ______ *(2-4)* **11.** 7 ______ *(2-4)*

12. 1 ______ *(2-4)* **13.** 5 ______ *(2-4)*

14. *(2-1)* A spring flows at a rate of 75 gallons per minute. About how many hours does it take to produce 1,000,000 gallons?

______

15. *(1-10)* Make a stem-and-leaf plot for the fund-raiser data.

Gift Wrap Sets Sold for Fund-Raiser			
12	2	6	15
21	14	15	4
26	18	11	15
8	12	14	15

Stem	Leaf

Name ___________________________

Daily Review
2-10

Daily Cumulative Review

Write each number in decimal form. *(Lesson 2-9)*

1. 6 hundredths ________ **2.** 6 ________ **3.** 6 thousandths ________

4. four and five thousandths ________ **5.** seven and sixty thousandths ________

Write each as an equivalent decimal using hundredths. *(Lesson 2-8)*

6. 0.3 ________ **7.** 0.1 ________ **8.** 0.7 ________ **9.** 4 ________

Mixed Review

Write >, <, or = to complete.

10. *(2-5)* 400,512 ◯ 400,152

11. *(2-5)* 101,609 ◯ 101,906

12. *(2-3)* A number has a 4 in the hundredths place. You multiply it by 10. Where will the 4 be in the product?

____

13. *(1-11)* Elise, Felicia, Luke, and Heather have started a band, but they are having problems. The drummer and her trumpet-playing brother have to practice outside because of the noise. The drummer and keyboard players names are each 7 letters and too long for their name tags. Heather does not play the keyboard. Which instrument does each band member play if the fourth instrument is a guitar?

____

____

Name ____________________

Daily Cumulative Review

Complete the number line. *(Lesson 2-10)*

1.

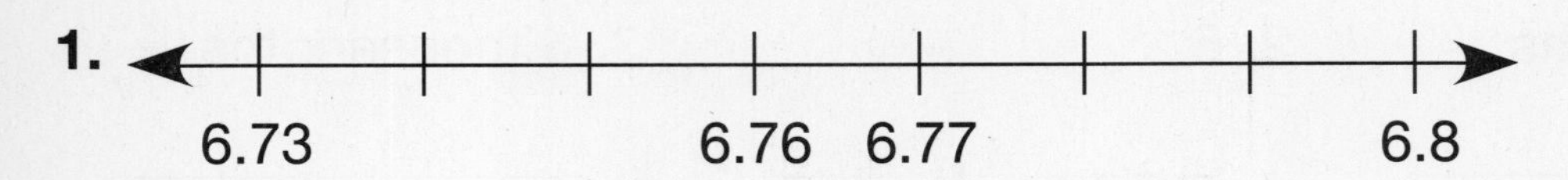

2. Name two numbers between 6.75 and 6.8.

____

Write each number in decimal form. *(Lesson 2-9)*

3. two and three hundred sixty thousandths ____________

4. nine and seventy-five thousandths ____________

Mixed Review

5. *(1-9)* Use the table to make a line graph.

Year	1990	1991	1992	1993	1994	1995	1996
Wins	19	22	25	18	20	24	23

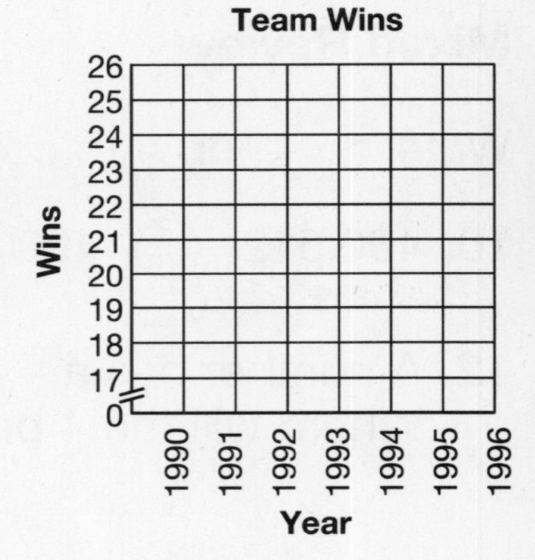

6. *(1-9)* Between which years shown on the graph did the number of wins decrease?

____

7. *(2-2)* Write in word form: 370,105,246 ____________________

____

8. *(2-4)* Write in standard form: four hundred twenty-eight billion, sixty million, three hundred thousand

____

9. *(2-1)* A roll of pennies holds 100 pennies. How many pennies are in 10,000 rolls?

____

Name ______________________________

Daily Cumulative Review

Write >, <, or = to complete. *(Lesson 2-11)*

1. 3.05 ◯ 3.50 **2.** 0.7 ◯ 0.70 **3.** 1.5 ◯ 1.09

4. 6.15 ◯ 6.25 **5.** 9.90 ◯ 8.90 **6.** 2.1 ◯ 2.10

Use the number line shown to answer 7–8. *(Lesson 2-10)*

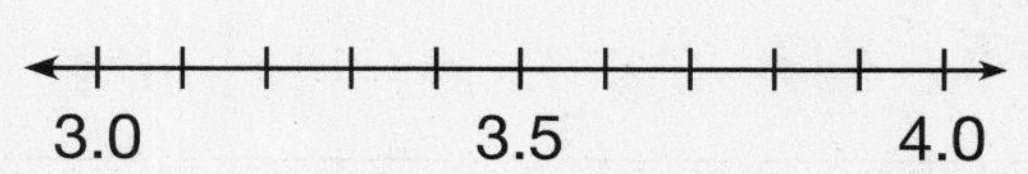

7. Name two numbers between 3.1 and 3.6. ____________________

8. Name two numbers between 3.6 and 4.0. ____________________

Mixed Review

9. *(1-6)* If there are an average of 250 words on one typewritten page, how many words are on 12 typewritten pages?

____

10. *(1-8)* Why is a graph with a scale of 10 easier to read than a graph with a scale of 25?

____

____

Write each number in decimal form.

11. *(2-7)* three and sixty hundredths ____________

12. *(2-7)* four and four hundredths ____________

13. *(2-7)* five tenths ____________

Write each number in standard form.

14. *(2-4)* three billion, fifty million ____________

15. *(2-4)* forty billion, seven hundred thousand ____________

16. *(2-4)* two billion, six hundred ____________

Name ______________________________

Daily Review 2-13

Daily Cumulative Review

Round each number to the place of the underlined digit. *(Lesson 2-12)*

1. 2.945 ________ **2.** 3.05 ________ **3.** 4.497 ________

4. 9.706 ________ **5.** 6.052 ________ **6.** 0.749 ________

Use the table to answer 7–9. *(Lesson 2-11)*

7. Which player had the highest free throw percentage?

____

8. Which of these players had the lowest free throw percentage?

____

9. Order the players from highest to lowest free throw percentage. ______________________________

1996–1997 NBA Free Throw Leaders

Player	Team	Free Throw Percentage
Elie	Houston	0.896
Brandon	Cleveland	0.902
Hornacek	Utah	0.899
Pierce	Denver/Charlotte	0.897
Price	Golden State	0.906

Mixed Review

Write two decimals that name each shaded part.

10. ________ *(2-8)*

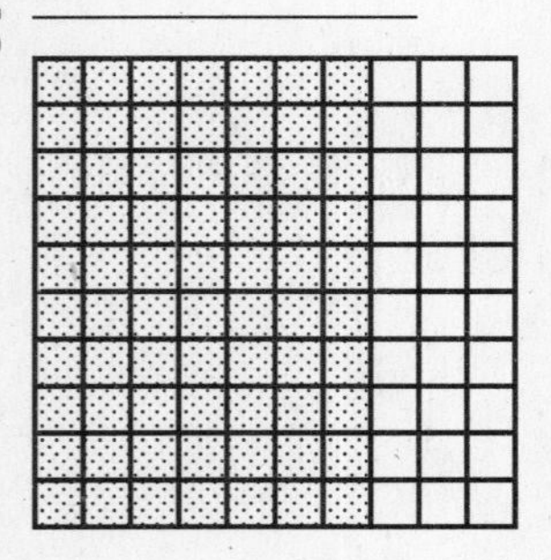

11. ________ *(2-8)*

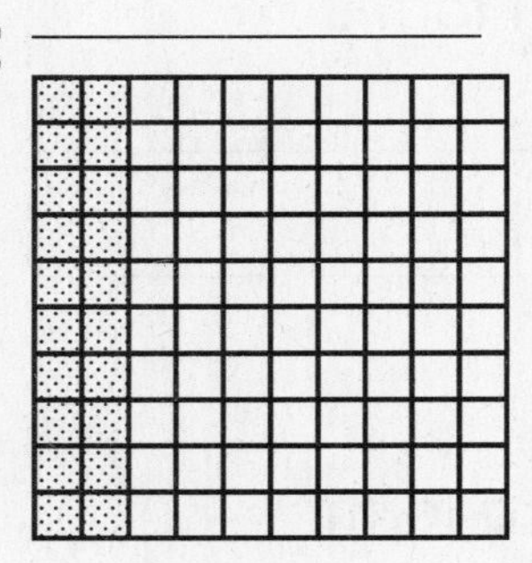

12. ________ *(2-8)*

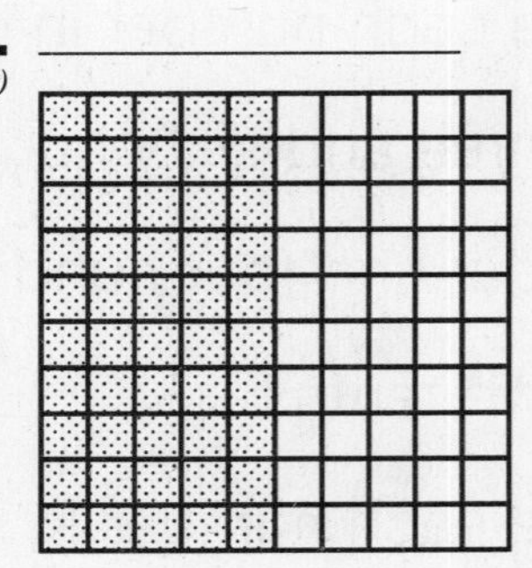

13. *(2-6)* What is the greatest number that rounds to 140,000,000 when rounded to the nearest ten million?

____

Name ______________________

Daily Cumulative Review

Draw a picture to solve. *(Lesson 2-13)*

1. Mike's mother agreed to give rides home to Davis, Neal, and Luis after basketball practice. From the school, she drove 3 miles east to Neal's house. Then she drove 1 mile west and 5 miles south to Davis' house. Then she drove 2 miles west to Luis' house. From there, she drove north 4 miles home.

a. How far did Mike's mother drive? ____________

b. How far is Mike's house from the school and in what direction? ______________________

c. How far does Luis live from Davis and in what direction? ______________________

Round each number to the place of the underlined digit. *(Lesson 2-12)*

2. 2.<u>4</u>61 ________ **3.** 7.<u>0</u>36 ________ **4.** 5.0<u>2</u>7 ________ **5.** 0.<u>0</u>13 ________

Mixed Review

6. Order these numbers from least to greatest.
(2-5) 13,907,021 13,097,037 14,011,237 14,101,542

____

7. Make a stem-and-leaf plot for the data in the table.
(1-10)

Letters in Last Name					
4	6	4	8	8	10
9	10	5	6	5	8

Stem	Leaf

8. What is the mode of the data in **7**? ________
(1-10)

9. What is the median the data in **7**? ________
(1-10)

Using the digits 0, 1, 3, and 9, write

10. the greatest decimal possible, in thousandths. ____. ____ ____ ____
(2-9)

11. the least decimal possible, in thousandths. ____. ____ ____ ____
(2-9)

Name ______________________________

Daily Cumulative Review

Estimate each sum or difference. *(Lesson 2-14)*

1. 741 + 32

2. 497 + 812

3. 377 − 102

4. \$11.93 − 2.55

Draw a picture or use another strategy to solve. *(Lesson 2-13)*

5. Antonio lifts weights every 5 days. He swims every 3 days. If he lifted weights and swam on October 6, what is the next date he will do both exercises?

____

6. Sergio, David, Jon, and William live on the same street. William lives west of the others. Jon lives east of Sergio and west of David. In what order do the boys live from west to east?

____

Mixed Review

Round to the nearest hundred thousand.

7. 6,781,532 ____________ *(2-6)*

8. 97,499 ____________ *(2-6)*

9. Write in word form: 40,061,020 *(2-2)*

____

Write =, <, or > to complete.

10. 0.50 ◯ 0.5 *(2-8)*

11. 2.30 ◯ 23.0 *(2-8)*

12. 0.70 ◯ 0.07 *(2-8)*

13. Draw place-value blocks to show the decimal 1.37. *(2-7)*

Name ______________________________

Daily Review 2-16

Daily Cumulative Review

Find each sum or difference. Then estimate to check your answer. *(Lesson 2-15)*

1. $\begin{array}{r} 237 \\ +\ 356 \\ \hline \end{array}$ **2.** $\begin{array}{r} 680 \\ +\ 928 \\ \hline \end{array}$ **3.** $\begin{array}{r} 1{,}937 \\ -\ 458 \\ \hline \end{array}$ **4.** $\begin{array}{r} 416 \\ -\ 273 \\ \hline \end{array}$

Estimate. Write >, <, or = to complete. *(Lesson 2-14)*

5. 87 + 42 ◯ 120

6. $6.99 − $3.00 ◯ $4

7. 21 + 32 + 61 ◯ 110

8. $89 − $12 ◯ $70

Mixed Review

9. Name the number shown by each letter.
(2-10)

A ________ *B* ________

C ________ *D* ________

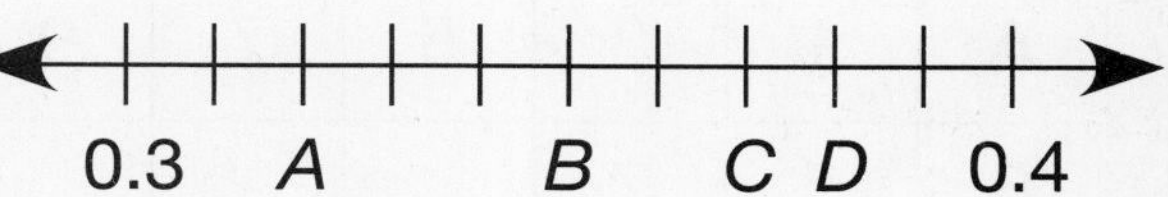
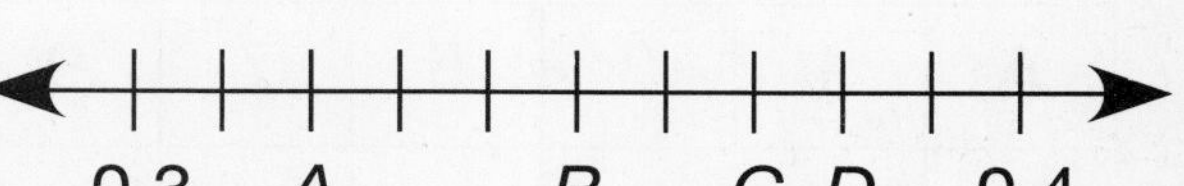

Write each number using exponents.

10. 100,000 ________ *(2-3)*

11. 1,000,000 ________ *(2-3)*

12. 100 ________ *(2-3)*

Use the line graph to answer the questions.

13. What does this line graph show?
(1-2)

____

____

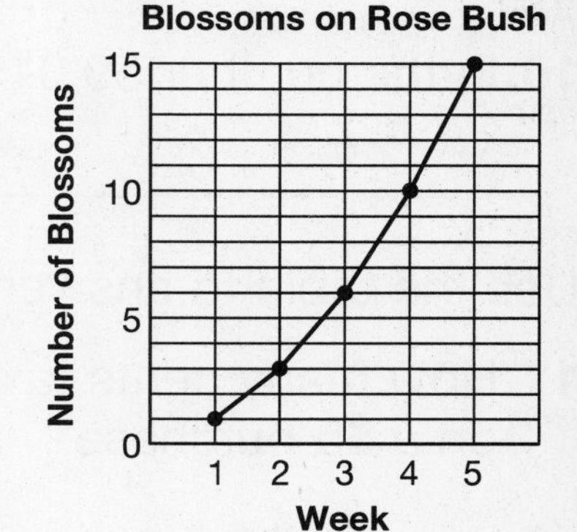

14. How many blossoms were on the plant in the 4th week? ________
(1-2)

15. What does the ordered pair (2, 3) stand for?
(1-2)

____

Name ____________________

Daily Review
2-17

Daily Cumulative Review

Use place-value blocks to add or subtract. *(Lesson 2-16)*

1. 0.3 7
+ 0.6 1

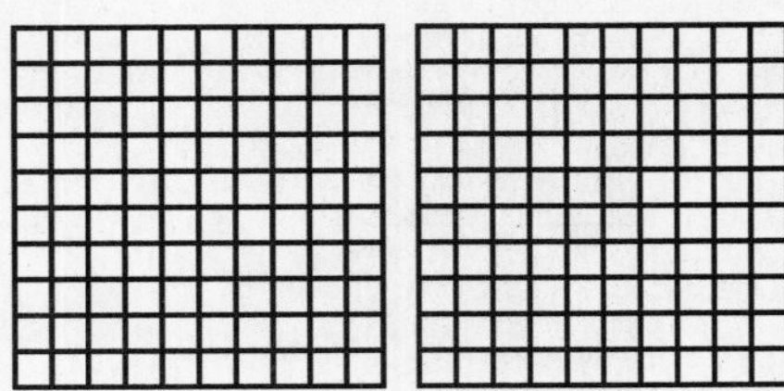

2. 0.6 4
− 0.4 6

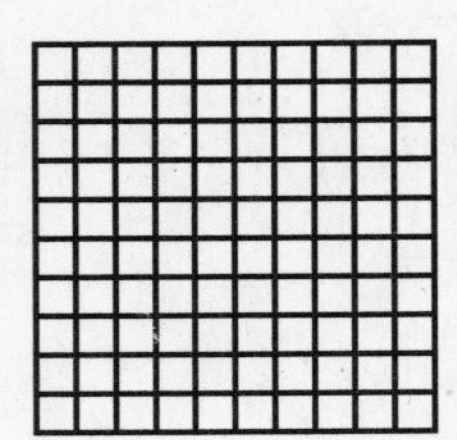

Find each sum or difference. Then estimate to check your answer. *(Lesson 2-15)*

3. 127 + 398 + 35 + 137 = ____________

4. 15,261 − 4,982 = ____________ **5.** 6,000 − 366 = ____________

Mixed Review

6. Complete the table. Write its rule using a variable.
(1-7)

A	1	3	5	7	9
B	5	7			

Rule: ____________

Write each number in decimal form.

7. five and thirty-six thousandths ____________
(2-9)

8. eight and four hundredths ____________
(2-9)

9. six and one hundred seven thousandths ____________
(2-9)

10. In the number 59,015,576,428, give the place value of each 5.
(2-4)

____

Use the table to answer the questions.

11. How many cents tax is there on a $5 purchase? ____________
(2-12)

12. What is the tax on a $15 item? ____________
(2-12)

Sales Tax Rate at 6.135%	
Subtotal	**Tax**
$5	0.30675
$10	0.6135
$15	0.92025

Name ______________________________

Daily Review 2-18

Daily Cumulative Review

Find each sum. *(Lesson 2-17)*

1. $\begin{array}{r} 1.83 \\ +\ 0.98 \\ \hline \end{array}$ **2.** $\begin{array}{r} 6.07 \\ +\ 2.19 \\ \hline \end{array}$ **3.** $\begin{array}{r} 2.16 \\ +\ 7.30 \\ \hline \end{array}$ **4.** $\begin{array}{r} 7.29 \\ +\ 1.05 \\ \hline \end{array}$ **5.** $\begin{array}{r} 6.00 \\ +\ 2.79 \\ \hline \end{array}$

Complete. Use place-value blocks or drawings to help you.
(Lesson 2-16)

6. 1.83 + ______ = 4.32

7. 4.21 + 3.09 = ______

8. 8.20 − ______ = 3.42

9. 6.1 − ______ = 5.3

Mixed Review

Shade in the grids to show each decimal.

10. 0.36
(2-7)

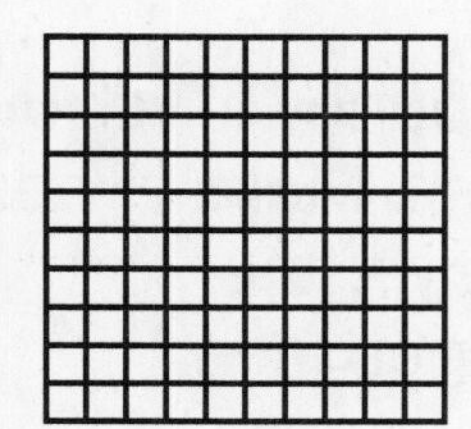

11. 1.2
(2-7)

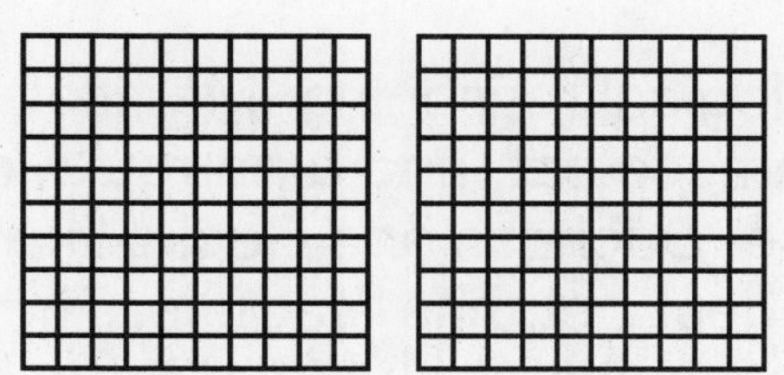

Use the stem-and-leaf plot to answer each question.

12. How many trees were measured? ________
(1-3)

13. A sugar maple grew the most. How much did it grow? ________
(1-3)

14. Two silver maples grew the same amount. How much did they grow? ________
(1-3)

Growth of Maple Trees in Inches

Stem	Leaf
0	9
1	1 2 6 8 8
2	4 8

What is the value in dollars of the money in each stack?

15. ten thousand $10 bills
(2-1)

____

16. ten $1,000 bills
(2-1)

____

Name ______________________________

Daily Review
2-19

Daily Cumulative Review

Find each difference. *(Lesson 2-18)*

1. 1.23 − 0.40

2. 0.80 − 0.02

3. 5.06 − 2.90

4. \$20.00 − 2.98

5. \$7.09 − 2.63

Find each sum. *(Lesson 2-17)*

6. 9.64 + 2.67

7. 4.89 + 3.06

8. 0.23 + 1.69 + 0.98

9. 12.00 + 1.57

10. 3.99 + 2.54

Mixed Review

In each group, circle equivalent decimals.

11. *(2-8)* 7.0 0.7 0.70

12. *(2-8)* 0.50 0.05 0.5

13. *(1-11)* Use logical reasoning. Martina's family has a Basset hound, a Poodle, a Siamese cat, and a parrot. A dog is the oldest pet and Mella is next in age. Duchess and Socks like to chase the cat. Popeye, the youngest pet, has feathers. The Basset hound is younger than Duchess. List the pets in order of age.

____

____

Write <, >, or = to complete.

14. *(2-5)* 62,301 ◯ 503,210

15. *(2-5)* 30,050 ◯ thirty thousand, fifty

16. *(2-5)* 998,000 ◯ 989,000

17. *(2-5)* 6,000,000 ◯ sixty million

18. *(2-10)* Complete the number line.

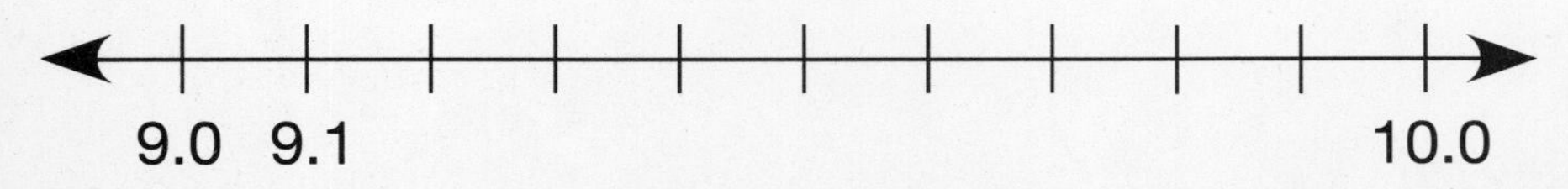

Name ______________________________

Daily Review 3-1

Daily Cumulative Review

Write the number sentence or sentences you would use. Then solve each problem. *(Lesson 2-19)*

1. Gena has earned a total of 267 test points. She made 92 on the first test and 86 on the second test. What score did she receive on the third test?

____

2. Rich had $2.00. He bought 3 bananas for 60¢, 2 apples for 70¢, and 1 apricot for 15¢ at a fruit stand. How much money does he have left?

____

Find each difference. *(Lesson 2-18)*

3. $7 - 3.55 =$ ________

4. \$7.50 − \$6.78 = ________

5. $6.5 - 2.69 =$ ________

6. \$2.08 − \$0.68 = ________

Mixed Review

Write $>$, $<$, or $=$ to complete.

7. *(2-11)* 0.337 ◯ 0.373

8. *(2-11)* 0.90 ◯ 0.9

Use the data to complete **9–11**.

Cars Crossing Bridge (per day)					
23	44	36	27	24	44
32	36	44	28	28	23
41	25	32	39	36	42

Stem	Leaf

9. *(1-10)* Make a stem-and-leaf plot to show the Cars Crossing Bridge data.

10. *(1-10)* What is the mode? ________

11. *(1-10)* What is the range? ________

Name ______________________

Daily Review 3-2

Daily Cumulative Review

Find each product. Use mental math. *(Lesson 3-1)*

1. $20 \times 60 =$ ________ **2.** $25 \times (4 \times 17) =$ ________

3. $80 \times 30 =$ ________ **4.** $2 \times (50 \times 9) =$ ________

Write the number sentence or sentences you would use. Then solve each problem. *(Lesson 2-19)*

5. Daniel wants to buy a pair of shoes that cost $96.34 including tax. He has $14 in his wallet and $81.50 in his savings account. Does he have enough money to buy the shoes? If so, how much will he have left over?

____

6. Brianna wants to buy a CD that costs $12. Tax is $0.76. If she pays with a twenty-dollar bill, how much change should she receive?

____

Mixed Review

Write each number in decimal form.

7. four hundred six thousandths ________
(2-9)

8. four hundred and six thousandths ________
(2-9)

9. Name two decimals with digits in the tenths place that could be rounded to the ones place as 5.
(2-12)

____

Use the line graph to answer **10–11**.

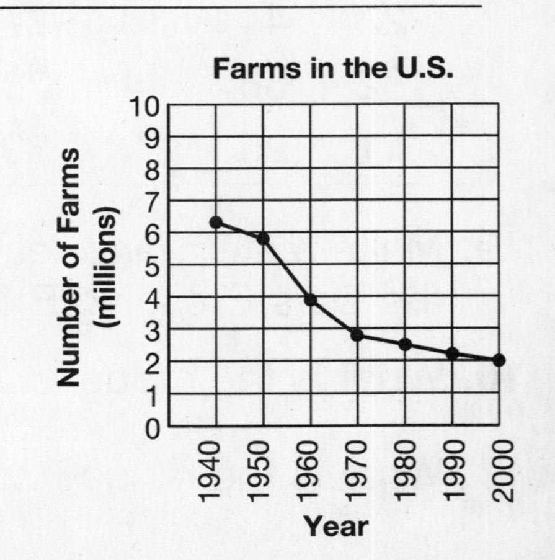

10. What is the trend in the number of farms?
(1-2)

____

11. About how many farms were there in 1970?
(1-2)

____

Name ______________________

Daily Review
3-3

Daily Cumulative Review

Estimate each product. *(Lesson 3-2)*

1. 69×5 ________ **2.** 18×9 ________ **3.** 47×11 ________

4. 73×51 ________ **5.** 82×41 ________ **6.** 803×89 ________

Complete. *(Lesson 3-1)*

7. $30 \times$ ________ $= 2{,}100$ **8.** $20 \times$ ________ $= 22{,}000$

9. $60 \times$ ________ $= 48{,}000$ **10.** $90 \times$ ________ $= 45{,}000$

Mixed Review

Use place-value blocks or drawings to find each sum or difference.

11. *(2-16)* $2.31 - 0.71$

12. *(2-16)* $6.7 - 5.8$

13. *(2-16)* $2.38 + 1.80$

14. *(2-16)* $1.6 + 0.9$

15. *(2-11)* Compare 2.132 and 2.106. Which is greater? ________

Write the operation needed for each problem. Then solve.

16. *(1-6)* There are 8,910 books in the school library and 192,347 in the public library. How many books are there in all?

____

17. *(1-6)* Chase earned $145 in 5 days. If he earned the same amount each day, how much did he earn in one day?

____

18. *(2-6)* Use the number line to help you round 1,876,650 to the nearest million.

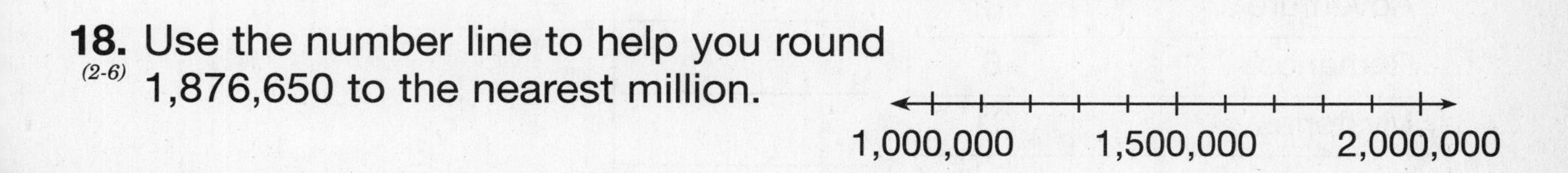

____

Name ____________________

Daily Review 3-4

Daily Cumulative Review

Find each product. Estimate to check. *(Lesson 3-3)*

1. $\begin{array}{r} 81 \\ \times 19 \\ \hline \end{array}$ **2.** $\begin{array}{r} 37 \\ \times 59 \\ \hline \end{array}$ **3.** $\begin{array}{r} 48 \\ \times 61 \\ \hline \end{array}$ **4.** $\begin{array}{r} 678 \\ \times \quad 7 \\ \hline \end{array}$ **5.** $\begin{array}{r} 196 \\ \times \; 21 \\ \hline \end{array}$

Estimate each product. *(Lesson 3-2)*

6. 36×24 ________ **7.** 303×72 ________ **8.** 85×38 ________

Mixed Review

Round each number to the place of the underlined digit.

9. $6.\underline{0}34$ *(2-12)* ________

10. $\underline{1}.578$ *(2-12)* ________

11. $0.\underline{5}49$ *(2-12)* ________

12. $6.9\underline{1}8$ *(2-12)* ________

13. *(2-18)* Complete. $9.12 -$ ________ $= 5.07$

14. *(2-15)* Find $2,000 - 1,603$ mentally. Explain your reasoning.

____

____

15. *(1-8)* Amanda decided to organize the bookshelf in the den. She sorted the books according to type. Use the data to make a bar graph.

Biographies	3
Reference books	24
Science Fiction	27
Adventure	12
Romance	6
Mysteries	21

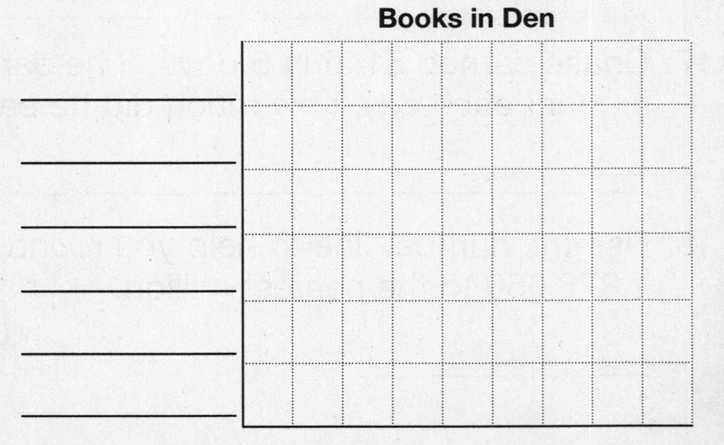

Name ______________________________

Daily Cumulative Review

Use mental math to find each product. *(Lesson 3-4)*

1. $701 \times 8 =$ ________ **2.** $71 \times 3 =$ ________

3. $198 \times 4 =$ ________ **4.** $19 \times 7 =$ ________

Find each product. Estimate to check. *(Lesson 3-3)*

5. $\begin{array}{r} 28 \\ \times \ 7 \\ \hline \end{array}$ **6.** $\begin{array}{r} 56 \\ \times 58 \\ \hline \end{array}$ **7.** $\begin{array}{r} 44 \\ \times 80 \\ \hline \end{array}$ **8.** $\begin{array}{r} 463 \\ \times \ 9 \\ \hline \end{array}$

Mixed Review

9. $2.06 + 3.45 + 0.37 =$ ________
(2-17)

10. Write one million, one hundred, and one tenth in decimal form.
(2-7)

____

11. Name the number shown by each letter.
(2-10)

A ________ *B* ________

C ________ *D* ________

A B C D
11.0 11.5 12.0

12. A class has 20 students. There are 4 more boys than girls. How many girls are there? ________
(1-11)

13. Use the table to make a line graph.
(1-9)

Leah's Height	
Age	Height (inches)
11	58
12	58.5
13	59
14	60.5
15	61.5
16	62
17	64

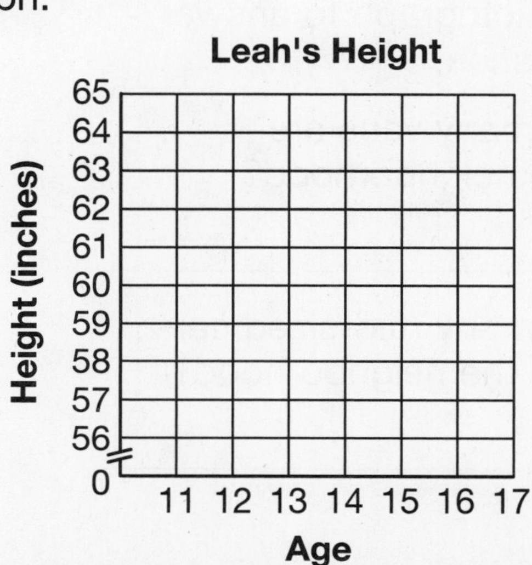

Name ______________________

Daily Review 3-6

Daily Cumulative Review

Choose a method. Find each product. *(Lesson 3-5)*

1. 35×87

2. 800×60

3. 741×29

4. 602×135

Use mental math to find each product. *(Lesson 3-4)*

5. 202×30

6. 99×6

7. 406×5

8. 198×3

Mixed Review

9. Find the difference of 5 and 2.36. ________
(2-19)

10. 90 × ________ = 54,000
(3-1)

11. 409 − ________ = 312
(2-15)

Write >, <, or = to complete.

12. 491 + 293 ◯ 800
(2-14)

13. 805 − 697 ◯ 100
(2-14)

14. Write which decimals are equivalent. 0.09 0.9 0.90
(2-8)

____

Use the pictograph to answer each question.

15. How many vans are in the neighborhood?
(1-1)

____

16. How many mid-sized cars are in the neighborhood?
(1-1)

____

Vehicles in Neighborhood

Truck	🚗 🚗
Van	🚗 half 🚗
Small Car	🚗
Mid-sized car	🚗 🚗 🚗
Full-sized car	🚗

🚗 = 2 vehicles

Name ______________________

Daily Review
3-7

Daily Cumulative Review

Find the LCM for each pair or set of numbers. *(Lesson 3-6)*

1. 2 and 7 ________ **2.** 4 and 8 ________ **3.** 12 and 8 ________

4. 2, 8, and 20 ________ **5.** 6, 9, and 12 ________

Find each product. *(Lesson 3-5)*

6. $\begin{array}{r} 49 \\ \times 50 \\ \hline \end{array}$ **7.** $\begin{array}{r} 600 \\ \times 70 \\ \hline \end{array}$ **8.** $\begin{array}{r} 25 \\ \times 43 \\ \hline \end{array}$ **9.** $\begin{array}{r} 360 \\ \times 90 \\ \hline \end{array}$

Mixed Review

10. Explain how you could show $3.87 using dollars, dimes, and pennies.
(2-16)

____

11. Mountains rise high in the sky but trenches are deep in the ocean. The Mariana Trench is the lowest place on earth at 35,840 feet beneath the surface of the Pacific Ocean. The Philippine Trench is slightly deeper than the Kermadec Trench, but neither of them is as deep as the Tonga Trench. List these Pacific trenches from deepest to shallowest.
(2-13)

____

12. Write in decimal form: three and eight thousandths. ________
(2-9)

13. Subtract 12.68 from 20. ________
(2-18)

14. The product of 392 and what number is about 20,000? ________
(3-2)

15. Emma bought 8 ounces of cream cheese. She already had 5 ounces at home. Does she have enough for a recipe that calls for 12 ounces of cream cheese? Explain.
(2-19)

____

Name ______________________________

Daily Review
3-8

Daily Cumulative Review

Plan and solve. Make a decision. *(Lesson 3-7)*

Emma's parents have both been offered new jobs 45 miles away. They are deciding between moving and staying in their current home.

Facts and Data	
Moving	Staying
The move will cost $1,000.	Rent is $200 lower per month.
Shorter work commutes would save $100 each month in gasoline costs.	Daily commuting would take 2 hours for each parent.
Utility bills would be $30 per month lower.	A neighbor would charge $85 per month to watch Emma after school.
Emma could have a horse.	Emma stays in the same school.

1. How much rent would be saved in a year by not moving? ________

2. How much would the neighbor charge for 9 months? ________

3. How much would be saved in gasoline and utilities in a year if they moved? ________

4. Should they move or stay? Explain. ______________________________

____

Find the LCM for each pair or set of numbers. *(Lesson 3-6)*

5. 2 and 9 ________

6. 8, 12, and 24 ________

Mixed Review

Write >, <, or = to complete.

7. 5.2 ◯ 5.29 *(2-11)*

8. 6.07 ◯ 6.7 *(2-11)*

9. 4.0 ◯ 4 *(2-11)*

10. Find the sum of 3.54 and 2.9 ________ *(2-17)*

Name ______________________

Daily Review
3-9

Daily Cumulative Review

Find each product *(Lesson 3-8)*

1. 6.43×10 ________

2. 0.571×100 ________

3. 4.95×1000 ________

4. $0.003 \times 10 =$ ________

$0.003 \times 100 =$ ________

$0.003 \times 1000 =$ ________

5. $0.801 \times 10 =$ ________

$0.801 \times 100 =$ ________

$0.801 \times 1000 =$ ________

Plan and solve. *(Lesson 3-7)*

6. You can buy a season pass for $36 for all 12 ball games or pay $4 per ticket for each game you attend. How many games would you have to attend with the season pass for it to be the better buy? Explain.

____

Mixed Review

Use mental math to find each answer.

7. $302 \times 5 =$ ________ *(3-4)*

8. $299 \times 4 =$ ________ *(3-4)*

9. $5{,}000 - 3{,}999 =$ ________ *(2-15)*

10. $0.42 + 1.99 =$ ________ *(2-17)*

11. *(3-5)* Estimate the product of 48 and 537. Is it closer to 25,000 or 30,000? Explain.

____

Complete. Use place-value blocks or drawings to help you.

12. $5.67 -$ ________ $= 1.41$ *(2-16)*

13. $1.56 +$ ________ $= 6.87$ *(2-16)*

14. $4.8 -$ ________ $= 2.64$ *(2-16)*

15. $4.71 +$ ________ $= 8.40$ *(2-16)*

16. $1.29 -$ ________ $= 0.57$ *(2-16)*

17. $0.18 +$ ________ $= 1.32$ *(2-16)*

Name ______________________________

Daily Review 3-10

Daily Cumulative Review

Estimate each product. Explain what you did. *(Lesson 3-9)*

1. 36.4×5 ______________

2. 3.87×12 ______________

3. 48.2×7 ______________

4. 92.1×478 ______________

Place the decimal point in the product. Write extra zeros if necessary. *(Lesson 3-8)*

5. $0.237 \times 100 = 2\ 3\ 7$

6. $8.51 \times 100 = 8\ 5\ 1$

7. $1.089 \times 100 = 1\ 0\ 8\ 9$

8. $0.607 \times 100 = 6\ 0\ 7$

Mixed Review

Complete. For each product the factors are the same.

9. *(3-1)* ______ $\times$ ______ $= 3{,}600$

10. *(3-1)* ______ $\times$ ______ $= 6{,}400$

11. *(2-18)* ______ $\times$ ______ $= 40{,}000$

12. *(3-1)* ______ $\times$ ______ $= 250{,}000$

13. *(1-6)* There are 50 water balloons in one packet. How many packets must you buy to get 200 water balloons? ________

For **14** and **15** decide if each problem needs an exact answer or an estimate. Then solve each problem.

14. *(3-3)* If a tree grows 4 feet every year, about how many feet does it grow in 21 years? ______________

15. *(3-3)* A bakery sold 112 combo-sacks with 4 cookies in each sack. How many cookies did they sell? ______________

16. *(2-12)* Charlie owes Allison 36¢ but he only has dimes. What is the nearest amount he can give her? ______________

17. *(2-19)* Find the difference of 6 and 3.23. ______________

18. *(2-19)* Find the sum of $1.5 + 1.05 + 10.5$. ______________

Name ______________________

Daily Review 3-11

Daily Cumulative Review

Find each product. *(Lesson 3-10)*

1. $2.3 \times 7 =$ ________

2. $4.17 \times 9 =$ ________

3. $\$5.65 \times 3 =$ ________

4. $\$1.25 \times 21 =$ ________

Is each product greater than 1,000? Write yes or no. Explain. *(Lesson 3-9)*

5. 49.2×19 ______________________

6. 149.5×9 ______________________

7. 10×9.76 ______________________

Mixed Review

Estimate. Write >, <, or = to complete.

8. *(2-14)* $9.82 + 4.59$ ○ 14

9. *(2-14)* $216 - 109$ ○ 100

Solve.

10. *(2-19)* $9.43 - 0.37$

11. *(2-17)* $0.84 + 2.76$

12. *(3-4)* 98×7

13. *(3-5)* 75×20

Round to the nearest hundred thousand.

14. *(2-6)* 90,006 ______________

15. *(2-6)* 124,899,160 ______________

16. *(2-6)* 364,749,688 ______________

17. *(2-6)* 1,450,099 ______________

18. *(2-10)* Use the number line to answer. Name nine numbers between 2.3 and 2.4

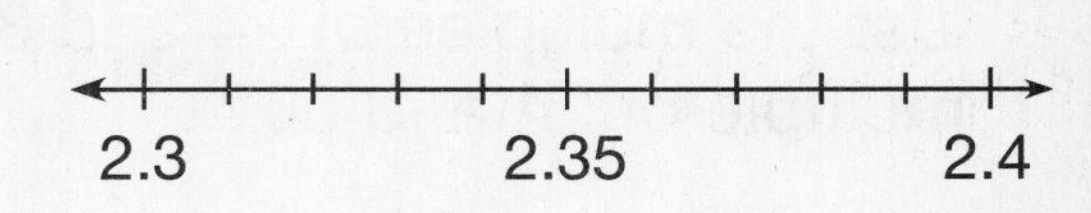

____

____

Name ______________________

Daily Review
3-12

Daily Cumulative Review

Solve each problem. *(Lesson 3-11)*

1. During the game against Edgarstown, Pam made 12 baskets and Bettina made 7 baskets. For each basket, 2 points were scored.

a. How many points did Pam score? ________

b. How many points did Bettina score? ________

c. How many points did the two girls score? ________

2. Maruka bought 3 pairs of earrings that cost $5.99 each. How much change would she receive from a $20 bill? ________

Choose the number that is closest to the actual product. *(Lesson 3-10)*

3. $3.06 × 21 ________ **A.** $6 **B.** $60 **C.** $600

4. $1.98 × 1000 ________ **A.** $2 **B.** $200 **C.** $2000

5. 6.005 × 50 ________ **A.** 30 **B.** 300 **C.** 3000

Mixed Review

Estimate each product.

6. 101 × 89 ____________ *(3-2)*

7. 59 × 31 ____________ *(3-2)*

8. *(2-15)* Find 3,998 + 6,998 mentally. Explain why it is easier to do this sum mentally than by writing it out.

____

____

9. *(3-6)* List the multiples of 24 and 36. What is the least common multiple of 24 and 36?

____

____

Name ________________________________

Daily Cumulative Review

Use the 10 × 10 grid to show 0.4 of 0.8. *(Lesson 3-12)*

1. 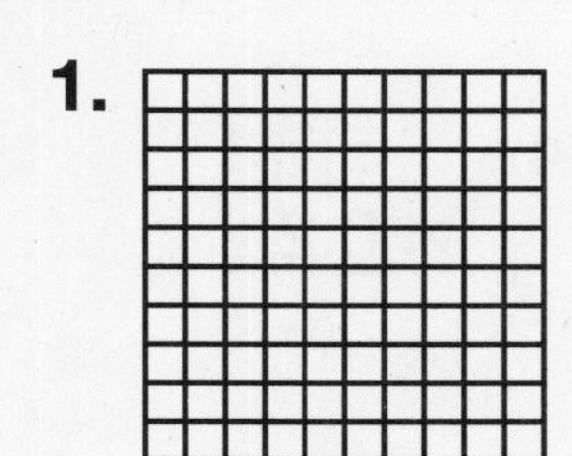

a. Use horizontal stripes to shade 0.4 on the grid as 4 rows.

b. Use vertical stripes to shade 0.8 on the grid as 8 columns.

c. Count the double-striped squares. 0.4 of 0.8 is __________.

Solve. *(Lesson 3-11)*

2. A bookstore charges $4.95 for new paperbacks, $2.95 for used paperbacks, and $10.95 for used hardbacks.

a. Mrs. Easley bought 3 new paperbacks and 2 used paperbacks. How much did she spend? __________

b. Allison bought 1 used hardback and 3 used paperbacks. How much did she spend? __________

Mixed Review

Complete. Use place-value blocks or drawings to help you.

3. 3.09 − __________ = 1.98 (2-16)

4. 5 − 3.63 = __________ (2-18)

5. (2-19) The Rameriz family is driving 1,060 miles to their new home. They drove 328 miles the first day and 341 miles the second day. How many more miles do they have to travel? Write the number sentence or sentences you would use. Then solve the problem.

____

6. (2-9) Using the digits 2, 4, 6, and 8, write the greatest decimal possible, in thousandths. ___ . ___ ___ ___

Name ______________________________

Daily Review 3-14

Daily Cumulative Review

Find each product. Round to the nearest cent when necessary. *(Lesson 3-13)*

1. $\$9.35 \times 0.1$

2. $\$0.37 \times 4.5$

3. 640×0.008

4. 5.71×0.22

Find each product. You can use 10 × 10 grids to help. *(Lesson 3-12)*

5. 0.5 of 0.4 ______

6. 0.7 of 0.3 ______

7. 0.8 of 0.1 ______

8. 0.4 of 0.9 ______

9. 0.1 of 0.1 ______

10. 0.9 of 0.9 ______

11. 0.5 of 0.5 ______

12. 0.3 of 0.4 ______

Mixed Review

Round each number to the place of the underlined digit.

13. $4.\underline{8}31$ *(2-12)* ______

14. $0.2\underline{8}6$ *(2-12)* ______

15. $3.\underline{3}90$ *(2-12)* ______

Complete.

16. 70 × ______ = 4,900 *(3-1)*

17. 60 × ______ = 54,000 *(3-1)*

Use the table to answer each question.

Monthly Internet Rates	
Plan A	Plan B
10 hours: $9.95	Unlimited access: $19.95
Each additional hour: $2.00	

18. How much would 15 hours of internet use cost using Plan A? *(3-7)* ______

19. How much would you save with plan B if you were online for 20 hours? *(3-7)* ______

Name ______________________

Daily Review 3-15

Daily Cumulative Review

Between which two numbers will each product be found? *(Lesson 3-14)*

1. 4.5×7.2 ________

A. 28 and 35 **B.** 35 and 40 **C.** 280 and 350

2. 31.7×9 ________

A. 40 and 50 **B.** 27 and 36 **C.** 270 and 360

3. 2.91×6.8 ________

A. 8 and 10 **B.** 12 and 21 **C.** 80 and 100

Find each product. Round to the nearest cent when necessary. *(Lesson 3-13)*

4. $\begin{array}{r} \$2.35 \\ \times\ 0.04 \\ \hline \end{array}$

5. $\begin{array}{r} 6.53 \\ \times\ 1.03 \\ \hline \end{array}$

6. $\begin{array}{r} \$5.50 \\ \times\ 0.005 \\ \hline \end{array}$

7. $\begin{array}{r} \$12.60 \\ \times\ \quad 6 \\ \hline \end{array}$

Mixed Review

8. Write three and nine hundredths in decimal form. ________
(2-7)

Write each number using exponents.

9. 100,000 ________ *(2-3)*

10. 100 ________ *(2-3)*

11. 1,000,000 ________ *(2-3)*

12. If 100 people attend a dinner theater and pay $9.75 each, how much did the theater collect? ________
(3-8)

13. One lap of a dirt track is 0.125 of a mile. How far does a car travel
(3-10)

a. in 3 laps? ________ **b.** in 8 laps? ________

14. Find the sum of 2.45 and 1.9. ________
(2-17)

Name ______________________

Daily Review 3-16

Daily Cumulative Review

Find each product. *(Lesson 3-15)*

1. $0.05 \times 0.003 =$ ________ **2.** $0.004 \times 0.07 =$ ________

3. $6.2 \times 0.001 =$ ________ **4.** $4.03 \times 0.08 =$ ________

Estimate low and high. Then find each product. *(Lesson 3-14)*

5. $7.3 \times 8 =$ ________ **6.** $6.9 \times 3 =$ ________

Estimate: ________ Estimate: ________

7. $4.5 \times 2.1 =$ ________ **8.** $1.8 \times 3.9 =$ ________

Estimate: ________ Estimate: ________

Mixed Review

Estimate each product. Explain what you did.

9. 6.8×5 ________________
(3-9)

10. 9×1.04 ________________
(3-9)

11. Give two numbers whose product is about 400.
(3-2)

____

12. Order 8.27, 8.72, 8.07, 8.20 from least to greatest.
(2-11)

____

13. A plane ticket costs \$105 per person. The same trip costs \$25 for gas and \$50 for meals.
(3-7)

a. Write a list of reasons why flying might be the better choice.

____

b. Write a list of reasons why driving might be the better choice.

____

____

Name ______________________________

Daily Cumulative Review

Use the Guess and Check Strategy to solve each problem. *(Lesson 3-16)*

1. Marissa has 13 guppies and swordtails in her aquarium. She has 3 more guppies than swordtails.

a. What is a reasonable first guess for the number of guppies?

____

b. She has 13 fish in all. Is it possible for her to have 10 guppies and 3 swordfish?

____

c. How many of each fish does she have?

____

2. Alex mowed 6 lawns last week. He charges $20 for medium-sized lawns and $12 for small lawns. He earned $104 last week. How many of each size lawn did he mow?

____

Find each product. Write zeros where needed. *(Lesson 3-15)*

3. 4.6×0.03

4. 0.21×0.15

5. 7.8×0.09

6. 1.05×9.6

Mixed Review

7. *(2-13)* Jesse is taller than Riley but shorter than Sam. Tom is the tallest of the four. Who is the shortest? __________

8. *(3-11)* The Band Boosters sold cupcakes for 50¢ each and cookies for 10¢ each. If you bought 2 cupcakes and 3 cookies, how much did you spend? __________

Name ______________________________

Daily Review
4-2

Daily Cumulative Review

Find each quotient. *(Lesson 4-1)*

1. $42 \div 7 =$ ________ **2.** $40 \div 5 =$ ________ **3.** $54 \div 6 =$ ________

4. $56 \div 8 =$ ________ **5.** $24 \div 4 =$ ________ **6.** $36 \div 9 =$ ________

Use Guess and Check or any strategy to solve each problem.
(Lesson 3-16)

7. Brenna has saved $125. She earns $20 each week helping her grandma in her store after school. How many weeks will it be before she has enough money to buy a saddle that costs $245?

____

8. In Mr. Lander's class, the boys outnumber the girls by 3. There are 21 students in his class. How many girls and how many boys are there in Mr. Lander's class?

____

Mixed Review

Complete.

9. *(3-3)* 87×45

10. *(2-15)* $506 - 349$

11. *(2-18)* $3.68 - 1.47$

12. *(2-17)* $6.09 + 3.27$

13. *(3-9)* Estimate the product of 5.763 and 6.103. ________

14. *(3-11)* Derrick took $35 to the mall. He bought two shirts for $14.26 each and spent $4.32 on lunch. How much money did he have left?

____

15. *(2-1)* In 1927, Charles Lindbergh flew 3,610 miles from New York to Paris. Use your calculator to find about how many times he would have had to make the trip to fly a million miles.

____

Name ______________________

Daily Review 4-3

Daily Cumulative Review

Use number sense and basic facts to divide mentally. *(Lesson 4-2)*

1. $35 \div 5 =$ ________

$350 \div 5 =$ ________

$3,500 \div 5 =$ ________

$35,000 \div 5 =$ ________

2. $24 \div 2 =$ ________

$240 \div 2 =$ ________

$2,400 \div 2 =$ ________

$24,000 \div 2 =$ ________

Identify each number in the equation $6 \times 8 = 48$ and $48 \div 6 = 8$ as a factor, a product, a divisor, a dividend, or a quotient. *(Lesson 4-1)*

3. 6 ↓ ________ × 8 ↓ ________ = 48 ↓ ________

4. 48 ↓ ________ ÷ 6 ↓ ________ = 8 ↓ ________

Mixed Review

5. (3-8) A charity fund-raiser collected $100 each from 37 people. The goal was $5,000. How much more does the charity need to collect?

____

6. (3-10) Connie jogs to the river and back every day, a total distance of 1.4 miles. How many miles does she jog in 4 weeks?

____

7. (2-2) Suppose Mr. Midas buys a house for $1,573,500. He writes this amount in word form on a check. What does he write?

____

____

Name ______________________________

Daily Review
4-4

Daily Cumulative Review

Estimate each quotient. *(Lesson 4-3)*

1. 490 ÷ 60 = __________ **2.** 277 ÷ 4 = __________

3. 539 ÷ 9 = __________ **4.** 119 ÷ 3 = __________

Use patterns and basic facts to divide mentally. *(Lesson 4-2)*

5. 3,500 ÷ 7 = __________ **6.** 63,000 ÷ 9 = __________

7. 420 ÷ 6 = __________ **8.** 7,200 ÷ 8 = __________

Mixed Review

Find each product.

9. *(3-4)* 587 × 11 = __________ **10.** *(3-1)* (5 × 37) × 20 = __________

11. *(3-14)* Between which two numbers will the product 9.7 × 6.3 be found?

A. 15 and 17 B. 54 and 70 C. 540 and 700

____

12. *(2-19)* Amber wanted to buy a computer game that costs $67.98. She saved until she had $70. When she went to buy the game, she found it on sale for $47.48. How much money did she have left?

____

13. *(3-7)* You and a friend go to a county fair that has 6 rides. Each ride takes one ticket. You can buy 4 ride tickets for $5 or a pass with unlimited rides for $20.

a. If you go on each ride twice, how much would it cost using tickets? __________

b. How many rides would you have to go on before the pass is the better buy? __________

Name ____________________

Daily Review
4-5

Daily Cumulative Review

Complete. You may use play money to help. *(Lesson 4-4)*

1.

```
   $[ ].1 3 R[ ]
8)$1 7.0 5
 − 1 6
   [ ]0
   − 8
     [ ]5
   − [ ][ ]
         1
```

2.

```
  $[ ].5 9 R[ ]
5)$7.9 8
− [ ]
  [ ]9
− [ ][ ]
    [ ]8
  − [ ][ ]
      [ ]
```

Estimate each quotient. *(Lesson 4-3)*

3. 319 ÷ 8 __________

4. 269 ÷ 4 __________

5. 362 ÷ 6 __________

6. 570 ÷ 7 __________

Mixed Review

7. Estimate the product of 195 and 97. __________
(3-2)

8. Estimate the sum of 459 and 212. __________
(2-14)

9. Lindsey and Leah each solve 307 multiplied by 386. Lindsey's answer is 118,502. Leah's answer is 95,432. Which answer is reasonable? Explain.
(3-5)

____

10. Christopher's Mom is on a low-fat diet. While helping her grocery shop, he compared the grams of saturated fat in four snack foods. List the snacks in order of least to most fat.
(2-5)

____

____

____

____

Snack	Grams of Saturated Fat per Serving
Mixed nuts	2.5
Chips	1.5
Popcorn	2.25
Pretzels	1.75

Name ____________________

Daily Review 4-6

Daily Cumulative Review

Divide. Use multiplication to check. *(Lesson 4-5)*

1. $6\overline{)835}$ **2.** $3\overline{)673}$ **3.** $5\overline{)408}$ **4.** $7\overline{)826}$

Divide. You may use play money to help. *(Lesson 4-4)*

5. $2\overline{)\$5.26}$ **6.** $4\overline{)\$1.29}$ **7.** $3\overline{)\$7.45}$ **8.** $8\overline{)\$8.96}$

Mixed Review

Complete.

9. *(2-16)* $\begin{array}{r} 2.58 \\ -\ 2.14 \\ \hline \end{array}$

10. *(2-15)* $\begin{array}{r} 900 \\ -\ 466 \\ \hline \end{array}$

11. *(3-2)* $\begin{array}{r} 704 \\ \times\ 48 \\ \hline \end{array}$

12. *(3-5)* $\begin{array}{r} 320 \\ \times\ 200 \\ \hline \end{array}$

13. *(3-15)* Is the product of 0.05 and 6.38 greater or less than 6.38? Explain.

____

14. *(4-1)* There are 36 paper napkins in a package. If 4 napkins are used at each meal, how many meals will one package last?

____

15. *(3-16)* A baseball team is giving away gloves and hats to promote their team. If the gloves cost the team $15 each and the hats cost $3.00 each, how much will it cost the team for 2 gloves and 5 hats?

____

Name ______________________

Daily Review 4-7

Daily Cumulative Review

Use any strategy to solve each problem. *(Lesson 4-6)*

1. Mrs. Bill is buying six-packs of sodas for her class of 22. Each student will get one soda. She plans to drink coffee.

a. How many six-packs does she need to buy? __________

b. How many sodas will be left over? __________

2. The science lab tables will seat 4 students each. How many tables will be needed for a class of 23?

____

Divide *(Lesson 4-5)*

3. $6\overline{)801}$ **4.** $4\overline{)673}$ **5.** $3\overline{)429}$ **6.** $7\overline{)900}$

Mixed Review

7. Find the LCM for 4, 6, and 9. __________
(3-6)

Place the decimal point in the product. Write extra zeros if necessary.

8. $0.025 \times 100 = 2\ 5$ *(3-8)*

9. $0.8 \times 1000 = 8\ 0\ 0$ *(3-8)*

Complete.

10. $2{,}400 \div$ __________ $= 400$ *(4-2)*

11. $56{,}000 \div$ __________ $= 80$ *(4-2)*

12. Jay sold a box of books at a yard sale for \$51. He sold some of the books for \$2 each and some for \$3 each. If there were 20 books in the box, how many did he sell at each price?
(3-16)

____

Name ___________________________

Daily Review 4-8

Daily Cumulative Review

Divide. Check your answer. *(Lesson 4-7)*

1. $5\overline{)379}$ **2.** $7\overline{)243}$ **3.** $2\overline{)176}$ **4.** $3\overline{)539}$

Use any strategy to solve each problem. *(Lesson 4-6)*

5. Hotdog buns come 8 to a package. Janice needs 36 buns for a cookout. How many packages should she buy? ___________

6. Kashan's father is going to be 38. Kashan found birthday candles that are packaged 12 to a box. How many boxes should she buy for his cake and how many candles will be left over?

____

Mixed Review

7. Write which decimals are equivalent.
(2-8)

0.9 0.09 0.90 ___________________________

8. Name the number shown by each letter.
(2-10)

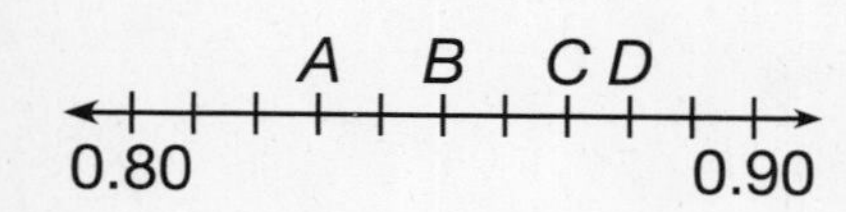

A ___________ *B* ___________ *C* ___________ *D* ___________

9. A cola sells for $0.59. A six-pack of the same cola sells for $1.59. How much would you save on 6 colas by buying the six-pack?
(3-11)

____

Name ______________________________

Daily Review 4-9

Daily Cumulative Review

Divide. Multiply to check. *(Lesson 4-8)*

1. $9\overline{)987}$ **2.** $4\overline{)1203}$ **3.** $7\overline{)734}$ **4.** $6\overline{)6034}$

Divide. Check your answer. *(Lesson 4-7)*

5. $5\overline{)247}$ **6.** $3\overline{)128}$ **7.** $8\overline{)576}$ **8.** $2\overline{)179}$

Mixed Review

9. Estimate the quotient of 549 ÷ 7. __________
(4-3)

10. Find the product of 0.5 and 0.5. __________
(3-12)

11. Order these numbers from least to greatest.
(2-5)
6,014,000; 60,140,000; 614,000; 6,100,400

____

12. Write three hundred and sixteen thousandths in decimal form.
(2-9)

____

13. Find 2000 − 998 mentally. Explain your reasoning.
(2-15)

____

14. Estimate low and high. Then find the product of 3.9 and 14.7.
(3-14)

____

Name ______________________________

Daily Review
4-10

Daily Cumulative Review

Complete each sentence using a number from the number bank. *(Lesson 4-9)*

Test Scores: 76, 82, 89, 92, 92, 97

Number Bank
6
88
89
90.5
92
528

1. The mode of the test scores is __________ because it is the number that appears most.

2. To find the mean, you would divide __________ by __________ and get __________.

3. The median is __________ because it is halfway between the middle numbers __________ and __________.

Divide. Multiply to check. *(Lesson 4-8)*

4. $9\overline{)3619}$

5. $2\overline{)8005}$

6. $6\overline{)723}$

Mixed Review

7. *(3-9)* Estimate the product 47.3×8. Explain what you did.

____

8. *(3-4)* Would you use the distributive property to find 730×2? Explain.

____

9. *(4-5)* The school purchased 123 boxes of paper for the 3 fifth grade teachers. If each teacher gets the same amount of paper, how many boxes would they get?

____

Name ______________________________

Daily Review 4-11

Daily Cumulative Review

Match each number sentence with the property it shows. *(Lesson 4-10)*

______ **1.** $1 \times 99 = 99$

______ **2.** $5 \times (2 \times 79) = (5 \times 2) \times 79$

______ **3.** $6 \times 0 = 0$

______ **4.** $7 \times 33 = 33 \times 7$

a. Zero Property

b. One Property

c. Commutative Property

d. Associative Property

Find the mean, median, and mode for each set of data. *(Lesson 4-9)*

5. 7, 13, 13, 16, 20, 24, 26

______, ______, ______

6. 76, 80, 82, 84, 93

______, ______, ______

Mixed Review

7. Complete the table. Give its rule using words and a variable.
(1-7)

A	1	3	5	7	9	11
B	8	10	12			

Rule: ______________________________

8. Julianna must read 500 pages this summer. So far she has read a book with 151 pages and another with 209 pages. She wants to reach the goal with one more book. How many pages does it need to have? Write the number sentence or sentences you would use. Then solve the problem.
(2-19)

____

____

Name ______________________

Daily Review 4-12

Daily Cumulative Review

Find each quotient. Multiply to check. *(Lesson 4-11)*

1. 9)$6 3.0 0 **2.** 5)$1 0.5 0 **3.** 7)$2 5 5.0 8

Write >, <, or = to complete. *(Lesson 4-10)*

4. $56 \times 1 = n$ **a.** n ◯ 56 **b.** n ◯ 1

5. $97 \times 6 = n$ **a.** n ◯ 97 **b.** n ◯ 6

6. $48 \times n = 0$ **a.** n ◯ 48 **b.** n ◯ 0

Mixed Review

Estimate high and low. Then find each product.

7. *(3-14)* $21.7 \times 8 =$ ________

Estimate: ________

8. *(3-14)* $2.96 \times 7 =$ ________

Estimate: ________

9. *(1-11)* Mrs. Lotridge has 4 children, 2 boys and 2 girls. Each child has a different color hair. Joanna, the youngest, does not have brown or black hair. Stan is not the oldest and does not have red hair. Kim, the blond, is younger than Stan. Robert has the darkest hair of all. List Mrs. Lotridge's children from oldest to youngest and their hair color.

____

____

10. *(4-6)* Martin baked 96 cookies for a bake sale. If he puts 5 cookies per baggie, how many baggies does he need? How many cookies will be left for him to eat?

____

Name ______________________________

Daily Cumulative Review

Find each quotient. *(Lesson 4-12)*

1. 5)1 2.0 6 5 **2.** 3)8.1 4 8 **3.** 7)3 5.8 0 5

Use a calculator to divide. Write each answer to the nearest cent. *(Lesson 4-11)*

4. 4)$840.19 **5.** 6)$654.79 **6.** 8)$160.97

Mixed Review

Multiply.

7. *(3-3)* 41×68

8. *(3-10)* $\$42.73 \times 9$

9. *(3-13)* 5.07×0.4

10. *(3-5)* 700×80

11. *(2-2)* Write 20,370,405 in word form.

____

____

12. *(2-6)* If 75,936,462 rounds to 75,940,000 to which place did you round?

____

13. *(3-16)* Mr. Frickes bought 12 cotton tee shirts sizes large and extra large for the art club to tie dye. There were two more large shirts than extra large shirts. How many of each size did he buy?

____

Name ______________________

Daily Review
4-14

Daily Cumulative Review

Find the factors for each number. *(Lesson 4-13)*

1. 14 ______________ **2.** 35 ______________

3. 24 ______________

4. 48 ______________

Find the length of the side of each square. *(Lesson 4-12)*

5. Perimeter = 16.492 cm

____

6. Perimeter = 20.32 in.

____

Mixed Review

7. Find the product of 0.9 of 0.5. ________
(3-12)

8. Find the LCM of 10 and 25. ________
(3-6)

9. Which is greater, the product of $20 \times 40 \times 300$ or $200 \times 4 \times 30$?
(3-1)

Explain. ______________

____

Meg and Amelia must decide between one-day passes for $30 or two-day passes for $50 at an amusement park. The park is open 10 hours every day.

10. If they stay the full 10 hours, what is the cost per hour for the one-day pass? ________
(3-7)

11. If they go both days for the full time, what is the cost per hour for the two-day pass? ________
(3-7)

Name ________________________________

Daily Review 4-15

Daily Cumulative Review

Use factor trees to find the prime factors of each number. *(Lesson 4-14)*

1. 18

2. 50

3. 27

Find the factors of each number. *(Lesson 4-13)*

4. 44 ____________________

5. 52 ____________________

6. 70 ____________________

7. 81 ____________________

Mixed Review

Complete.

8. *(4-7)* $7\overline{)574}$

9. *(3-15)* 2.7×0.03

10. *(3-3)* 468×17

11. *(2-18)* $5.00 - 2.17$

Use the graph to answer **12** and **13**.

12. *(1-1)* How many more children does the Allen family have than the Ford family?

____

13. *(4-9)* Find the mean, median, and mode for the set of data in the bar graph.

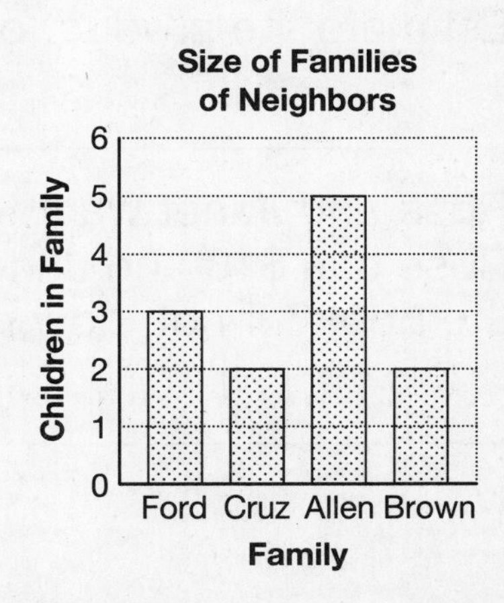

Name ______________________

Daily Review 5-1

Daily Cumulative Review

Work backward to solve the problem. *(Lesson 4-15)*

1. Jonathan went to an arcade. In the first hour he spent half his money. During the next hour, he spent 75¢. He spent half his remaining money before he left and had 50¢ left over.

a. How much did he have left? ______________

b. What operation undoes dividing his remaining money in half?

____

c. What operation undoes subtracting 75¢? ______________

d. How much money did he have when he went to the arcade?

____

Write whether each number is prime or composite. *(Lesson 4-14)*

2. 23 ____________ **3.** 33 ____________ **4.** 21 ____________

Mixed Review

Complete.

5. *(4-8)* $7\overline{)1421}$

6. *(3-3)* $\begin{array}{r} 366 \\ \times\ 55 \\ \hline \end{array}$

7. *(2-17)* $\begin{array}{r} 3.09 \\ 1.87 \\ +\ 6.1 \\ \hline \end{array}$

8. *(2-15)* $\begin{array}{r} 400 \\ -\ 37 \\ \hline \end{array}$

9. *(3-9)* Estimate the product of 78.9×7. Explain what you did.

____

10. *(2-19)* Rose and Janet want to buy a book for their mother that costs $36. Rose has $13 and Janet has $16. Do they have enough money to buy the book? If not, how much more money do they need?

____

Name ____________________

Daily Review
5-2

Daily Cumulative Review

You can use number sense and basic facts to divide with multiples of 10. *(Lesson 5-1)*

1. a. What basic fact would you use to find $240 \div 60$? __________

b. $240 \div 60 =$ __________

2. a. What basic fact would you use to find $56{,}000 \div 80$? __________

b. $56{,}000 \div 80 =$ __________

Use any strategy to solve each problem. *(Lesson 4-15)*

3. Bonnie had $1.33 left at the end of the week. She bought 2 candy bars for $0.55 each and 3 bottles of juice for $1.06 each. How much did she have at the beginning of the week?

____

4. Marco earns $4 an hour helping his dad. He worked 8 hours on Monday, 5 hours on Tuesday, 7 hours on Wednesday, and 2 hours on Thursday. Friday he spent 6 hours at the beach. How much money did Marco earn?

____

Mixed Review

5. *(1-1)* In a pictograph, each picture of a house stands for 20 houses. How many houses do $2\frac{1}{2}$ pictures stand for?

____

6. *(4-12)* Is $41.907 \div 6 = 16.1542$ a reasonable answer? Explain why or why not.

____

____

Name ______________________________

Daily Review
5-3

Daily Cumulative Review

Estimate each quotient. Give a high and low estimate. *(Lesson 5-2)*

1. 13,427 ÷ 30 ____________ **2.** 2,316 ÷ 90 ____________ **3.** 34,895 ÷ 80 ____________

4. 4,563 ÷ 60 ____________ **5.** 67,339 ÷ 80 ____________ **6.** 5,986 ÷ 70 ____________

Find each quotient. Use mental math. *(Lesson 5-1)*

7. 1,600 ÷ 80 = ____________ **8.** 72,000 ÷ 800 = ____________

9. 4,800 ÷ 60 = ____________ **10.** 5,400 ÷ 900 = ____________

Mixed Review

11. Estimate high and low. Then find the product of 15.3 and 45.5.
(3-14)

____

12. Estimate. Write >, <, or = to complete. 72 + 63 ◯ 130
(2-14)

13. Write the place-value position for each digit in the number 47,563,128.
(2-4)

1 ____________ 2 ____________ 3 ____________

4 ____________ 5 ____________ 6 ____________

7 ____________ 8 ____________

14. Find the mean, median, and mode for the set of data.
(4-9) 3, 4, 4, 4, 5, 6, 7, 7, 7, 13

mean ____________ median ____________ mode(s) ____________

15. The divisor is 4 and the dividend is 429. Divide. ____________
(4-7)

Name ______________________________

Daily Review
5-4

Daily Cumulative Review

Estimate each quotient using compatible numbers. *(Lesson 5-3)*

1. 638 ÷ 81 ________ **2.** 130 ÷ 62 ________ **3.** 2,671 ÷ 29 ________

4. 19,536 ÷ 59 ________ **5.** 23,932 ÷ 38 ________ **6.** 123,956 ÷ 33 ________

Estimate each quotient. Give a high and low estimate. *(Lesson 5-2)*

7. 2,239 ÷ 40 ________ **8.** 41,672 ÷ 60 ________ **9.** 6,637 ÷ 90 ________

Mixed Review

10. In the equations 5 × 8 = 40 and 40 ÷ 8 = 5, which number is:
(4-1)

a. a product? ______ **b.** a quotient? ______ **c.** a divisor? ______

11. Write >, <, or = to complete. 0.47 ◯ 0.5
(2-11)

12. Write two and eighty-eight thousandths in decimal form. ________
(2-9)

13. The average number of times Brianna visits the library each month is 5. About how many times does she visit in a year?
(1-6)

____

14. Suppose you wanted to find the mean, median, and mode of your test scores 87, 88, 89, 90, 91. How could you find them mentally?
(4-9)

____

____

15. Write five hundred two thousandths in decimal form. ________
(2-9)

Name ____________________

Daily Review
5-5

Daily Cumulative Review

Complete. *(Lesson 5-4)*

1. $52\overline{)163}$ = 3 R____
2. $24\overline{)99}$ = 4 R____
3. $13\overline{)71}$ = 5 R____

Estimate each quotient. Use compatible numbers. *(Lesson 5-3)*

4. 204 ÷ 37 ____________

5. 242 ÷ 8 ____________

6. 331 ÷ 41 ____________

7. 3,050 ÷ 49 ____________

8. 731 ÷ 80 ____________

9. 44,990 ÷ 49 ____________

Mixed Review

Complete each number sentence.

10. 81 × 7 = ____________ *(3-4)*

11. 0.017 × 5.4 = ____________ *(3-13)*

12. 21,000 ÷ ________ = 300 *(4-2)*

13. 532 ÷ 4 = ____________ *(4-5)*

14. 35,000 ÷ 5 = ____________ *(4-8)*

15. $16 − $8.85 = ____________ *(2-18)*

Round each number to the place of the underlined digit.

16. 9.<u>3</u>87 ________ *(2-12)*

17. 1.<u>9</u>61 ________ *(2-12)*

18. <u>0</u>.39 ________ *(2-12)*

19. Kaylin and Clare are reading a lunch menu. They can buy a chicken dinner which serves 2 for $13.50 or pepper steak for $7.75 each. *(3-7)*

a. How much will 2 pepper steak dinners cost? ____________

b. Give a reason the girls might choose the chicken dinner.

____

____

Name ______________________________

Daily Review
5-6

Daily Cumulative Review

Divide. Check your answer. *(Lesson 5-5)*

1. $27\overline{)1{,}080}$

2. $51\overline{)3{,}723}$

3. $34\overline{)1{,}700}$

4. $61\overline{)1{,}830}$

5. $78\overline{)1{,}716}$

6. $49\overline{)2{,}989}$

Complete. *(Lesson 5-4)*

7. $45\overline{)437}$ = 9 R____

8. $36\overline{)165}$ = 4 R____

9. $74\overline{)535}$ = 7 R____

Mixed Review

Write whether each equation is true or false. Explain how you know.

10. $21 \div 7 = 7 \div 21$ ______________________________
(4-10)

11. $59 \times 1 = 59$ ______________________________
(4-10)

12. $0 \times 49 = 49$ ______________________________
(4-10)

13. Find the product of $1.24 and 26.3. Round to the nearest cent.
(3-13)

____

14. Estimate the quotient of $391 \div 9$. ______________
(4-3)

15. The tag shows that the price has been lowered twice. What was the original price?
(4-15)

____

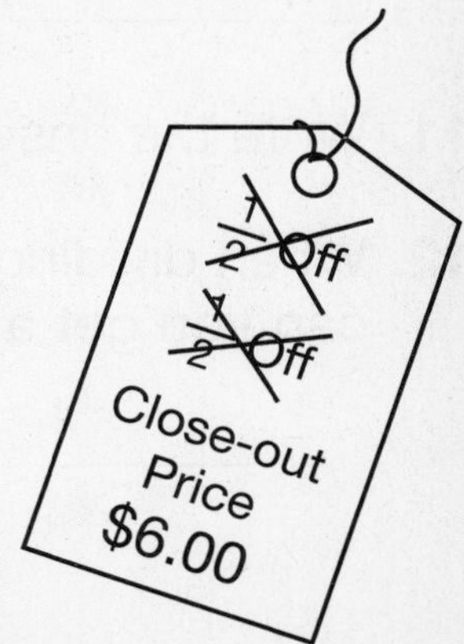

Name ______________________________

Daily Review 5-7

Daily Cumulative Review

Divide and check. Explain what calculation method you used and why. *(Lesson 5-6)*

1. $60\overline{)360}$

2. $24\overline{)366}$

3. $25\overline{)325}$

4. $20\overline{)4,400}$

5. $17\overline{)388}$

6. $35\overline{)35,000}$

Estimate. Use your number sense to choose the best answer for Exercises 7 and 8. *(Lesson 5-5)*

7. 9,377 ÷ 50 is ________

A. more than 200 **B.** less than 200 **C.** exactly 200

8. 4,287 ÷ 60 is ________

A. less than 70 **B.** more than 80 **C.** between 70 and 80

Mixed Review

9. *(2-7)* Write four and fifty hundredths in decimal form. ________________

10. *(3-9)* Estimate the quotient of 46.3 and 5.03. Explain what you did.

____

11. *(4-11)* Write the answer to the nearest cent. $6.58 ÷ 3 = ______________

12. *(4-5)* When dividing a 4-digit number by a 2-digit number, for what divisors can you get a remainder of 24? Explain.

____

Name ______________________________

Daily Review 5-8

Daily Cumulative Review

Divide and check. *(Lesson 5-7)*

1. 20)12,070 **2.** 40)4,200 **3.** 33)35,310

4. 11)2,222 **5.** 51)15,555 **6.** 27)27,164

Divide and check. Tell what calculation method you used and why. *(Lesson 5-6)*

7. 30)6,352 **8.** 40)32,000 **9.** 60)42,600

Mixed Review

Complete.

10. *(4-4)* 4)$12.36

11. *(3-15)* 1.7 × 0.068

12. *(2-18)* $20.00 − $11.76

13. *(4-13)* What are the factors of 54? ______________________________

Write whether each number is prime or composite.

14. *(4-14)* 13 __________ **15.** *(4-14)* 17 __________ **16.** *(4-14)* 21 __________

17. *(3-11)* Kiwi cost 24¢ each. Oranges cost 3 for $1.00. How much would 4 kiwi and 6 oranges cost? __________

Name ______________________

Daily Review
5-9

Daily Cumulative Review

Replace the variable with the given number and do the computation. *(Lesson 5-8)*

1. There are 4 lightbulbs in a package. How many lightbulbs are in n packages?

a. For $n = 3$

$4 \times n = 4 \times$ ______

= ______ lightbulbs

b. For $n = 8$

$4 \times n = 4 \times$ ______

= ______ lightbulbs

2. Mrs. Knox bought a 12-foot board. If she cuts a section n feet long, how much of the board does she have left?

a. For $n = 3$

$12 - n = 12 -$ ______

= ______ feet

b. For $n = 8$

$12 - n = 12 -$ ______

= ______ feet

Divide and check. *(Lesson 5-7)*

3. $3{,}355 \div 11 =$ ______

4. $12{,}060 \div 60 =$ ______

5. $48{,}073 \div 12 =$ ______

6. $83{,}204 \div 80 =$ ______

Mixed Review

7. *(3-11)* A baker can make 3 cakes from a 5-pound sack of flour. How many pounds of flour would be needed for 9 cakes?

______

8. *(3-4)* Use the distributive property to find 44×5.

______

9. *(3-8)* 100 suckers cost $0.06 each. How much do they cost all together?

______

Name ______________________________

Daily Review 5-10

Daily Cumulative Review

Use any strategy to solve the problem. *(Lesson 5-9)*

1. You are designing an office building with 4 stories. There will be 3 offices on each side with 2 offices in the front and back of each story. Each outside wall of each office has a window.

a. How many offices will be in the building? __________

b. How many offices will have only one window? __________

c. How many offices will have two windows? __________

Evaluate the expression for $n = 3$ and $n = 7$. *(Lesson 5-8)*

2. $n - 2$ ______ ______

3. $42 \div n$ ______ ______

4. $n + 8$ ______ ______

5. $n \times 6$ ______ ______

Mixed Review

6. Divide 585 by 26. __________
(5-5)

7. Find the product of 4.05 and 36.02. __________
(3-13)

Find the length of the side of each square.

8. *(4-12)*

Perimeter = 28.56 ft

____

9. *(4-12)*

Perimeter = 6.124 yd

____

10. How many tables are needed for 1,208 people if each table seats 4? __________
(4-8)

Name ______________________________

Daily Review 5-11

Daily Cumulative Review

Estimate to decide whether each quotient in Problems 1–3 is more or less than $1.00. *(Lesson 5-10)*

1. $6\overline{)\$7.23}$ ________

2. $18\overline{)\$16.98}$ ________

3. $9\overline{)\$9.36}$ ________

Use any strategy to solve each problem. *(Lesson 5-9)*

4. Leslie is building a square corral for her horse. Each side of the corral needs 8 fence posts. How many posts will she need?

____

5. Each apartment in a 5-floor apartment building needs 900 square feet of new carpet. If there are 4 apartments on each floor, how much carpet is needed?

____

Mixed Review

6. *(4-7)* The divisor is 7 and the dividend is 878. Divide. ________

7. *(4-10)* If you divide a number by 9 and get zero, what is the number? Explain how you know.

____

8. *(3-10)* Circle each multiplication sentence whose product is a whole number.

21.2×5 $\quad$ 6×9.5 $\quad$ 7.2×7 $\quad$ 16.5×4

9. *(5-5)* If your divisor is 29, what is the greatest possible remainder you could have?

____

10. *(3-16)* The sum of the ages of Carla and her younger brother, Daniel, is 23. The difference in their ages is 5. How old are they?

____

Name ______________________

Daily Review 5-12

Daily Cumulative Review

Use the information given to answer the questions. *(Lesson 5-11)*

Science Museum
Admission
Children: $4 Adults: $5
Senior Citizens: $4
Hours: 9:30 A.M.–6:00 P.M.

Show Times
Laser Light: 10:00, 12:00, 2:00, 4:00 (1 hour show)
Electricity: Every half hour starting at 9:30 (20 minute show)
Holograms: 11:00, 1:00, 3:00 (1 hour show)

1. Blythe, Baxter, their mother, and grandmother visit the science Museum. What is the cost of admission for the family? ______

2. If it takes $1\frac{1}{2}$ hours to drive to the museum and they need to be back home by 3:00, plan a schedule so that they could see each show, visit the nature exhibit, and eat a picnic lunch.

Time	Activity	Time	Activity
______	Leave Home	______	______
______	Arrive at museum	______	______
______	______	______	______
______	______	______	______
		3:00	Arrive at home

Divide and check. *(Lesson 5-10)*

3. $19\overline{)\$80.75}$

4. $15\overline{)\$9.00}$

5. $4\overline{)\$9.88}$

Mixed Review

6. Estimate 5,397 ÷ 52. Use compatible numbers. ______ *(5-3)*

7. What is the LCM for 5, 15, and 25? ______ *(3-6)*

8. Chloe wants to buy 21 ornaments for 79¢ each. Is $15 enough? Explain. ______ *(3-9)*

Name ____________________

Daily Review 6-1

Daily Cumulative Review

Complete the table. *(Lesson 5-12)*

	÷	10	100	1000
1.	3,265.4			
2.	377.1			
3.	982.56			
4.	62.43			
5.	7,400.5			

Use the information to answer the questions. *(Lesson 5-11)*

6. Mr. Burke plans to take his two children to dinner and a play. The play starts at 7:00 P.M. It takes 35 minutes to drive from home to the restaurant and then 25 minutes to the theater. He anticipates that they will need $1\frac{1}{2}$ hours to order, be served, and eat. He wants to be 15 minutes early to buy tickets for the play.

a. How much time will they spend driving? ____________

b. How much total time will they need for driving, eating, and buying tickets? ____________

c. What time do they need to leave home? ____________

Mixed Review

7. *(4-14)* Write the missing factors. 1, ____, ____, ____, ____, 32.

8. *(4-13)* Is 3 a factor of 651? Explain how you know.

____

9. *(5-3)* Which quotient is greater, 5,732 ÷ 21 or 5,732 ÷ 23? ____________

10. *(3-14)* How can you use estimation to know that the product of 6.5 and 3.89 is more than 18? ____________

Name ______________________________

Daily Review
6-2

Daily Cumulative Review

Write the name for each. *(Lesson 6-1)*

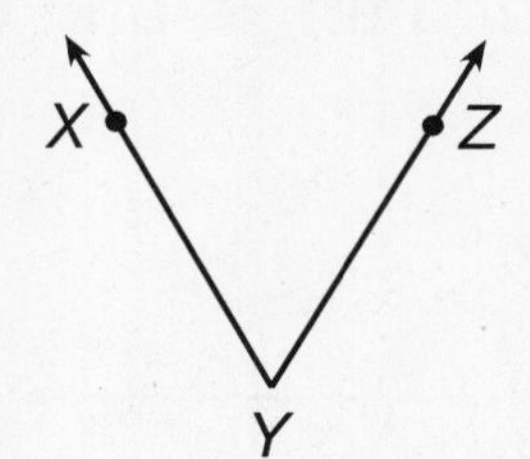

1. ______________________ **2.** ______________________

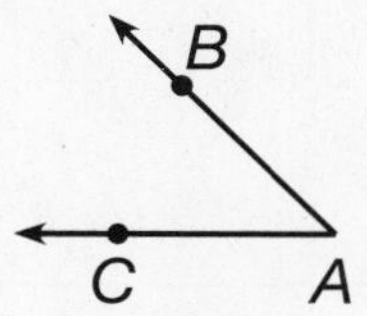

3. ______________________ **4.** ___ ______________________

Find each quotient. Use mental math. *(Lesson 5-12)*

5. 5.73 ÷ 10 = ________ **6.** 4.02 ÷ 100 = ________

7. 42.1 ÷ 10 = ________ **8.** 5 ÷ 1,000 = ________

9. 759.05 ÷ 100 = ________ **10.** 28.6 ÷ 1,000 = ________

Mixed Review

Use a calculator to divide. Write each answer to the nearest cent.

11. $6.14 ÷ 3 = ________ *(4-11)* **12.** $76.31 ÷ 8 = ________ *(4-11)*

13. *(4-6)* A test tube racks hold 5 tubes each. How many racks are needed to hold 28 test tubes?

____

14. *(3-12)* Write a number sentence that describes the shaded areas of the grid.

____

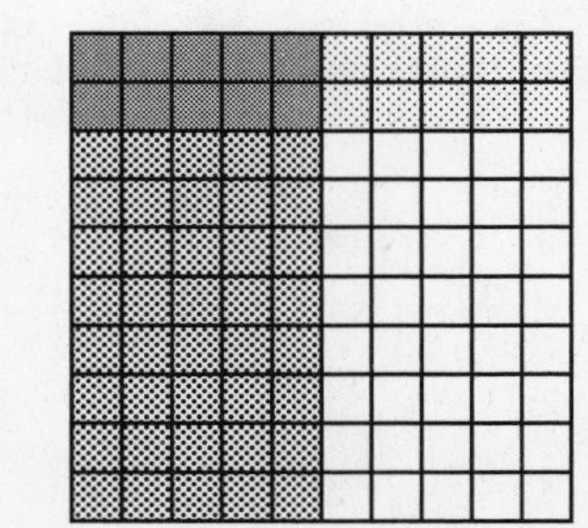

Name ______________________________

Daily Review 6-3

Daily Cumulative Review

Classify each angle as acute, right, obtuse, or straight. Extend the sides of each angle and measure it with a protractor. *(Lesson 6-2)*

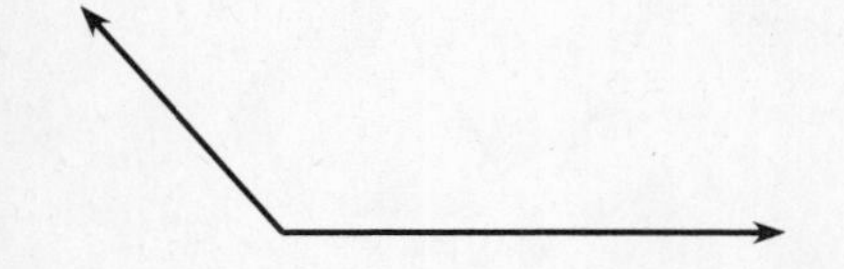

1. ____________________

2. ____________________

3. ____________________

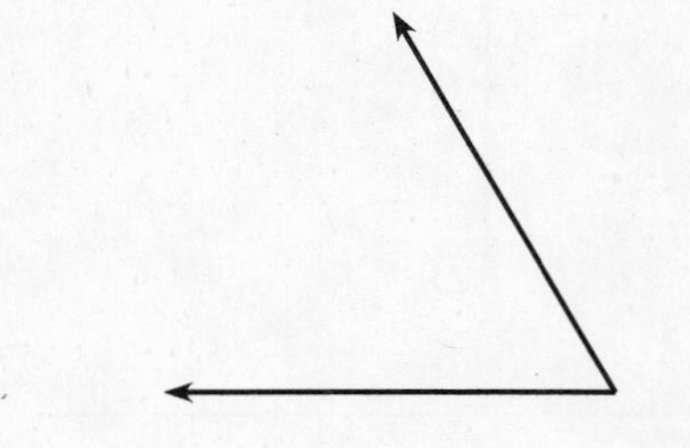

4. ____________________

Name each in the figure at the right. *(Lesson 6-1)*

5. Perpendicular lines

____________ ____________

6. Parallel lines

____

W X Z Y

Mixed Review

Multiply or divide.

7. 5)$7.9 5 *(4-4)*

8. 9)6,3 1 0 *(4-8)*

9. *(3-5)*

$$\begin{array}{r} 705 \\ \times\ 130 \\ \hline \end{array}$$

Name ______________________________

Daily Review 6-4

Daily Cumulative Review

Classify each triangle as equilateral, isosceles, or scalene. *(Lesson 6-3)*

1.

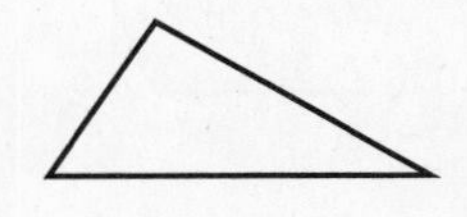

____

2.

____

3.

____

Choose the best estimate of each angle's measure. Then use a protractor to check your estimate. *(Lesson 6-2)*

4.

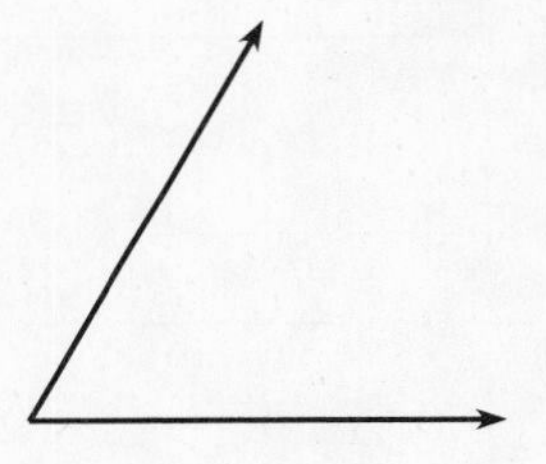

____

A. 20°
B. 60°
C. 100°

5.

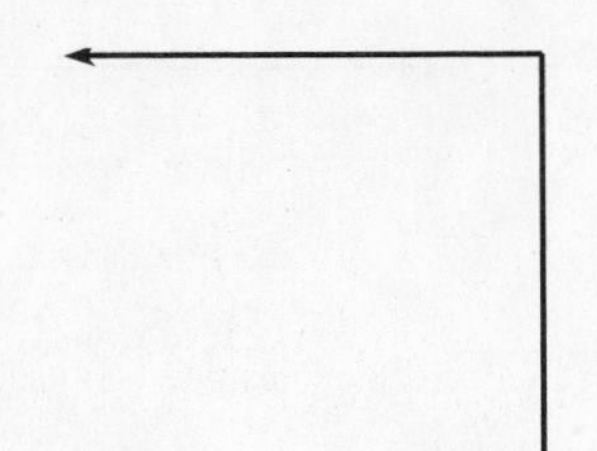

____

A. 90°
B. 120°
C. 160°

6.

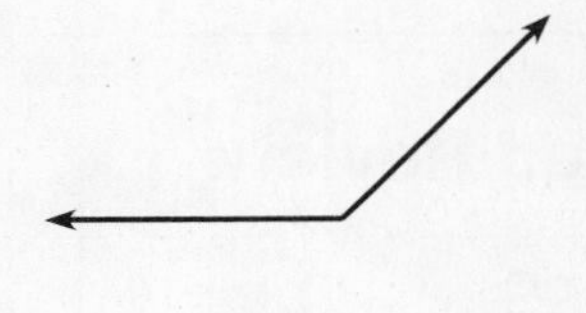

____

A. 45°
B. 90°
C. 135°

Mixed Review

7. *(4-3)* You know that 159 ÷ 4 is about 40.
Find estimates for 1,590 ÷ 4 and 15,900 ÷ 4. ______________

Multiply or divide.

8. *(5-7)* $69\overline{)715}$

9. *(4-12)* $8\overline{)50.56}$

10. *(3-13)* 4.4×0.6

11. *(3-5)* 679×200

Name ______________________________

Daily Review 6-5

Daily Cumulative Review

Write the name that best describes each figure. *(Lesson 6-4)*

1. 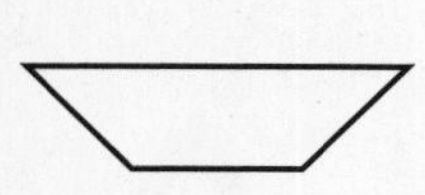

____

2. 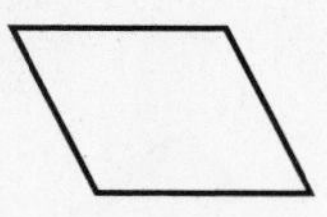

____

3. 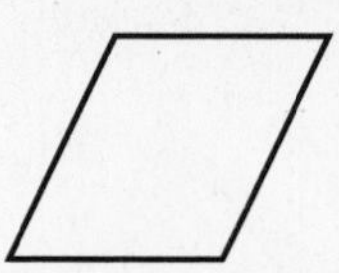

____

Classify each triangle as acute, right, or obtuse. *(Lesson 6-3)*

4. 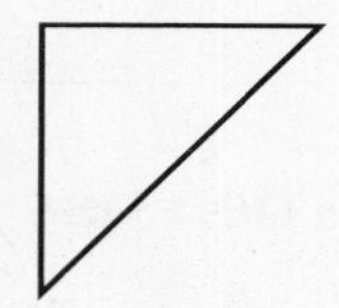

____

5. 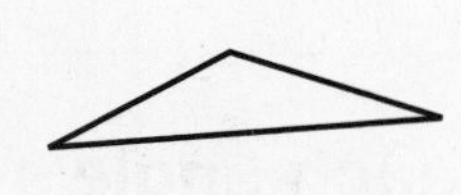

____

6. 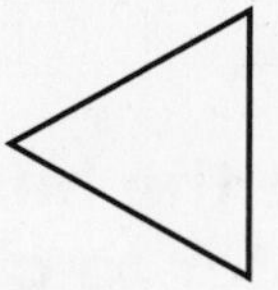

____

Mixed Review

7. $19 - 4.92 =$ ______________ *(2-18)*

8. $5.18 \times 3 =$ ______________ *(3-10)*

9. $280 \div 40 =$ ______________ *(5-1)*

10. $50 \times 9 \times 2 =$ ______________ *(5-1)*

11. *(3-11)* Mr. Walker bought wood varnish for $18.25 and a brush set for $6.75. What was the total cost? ______________

12. *(2-19)* Parking for a concert costs $3 for each car. If the attendant collected $1,671, how many cars were parked? __________

13. *(1-9)* Use the table to make a line graph

Average Monthly Temperatures °F			
June	79	October	63
July	82	November	51
August	81	December	43
September	74	January	38

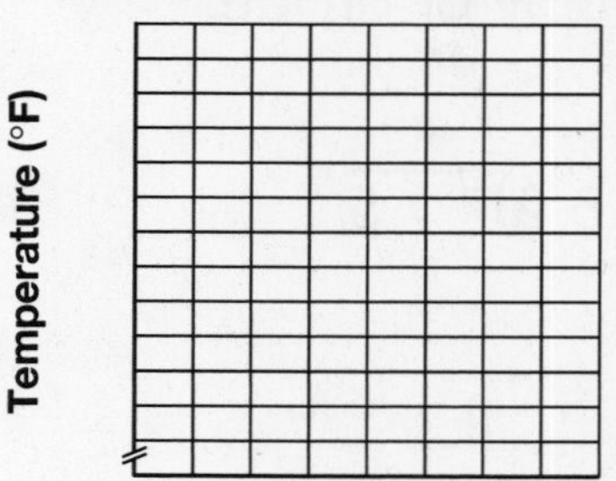

Name ______________________________

Daily Review 6-6

Daily Cumulative Review

Solve a simpler problem. *(Lesson 6-5)*

Mr. Lambert is arranging a canned-peach display in his grocery store.

1. Complete the table to find how many cans of peaches he will need to make the display 10 rows high.

Number of rows	1	2	3	4	5	6	7	8	9	10
Number of cans	1	3	6	10						

1 row:

2 rows:

3 rows:

2. If he wanted to make eleven rows, how many more cans would he have to include? ________

3. What would be the total number of cans if he had 11 rows? ________

Write the name that best describes each figure. *(Lesson 6-4)*

4. 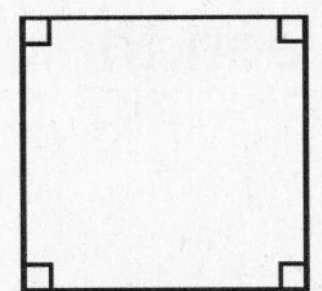

5. 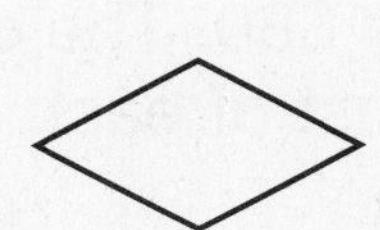

6. 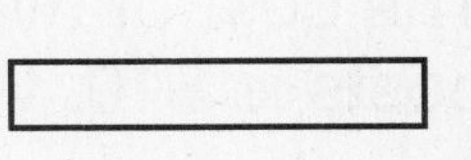

________________ ________________ ________________

Mixed Review

Divide.

7. $6\overline{)4\,5\,6}$ *(4-7)*

8. $8\overline{)\$7\,2.4\,8}$ *(4-4)*

9. $5\overline{)1{,}0\,0\,5}$ *(4-8)*

10. *(3-16)* Maruka chose two numbers less than 20. The product of the numbers is 72 and the sum of the numbers is 22. What are the numbers?

____

Name ______________________

Daily Review
6-7

Daily Cumulative Review

Circle the polygon congruent to the first one in each row. *(Lesson 6-6)*

1.  **A.** 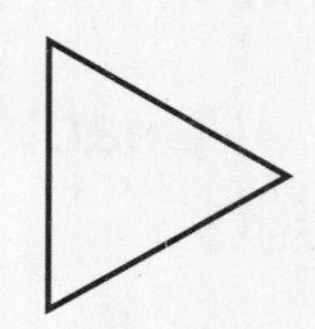 **B.** 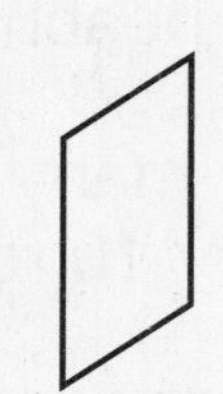 **C.** 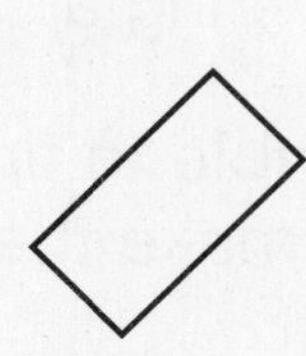

2. 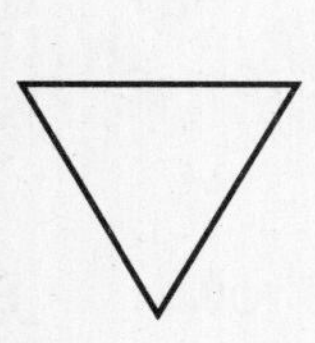 **A.** 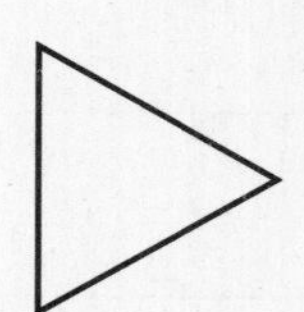 **B.** 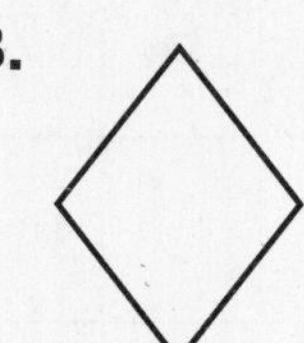 **C.** 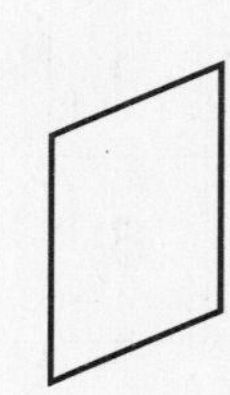

3. 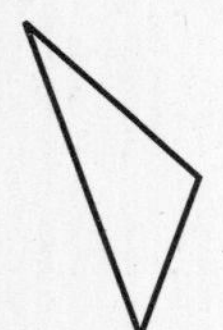 **A.** 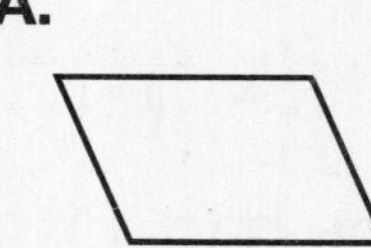 **B.** 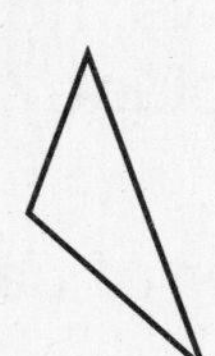 **C.** 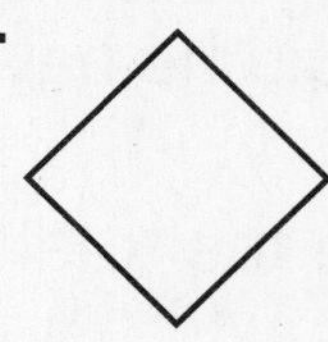

Use any strategy to solve each problem. *(Lesson 6-5)*

4. The cost of two paintings is $80. The difference between their costs is $10. What is the cost of each painting?

____

5. Five teams are playing in a tournament. If each of the five head coaches shakes hands with each of the other coaches, how many handshakes are there in all?

____

Mixed Review

6. Name the place that contains a 9 in 27.5936. ______________
(2-4)

7. How many 8-inch sections can be cut from a 120-inch ball of string?
(4-1)

____

8. Evaluate $n - 12$ for $n = 21$. ______________
(5-8)

Name ______________________

Daily Cumulative Review

For each pentomino pair, write whether you would flip, turn, or slide the figures to show that they are congruent. *(Lesson 6-7)*

1. 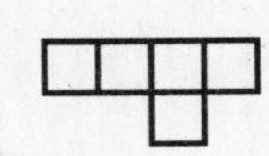

____

2.

____

3. 

____

Circle the polygon similar to the first one in each row. *(Lesson 6-6)*

4. 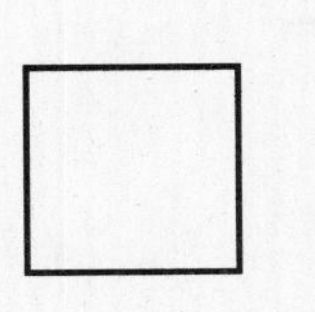 **A.** 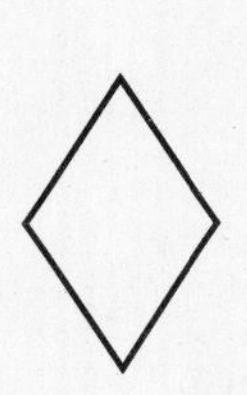 **B.** 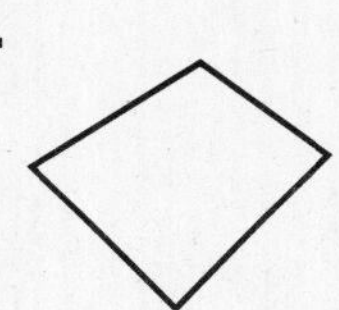 **C.** 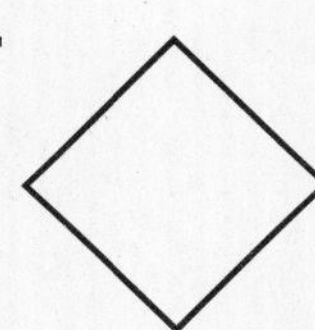

5. 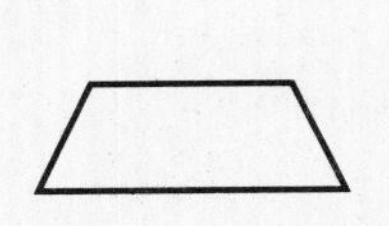 **A.** 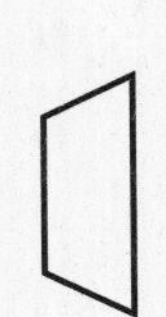 **B.** 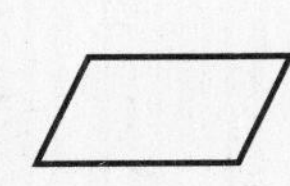 **C.** 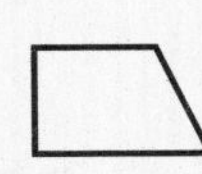

6. 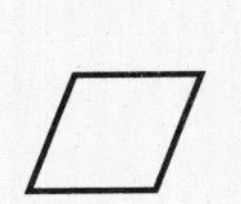 **A.**  **B.** 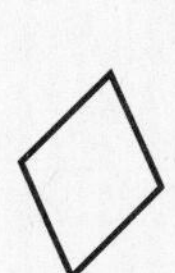 **C.** 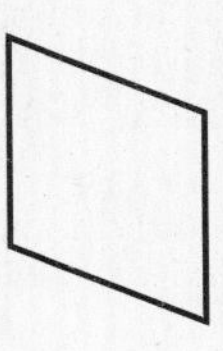

Mixed Review

7. Estimate the quotient 359 ÷ 4. ______________________
(4-3)

8. Is $325 ÷ 60 less than $5 or more than $5? ______________________
(5-10)

9. English muffins come 6 to a bag. At a parent-teacher breakfast, the Spanish Club served 53 muffins. How many bags did they open? How many muffins were left over? ______________________
(4-6)

Name ____

Daily Review 6-9

Daily Cumulative Review

Draw all lines of symmetry. *(Lesson 6-8)*

1.

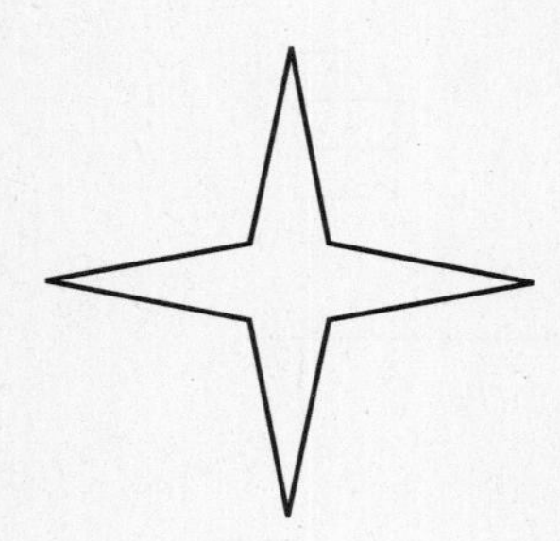

2.

3.

Write whether each picture shows a slide, flip, or turn. *(Lesson 6-7)*

4. ____________________

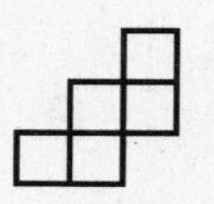

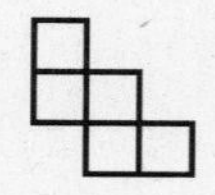

5. ____________________

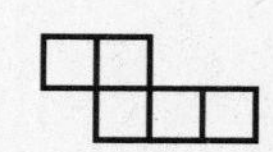

Mixed Review

6. Write $>$, $<$, or $=$ to complete.
(4-10)

$n \div 7 = 0$ **a.** n ◯ 7 **b.** n ◯ 0

7. $69\overline{)323}$
(5-4)

8. $36\overline{)7{,}344}$
(5-7)

9. $7\overline{)\$8.96}$
(4-4)

10. Estimate $15{,}876 \div 50$. Give a high and low estimate. ____________________
(5-2)

11. Tasha drew a triangle with a 95° angle. Could it be acute, right, or obtuse? ____________________
(6-3)

Name ______________________

Daily Cumulative Review

To make a good decision, you need to think about the details. Answer the following questions. *(Lesson 6-9)*

You must complete a geometry project by the end of the week. There are 2 projects from which to choose. You will be working by yourself.

Polygon Quilt
Draw a quilt design that includes all the polygons from this chapter. Include some similar and some congruent figures. Choose a color for each shape in your quilt.

Symmetry Puzzle
Draw a picture that includes at least 3 figures with symmetry. Trace your drawing on cardboard. Cut it into pieces to make a jigsaw puzzle. Cut along all lines of symmetry.

1. How much time do you have to work on the project?

____

2. Do you have the materials you need? ______________________

3. Which project would you choose to complete? Why?

____

Use the line of symmetry to complete each figure. *(Lesson 6-8)*

4.

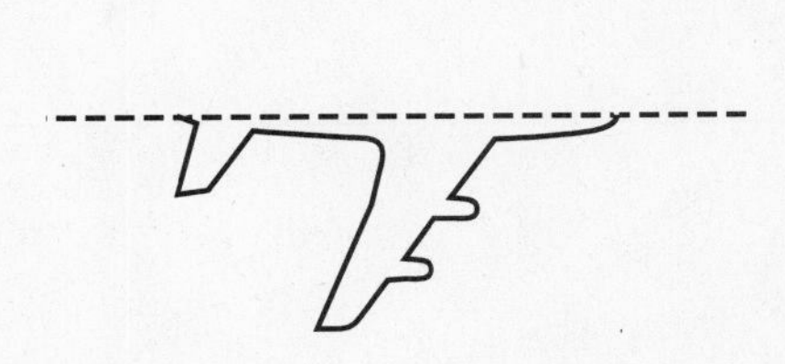

5.

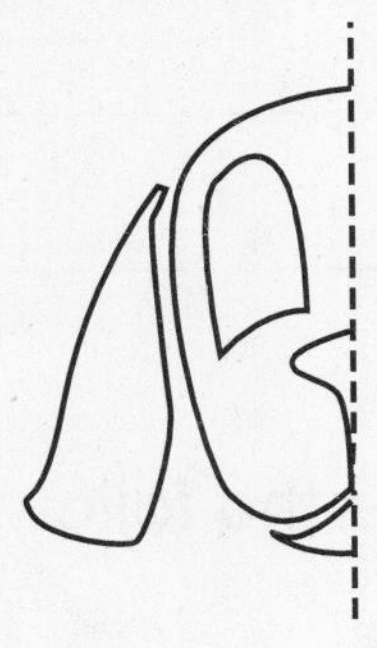

Mixed Review

Multiply or divide.

6. $4\overline{)337}$
(4-5)

7. $27\overline{)8,889}$
(4-5)

8. $\begin{array}{r} 167 \\ \times\ 89 \\ \hline \end{array}$
(4-5)

Name ______________________

Daily Review 7-2

Daily Cumulative Review

Write the fraction that names each shaded part. *(Lesson 7-1)*

1. ◉ ◉ ○ ◉ ○ ◉
◉ ○ ◉ ◉ ○ ○

2.

3.

_______ _______ _______

Decision making. You have 3 choices for a geometry project.
(Lesson 6-9)

Trapezoid Design	Rectangle Design	Rhombus Design
Make a design using 6 trapezoids.	Make a design using 10 rectangles.	Make a design using 5 rhombuses.

4. What materials will you use?

____

5. How long will it take? ______________________

6. Which project would you do? Explain your reasons for your decision.

____

____

Mixed Review

Use the figure to name the following.

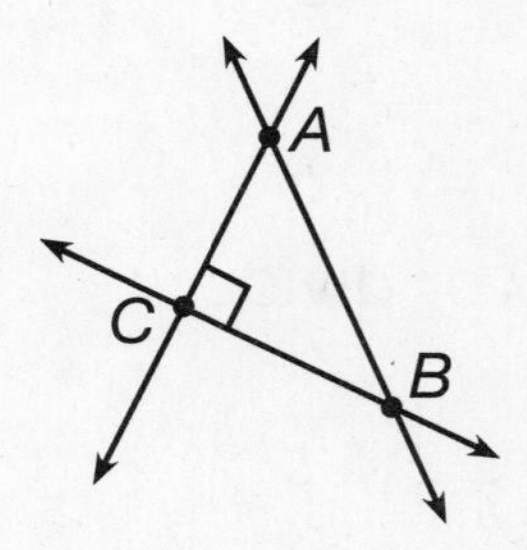

7. perpendicular lines ______________________
(6-1)

8. a right angle ______________________
(6-1)

9. the rays that form $\angle B$ ______________________
(6-1)

Name ______________________

Daily Review 7-3

Daily Cumulative Review

Write two fractions that name the shaded part. *(Lesson 7-2)*

1. 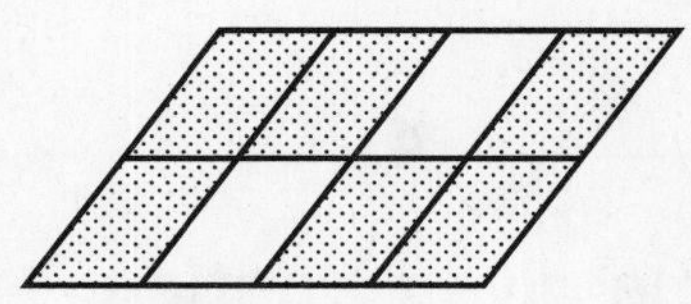

2. 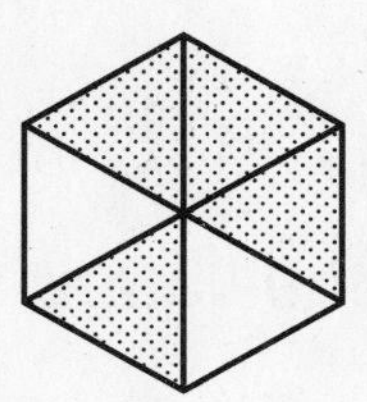

3. 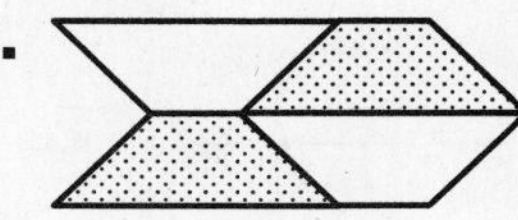

________ ________ ________

What part of each set is square? *(Lesson 7-1)*

4. 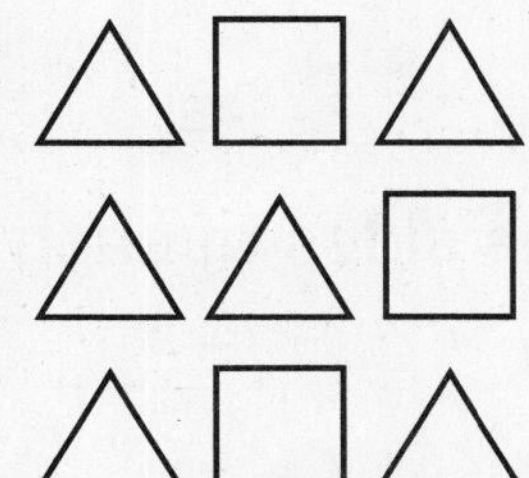

5. 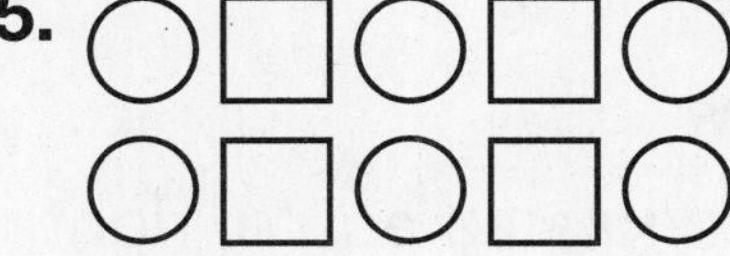

________ ________

Mixed Review

6. Write 3.4 in words. ______________________
(2-7)

7. Find the LCM of 8 and 24. ________
(3-6)

8. Find the mean, median, and mode for
(4-9) $3.25, $4.50, $5.50, $5.50, $6.25. ________

9. You are playing in a tournament with 4 teams. Each team plays
(6-5) until they lose. If there are no tied games, how many games will be played?

____

10. What is the greatest number that rounds to 41,000,000
(2-6) when rounded to millions place?

____

Name ______________________________

Daily Review 7-4

Daily Cumulative Review

Find equivalent fractions with a denominator of 9. *(Lesson 7-3)*

1. $\frac{3}{27}$ __________ **2.** $\frac{2}{3}$ __________ **3.** $\frac{12}{54}$ __________ **4.** $\frac{6}{18}$ __________

Which shading shows a fraction equivalent to the given fraction. *(Lesson 7-2)*

5. $\frac{1}{4}$ ________

6. $\frac{2}{3}$ ________

7. $\frac{5}{8}$ ________

A.

B.

C.

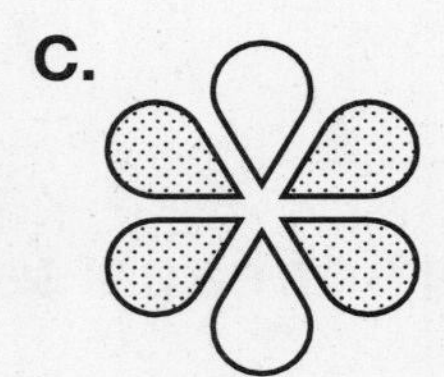

Mixed Review

Identify each angle as acute, right, or obtuse. Extend the sides of each angle. Then measure each with a protractor.

8. *(6-2)*

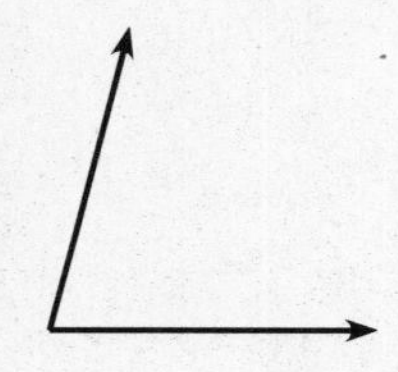

____

9. *(6-2)*

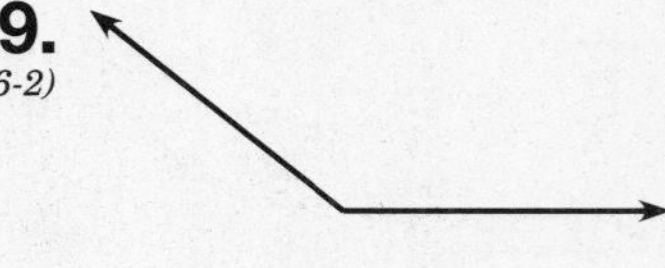

____

Classify each triangle as equilateral, isosceles, or scalene. Then classify each triangle as acute, right, or obtuse.

10. *(6-3)*

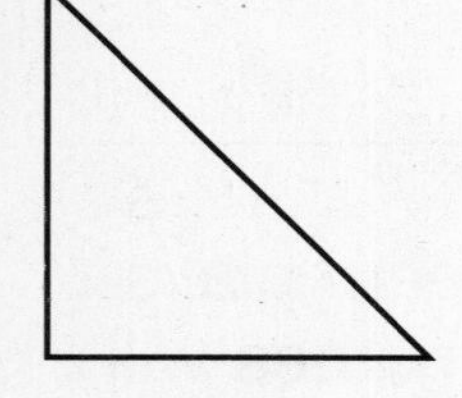

____

____

11. *(6-3)*

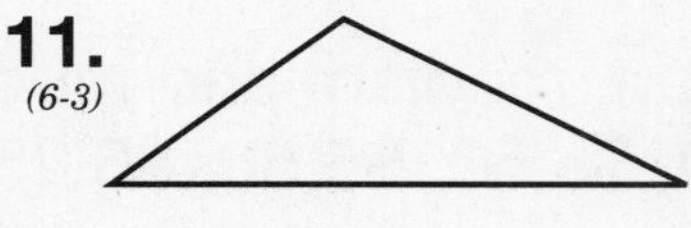

____

____

Divide.

12. $24 \div 3 =$ __________ *(4-1)*

13. $832 \div 4 =$ __________ *(4-7)*

14. $\$37.02 \div 6 =$ __________ *(4-11)*

15. $41.12 \div 8 =$ __________ *(4-12)*

Name ______________________________

Daily Cumulative Review

Find the greatest common factor for each pair. *(Lesson 7-4)*

1. 6 and 10 ________ **2.** 12 and 16 ________ **3.** 9 and 15 ________ **4.** 8 and 24 ________

5. 16 and 20 ________ **6.** 12 and 18 ________ **7.** 27 and 36 ________ **8.** 14 and 21 ________

Name the fractions in the box equivalent to each fraction below.
(Lesson 7-3)

$\frac{5}{15}$	$\frac{6}{8}$	$\frac{7}{21}$	$\frac{8}{12}$	$\frac{4}{16}$	$\frac{12}{18}$	$\frac{9}{12}$	$\frac{3}{12}$

9. $\frac{2}{3}$ ________ **10.** $\frac{1}{4}$ ________

11. $\frac{1}{3}$ ________ **12.** $\frac{3}{4}$ ________

Mixed Review

Round each number to the place of the underlined digit.

13. *(2-12)* $1\underline{2}.49$ ________ **14.** *(2-12)* $0.\underline{0}51$ ________ **15.** *(2-12)* $\underline{6}.097$ ________

Solve.

16. *(2-15)* $\begin{array}{r} 604 \\ +\ 197 \\ \hline \end{array}$ **17.** *(3-3)* $\begin{array}{r} 375 \\ \times\ \ 6 \\ \hline \end{array}$ **18.** *(3-13)* $\begin{array}{r} 2.34 \\ \times\ 0.5 \\ \hline \end{array}$ **19.** *(3-16)* $\begin{array}{r} 9.53 \\ -\ 0.9 \\ \hline \end{array}$

20. *(2-1)* An anteater can eat 30,000 ants in a day. In about how many days can an anteater eat 1 million ants? ________

21. *(5-8)* A chef uses 2 cups of olive oil and *n* cups of corn oil. Write an expression for the total number of cups used. ________

Name ________________________________

Daily Review
7-6

Daily Cumulative Review

Find the simplest form for each fraction. *(Lesson 7-5)*

1. $\frac{3}{24}$ ________ **2.** $\frac{12}{15}$ ________ **3.** $\frac{6}{14}$ ________ **4.** $\frac{16}{20}$ ________ **5.** $\frac{28}{36}$ ________

Find two numbers that have the given number as the greatest common factor. *(Lesson 7-4)*

6. 4 ________________________

7. 8 ________________________

8. 9 ________________________

9. 12 ________________________

Mixed Review

10. Which of the figures is not congruent to [figure]? ________
(6-7)

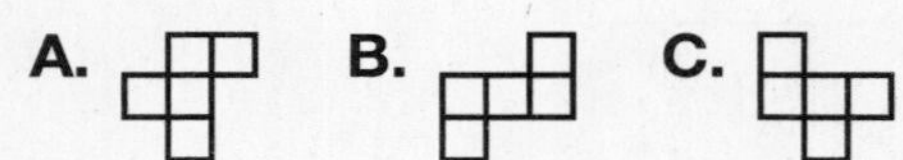

11. Which shows $\frac{3}{5}$? ________
(7-1)

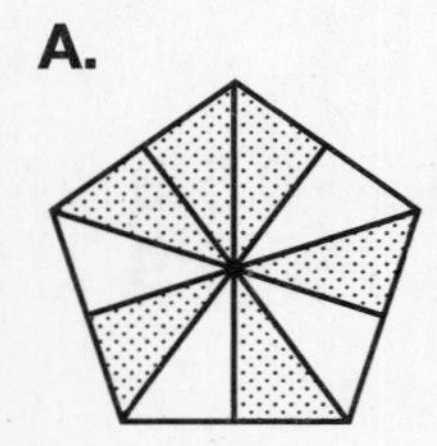

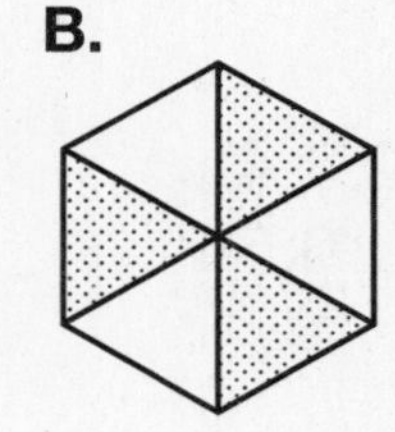

12. Give the rule using a variable. ________
(1-7)

A	B
5	1
10	2
15	3
20	4

13. What are the factors of 30? ________________________
(4-13)

Multiply or divide.

14. 99,000 ÷ ____________ = 110
(4-3)

15. 0.65 × 1,000 = ____________
(3-8)

Name ______________________________

Daily Review
7-7

Daily Cumulative Review

Compare each pair of fractions. You may use fraction strips or draw pictures. Write >, <, or = to complete. *(Lesson 7-6)*

1. $\frac{3}{5}$ ◯ $\frac{3}{7}$ **2.** $\frac{1}{8}$ ◯ $\frac{1}{7}$ **3.** $\frac{2}{6}$ ◯ $\frac{3}{9}$ **4.** $\frac{5}{9}$ ◯ $\frac{7}{9}$

Write whether each fraction is in simplest form. If it is not, find the simpler form. *(Lesson 7-5)*

5. $\frac{3}{8}$ **6.** $\frac{9}{12}$ **7.** $\frac{24}{36}$ **8.** $\frac{4}{9}$

________ ________ ________ ________

Mixed Review

Use the figure to answer questions 9–11.

9. Name parallel lines. ________________
(6-1)

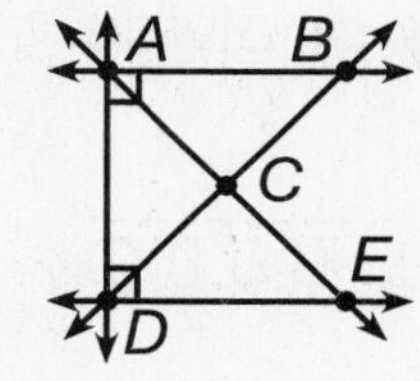

10. Classify triangle *ADE* as acute, right, or obtuse. ________________
(6-3)

11. Name a triangle congruent to triangle *ABC*. ________________
(6-6)

12. Estimate the quotient. 297 ÷ 3 ________________
(4-3)

13. Complete.
(5-8)

n	7	15	21	27	30	42
$n - 3$						

14. A kennel has for sale 18 cocker spaniels, half that many collies, and two more golden retrievers than collies. How many dogs are for sale?
(5-9)

____

Name ______________________

Daily Review 7-8

Daily Cumulative Review

Write >, <, or = to complete. *(Lesson 7-7)*

1. $\frac{3}{7}$ ◯ $\frac{7}{8}$ **2.** $\frac{5}{6}$ ◯ $\frac{3}{4}$ **3.** $\frac{3}{12}$ ◯ $\frac{6}{24}$

4. $\frac{3}{4}$ ◯ $\frac{4}{5}$ **5.** $\frac{2}{3}$ ◯ $\frac{5}{9}$ **6.** $\frac{6}{10}$ ◯ $\frac{9}{15}$

Order these fractions from least to greatest. Use fraction strips. *(Lesson 7-6)*

7. $\frac{1}{4}, \frac{1}{3}, \frac{1}{5}$ ________, ________, ________

8. $\frac{7}{10}, \frac{3}{5}, \frac{5}{7}$ ________, ________, ________

Mixed Review

Multiply or divide.

9. *(5-7)* $15\overline{)30{,}600}$ **10.** *(5-7)* $16\overline{)3{,}216}$ **11.** *(3-13)* 1.005×0.08

12. *(5-1)* 40,000 ÷ 200 = ________ **13.** *(5-4)* 84 ÷ 14 = ________

Identify each number as prime or composite.

14. *(4-14)* 11 ____________ **15.** *(4-14)* 21 ____________ **16.** *(4-14)* 51 ____________

17. *(5-10)* If you had $475.50 to give to 15 people, and each person gets the same amount, how much would each person get? ____________

18. *(6-8)* Draw a polygon that has exactly one line of symmetry.

Name ___________________________

Daily Review
7-9

Daily Cumulative Review

Make a table or use another strategy to solve each problem. *(Lesson 7-8)*

1. A brownie mix uses 2 eggs for 12 brownies. How many eggs are needed to make 48 brownies? ____________

2. After running about 3 minutes, you have used about 20 calories. How many calories have you used after running for 9 minutes? ____________

3. Jennifer earns $4.50 each afternoon babysitting for a neighbor. How much does she earn in 5 afternoons? ____________

Write >, <, or = to complete. *(Lesson 7-7)*

4. $\frac{5}{6} \bigcirc \frac{9}{12}$ **5.** $\frac{9}{12} \bigcirc \frac{6}{8}$ **6.** $\frac{2}{3} \bigcirc \frac{4}{5}$

7. $\frac{3}{15} \bigcirc \frac{4}{20}$ **8.** $\frac{3}{8} \bigcirc \frac{3}{10}$ **9.** $\frac{5}{9} \bigcirc \frac{2}{3}$

Mixed Review

Divide.

10. 43.6 ÷ ____________ = 4.36 *(5-12)*

11. 215 ÷ 18 = ____________ *(5-4)*

12. An angle's measure is more than 90° and less than 180°. How is it classified? ____________ *(6-2)*

Use a calculator to divide. Write each answer to the nearest cent.

13. $14.94 ÷ 7 = ____________ *(4-11)*

14. $32.85 ÷ 8 = ____________ *(4-11)*

15. How many 1,000s make 100,000,000? ____________ *(2-3)*

16. Estimate the product of 42 and 328. Is it closer to 12,000 or 20,000? *(3-5)*

____

17. Circle the fractions that are in simplest form. *(7-5)*

$\frac{7}{9}$ $\frac{12}{16}$ $\frac{18}{27}$ $\frac{13}{16}$ $\frac{2}{20}$ $\frac{9}{11}$

Name ______________________________

Daily Cumulative Review

Write the mixed or whole number and the improper fraction that name each shaded part. *(Lesson 7-9)*

1. 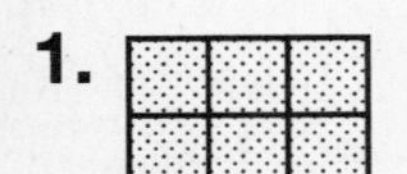 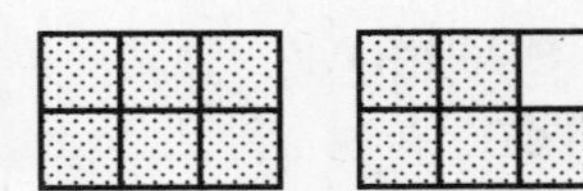

____

2. 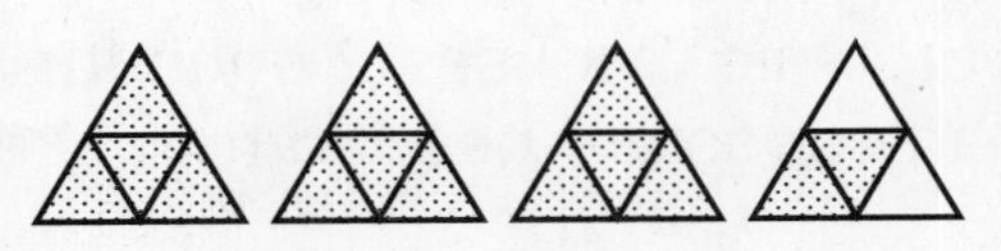

____

3. 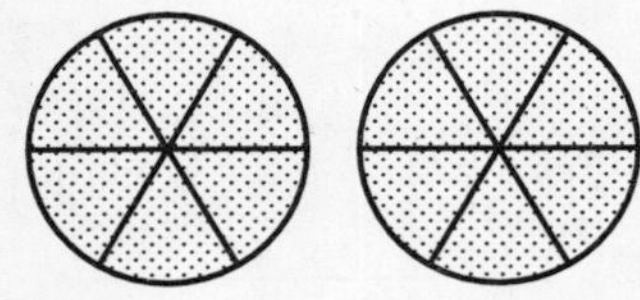

____

4. 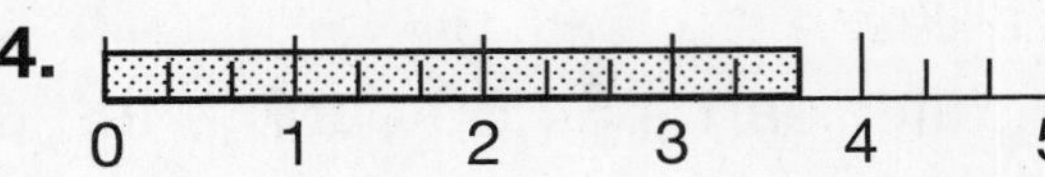

____

Make a table or use any other strategy to solve each problem.
(Lesson 7-8)

5. A package of 3 video tapes costs $8.75.
How much do 9 tapes cost? ______________

6. Cassie's family recycles about 75 aluminum cans each week. How many weeks will it take them to recycle 900 cans.? ______________

Mixed Review

Write the name that best describes each figure.

7. *(6-4)*

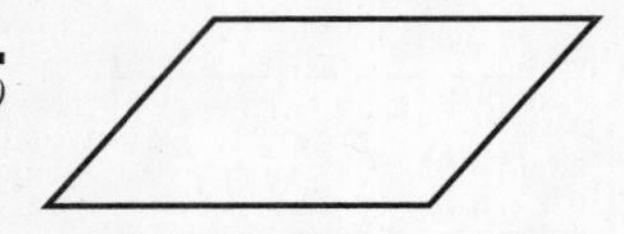

____

8. *(6-4)*

____

9. *(4-14)* Can a whole number ending in 6 be prime? Explain.

____

____

Name ______________________

Daily Review
7-11

Daily Cumulative Review

Write each improper fraction as a mixed number in simplest form or as a whole number. *(Lesson 7-10)*

1. $\frac{23}{4}$ = ______ **2.** $\frac{14}{7}$ = ______ **3.** $\frac{13}{3}$ = ______

4. $\frac{16}{5}$ = ______ **5.** $\frac{27}{6}$ = ______ **6.** $\frac{43}{8}$ = ______

Make a drawing that shows each fraction. *(Lesson 7-9)*

7. $\frac{6}{4}$

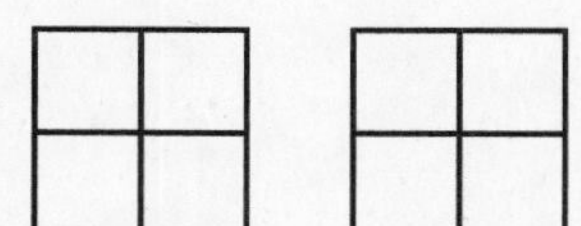

8. $\frac{7}{5}$

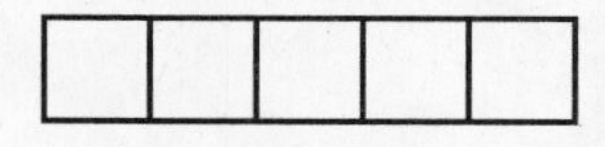

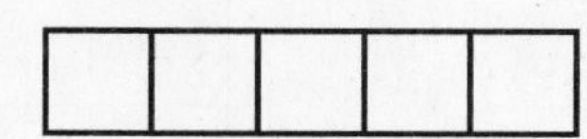

9. $\frac{8}{2}$

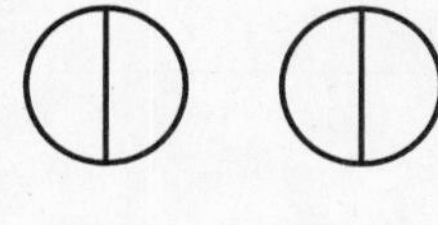

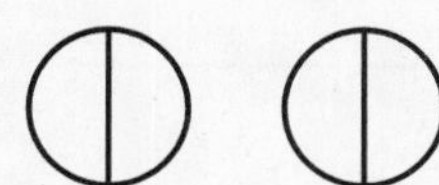

10. $\frac{4}{3}$

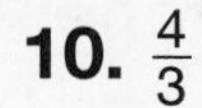

Mixed Review

Estimate each quotient. Give a high and low estimate.

11. 4,207 ÷ 50 *(5-2)* ______

12. 3,729 ÷ 70 *(5-2)* ______

13. 2,868 ÷ 30 *(5-2)* ______

14. *(4-10)* Write whether the equation 3 × 405 = 405 × 3 is true or false. Explain how you knew.

____

Name ______________________

Daily Review 7-12

Daily Cumulative Review

Give a mixed number for the shaded part of each picture.
Use $>$ or $<$ to compare each pair of mixed numbers. *(Lesson 7-11)*

1. 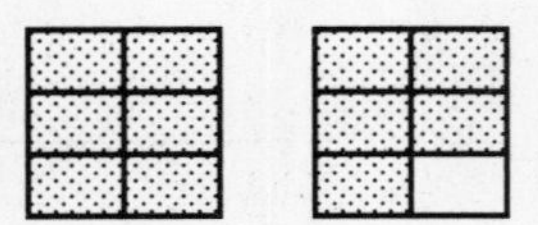 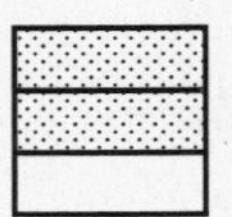

__________ ○ __________

2. 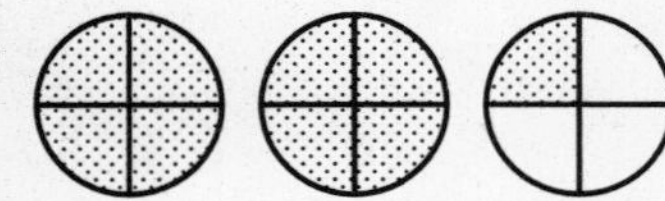 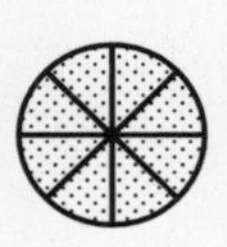 

__________ ○ __________

Write each number as an improper fraction. *(Lesson 7-10)*

3. $2\frac{1}{6}$ = __________ **4.** $3\frac{2}{5}$ = __________ **5.** $4\frac{2}{3}$ = __________

6. $1\frac{7}{8}$ = __________ **7.** $9\frac{1}{2}$ = __________ **8.** $5\frac{3}{7}$ = __________

Mixed Review

9. *(5-3)* Estimate using compatible numbers.

26,897 ÷ 88 __________________

10. *(4-12)* Find the length of the side of a square with perimeter 13.88 inches.

____

11. *(3-4)* Use the distributive property to find 290 × 4.

____

12. *(6-8)* Draw a triangle that has no lines of symmetry.

Name ______________________________

Daily Review 7-13

Daily Cumulative Review

Write the hundredths fraction and the percent shaded in each picture. *(Lesson 7-12)*

1. 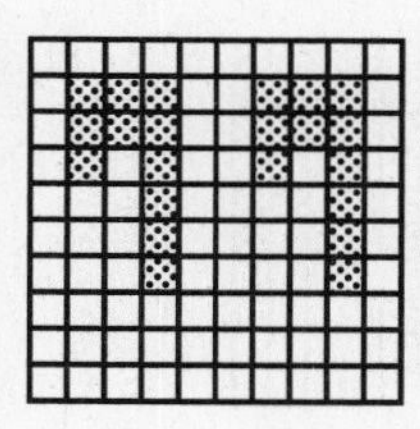

____

____

2. 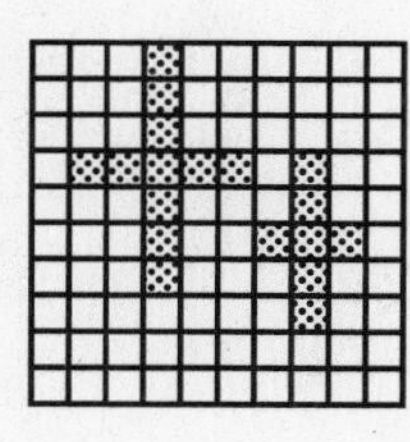

____

____

3. 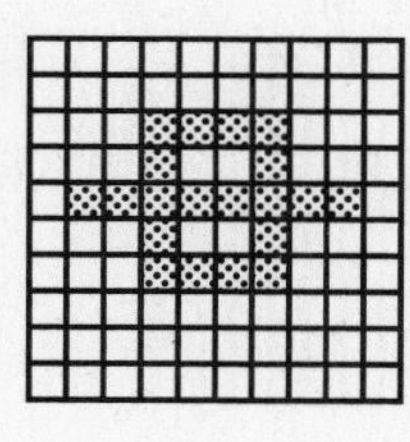

____

____

Compare. Use > or <. *(Lesson 7-11)*

4. $3\frac{5}{6}$ ◯ $3\frac{6}{7}$

5. $1\frac{2}{5}$ ◯ $1\frac{3}{8}$

6. $2\frac{7}{9}$ ◯ $2\frac{3}{4}$

Mixed Review

Multiply or divide.

7. *(4-5)* $4\overline{)423}$

8. *(3-13)*

$$\begin{array}{r} 1.5 \\ \times\ 1.5 \\ \hline \end{array}$$

9. *(3-3)* 10^3 = ____ × ____ × ____ = ______

10. *(2-8)* Write 0.9 as an equivalent decimal using hundredths. ______

Write >, <, or = to compare.

11. *(2-11)* 0.41 ◯ 0.39

12. *(2-11)* 0.4 ◯ 0.40

13. *(2-11)* 0.75 ◯ 0.7

14. *(4-14)* Use a factor tree to find the prime factors of 70.

70 = ____ × ____ × ____

Name ____________________________________

Daily Review 7-14

Daily Cumulative Review

Write a fraction, a decimal, and a percent that names each shaded part. *(Lesson 7-13)*

1. 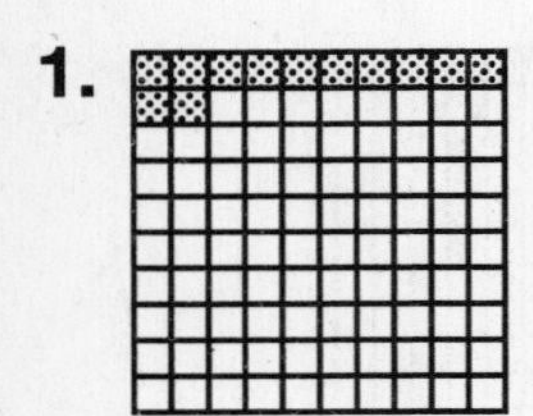

____

____

____

2. 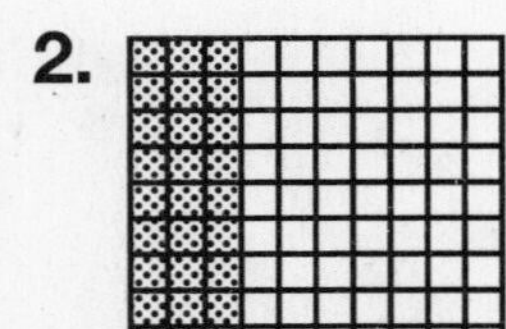

____

____

____

3. 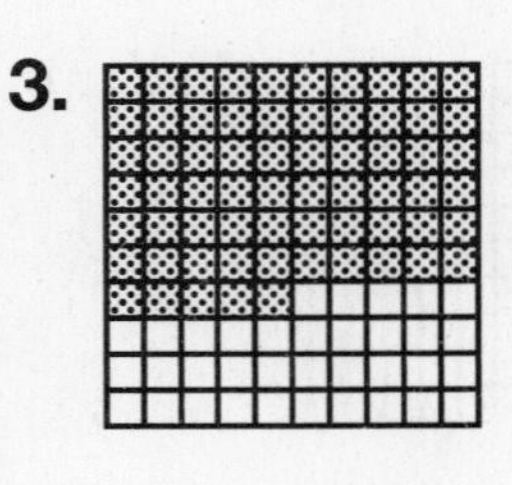

____

____

____

For each set, decide which does *not* belong. *(Lesson 7-12)*

4. ______ **A.** 33% **B.** $\frac{33}{100}$ **C.** $\frac{3}{10}$ **D.** 33 out of 100

5. ______ **A.** $\frac{4}{100}$ **B.** 40% **C.** $\frac{4}{10}$ **D.** 40 out of 100

6. ______ **A.** $\frac{100}{100}$ **B.** 100% **C.** 1 **D.** 1 out of 100

Mixed Review

7. Estimate the quotient of 997 ÷ 2. ______
(4-3)

8. Estimate high and low and then find the product of 7.4 and 2.6.
(3-14)

Estimate: ____________ Product: ________

Divide.

9. $5\overline{)3{,}604}$
(4-8)

10. $8\overline{)3.288}$
(4-12)

11. $36\overline{)415}$
(5-4)

Name ______________________________

Daily Review
8-1

Daily Cumulative Review

Compare survey results. *(Lesson 7-14)*

Phillipe read a survey in the newspaper about readers' favorite sports. He decided to survey 10 students in his class to see if the results would be the same. His results are shown in the table.

Favorite Sports of Readers		Votes for Favorite Sports of Students	
Basketball	35%	Basketball	4
Soccer	10%	Soccer	1
Football	40%	Football	2
Ice Skating	5%	Ice Skating	1
Baseball	10%	Baseball	2

Write fractions, decimals, and percents to describe Phillipe's survey results.

	Sport	Fraction	Decimal	Percent
1.	Basketball	________	________	________
2.	Soccer	________	________	________
3.	Football	________	________	________
4.	Ice skating	________	________	________
5.	Baseball	________	________	________

6. Which sport has the biggest difference between the two surveys? ________________

Write each as a percent. *(Lesson 7-13)*

7. 15 out of 100 ______

8. 0.35 ______

9. $\frac{11}{100}$ ______

Mixed Review

Find each product or quotient.

10. $427 \div 1000 =$ ____________ *(5-12)*

11. $6 \times 0.004 =$ ____________ *(3-15)*

12. $\$370.40 \div 20 =$ ____________ *(5-10)*

13. $\$9.18 \times 14 =$ ____________ *(3-13)*

Name ______________________

Daily Cumulative Review

Find each sum or difference. Simplify. *(Lesson 8-1)*

1. $\frac{2}{9} + \frac{4}{9}$ ________

2. $\frac{3}{10} + \frac{7}{10}$ ________

3. $\frac{7}{8} + \frac{3}{8}$ ________

4. $\frac{1}{7} + \frac{3}{7}$ ________

5. $\frac{4}{5} - \frac{3}{5}$ ________

6. $\frac{5}{6} - \frac{1}{6}$ ________

7. $\frac{3}{4} - \frac{1}{4}$ ________

8. $\frac{8}{9} - \frac{5}{9}$ ________

Compare the survey results. *(Lesson 7-14)*

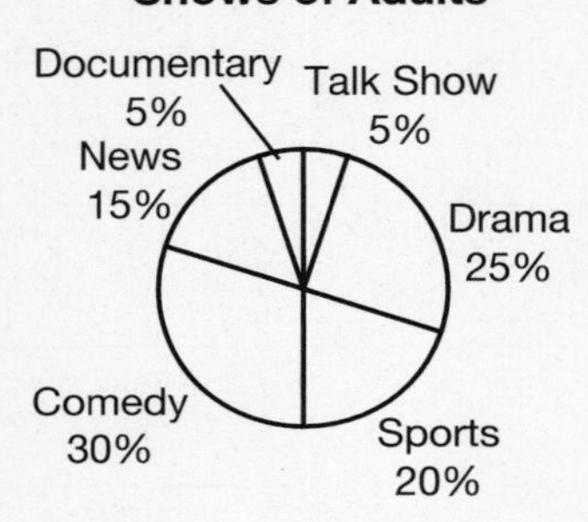

Favorite Evening Television Shows of 50 Students			
News	0	Talk show	0
Documentary	5	Drama	15
Comedy	20	Sports	10

9. How will you compare the results of the adults' survey with the results from the fifth graders.

____

10. What percent of students prefer comedy shows? ________

11. Which type of show had the same result in both surveys? ________

Mixed Review

12. Write whether $\frac{3}{12}$ and $\frac{1}{4}$ are equivalent. Explain how you decided.
(7-3)

____

13. What is the LCM of 4, 6, and 8? ________
(3-6)

Name ____________________

Daily Review
8-3

Daily Cumulative Review

Find each sum. You may use fraction strips or draw pictures to help. *(Lesson 8-2)*

1. $\frac{1}{2} + \frac{1}{6}$ **2.** $\frac{2}{5} + \frac{1}{10}$ **3.** $\frac{1}{8} + \frac{1}{2}$ **4.** $\frac{2}{3} + \frac{1}{2} + \frac{5}{6}$

________ ________ ________ ________

Find each sum or difference. Simplify. *(Lesson 8-1)*

5. $\frac{2}{5} + \frac{3}{5}$ **6.** $\frac{5}{8} + \frac{7}{8}$ **7.** $\frac{3}{10} + \frac{1}{10}$ **8.** $\frac{11}{12} - \frac{3}{12}$

________ ________ ________ ________

Mixed Review

Write $>$, $<$, or $=$ to complete.

9. *(7-7)* $\frac{2}{9} \bigcirc \frac{3}{11}$ **10.** *(7-7)* $\frac{7}{16} \bigcirc \frac{3}{8}$ **11.** *(7-7)* $\frac{9}{16} \bigcirc \frac{3}{4}$

Complete.

12. *(7-10)* $3 = \frac{\square}{4}$ **13.** *(7-10)* $7\frac{2}{3} = \frac{\square}{3}$ **14.** *(2-3)* $10^{\square} = 100{,}000$

15. *(7-1)* Estimate the fraction of the figure that is shaded. ________

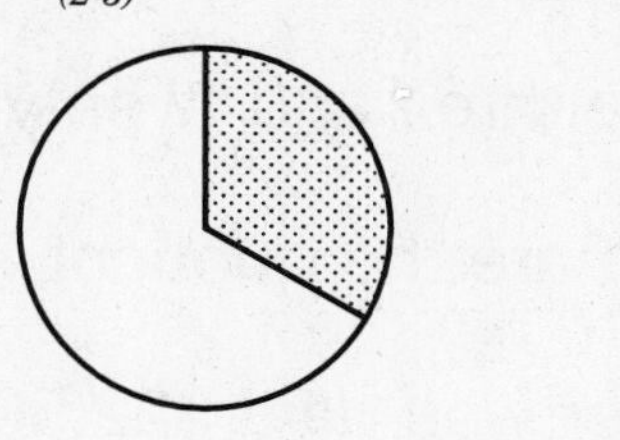

A. $\frac{1}{2}$ **B.** $\frac{1}{3}$ **C.** $\frac{1}{4}$

16. *(6-5)* Jadice jogs every morning to the gym. How many different routes can she take to the gym without backtracking?

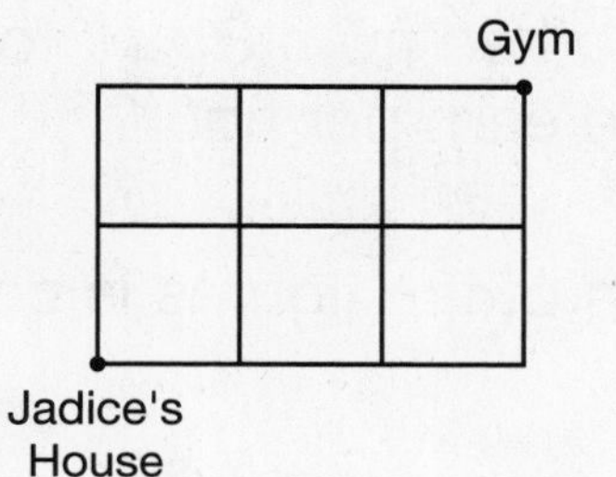

____

17. *(2-13)* Todd is shorter than Mario but taller than Doug. Sam is the tallest of the four. Who is the shortest? ________

Name ______________________

Daily Review 8-4

Daily Cumulative Review

Find the LCD for each pair of fractions. *(Lesson 8-3)*

1. $\frac{11}{12}$ and $\frac{1}{5}$ ______

2. $\frac{3}{10}$ and $\frac{1}{4}$ ______

3. $\frac{3}{8}$ and $\frac{5}{6}$ ______

4. $\frac{3}{12}$ and $\frac{1}{8}$ ______

Find each sum. You may use fraction strips or draw pictures to help. *(Lesson 8-2)*

5. $\frac{3}{10} + \frac{1}{5}$ ______

6. $\frac{5}{6} + \frac{1}{9}$ ______

7. $\frac{5}{12} + \frac{3}{4} + \frac{1}{6}$ ______

8. $\frac{3}{10} + \frac{1}{4} + \frac{1}{6}$ ______

Mixed Review

Solve.

9. 1.44 ÷ 4 = ______ *(4-12)*

10. 643 ÷ 40 = ______ *(5-4)*

11. 0.5 × 9.1 = ______ *(3-13)*

12. 387 × 24 = ______ *(3-9)*

13. 250 × 0.028 ______ *(3-10)*

14. 1,003 − 345 = ______ *(2-15)*

15. 6.003 − 4.39 = ______ *(2-18)*

16. 9.7 − 6.8 = ______ *(2-16)*

17. Write three and twenty-eight thousandths in decimal form. ______ *(2-5)*

18. Estimate the quotient 709 ÷ 8. ______ *(4-3)*

19. Javier was paid $22.50 for working on Monday. He worked from 8 A.M. to 2 P.M. How much did he earn per hour? ______ *(4-12)*

20. Which of the figures is congruent to ? ______ *(6-7)*

A. 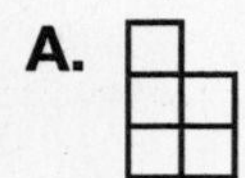

B. 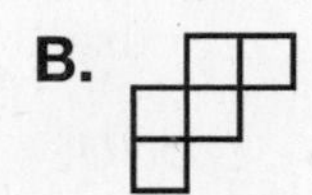

C.

D.

Name ____________________

Daily Cumulative Review

Find each sum. Simplify. *(Lesson 8-4)*

1. $\frac{1}{5} + \frac{1}{4}$ ______ **2.** $\frac{3}{7} + \frac{2}{3}$ ______ **3.** $\frac{5}{6} + \frac{2}{5}$ ______ **4.** $\frac{2}{3} + \frac{4}{9}$ ______

Find the LCD for each pair of fractions. *(Lesson 8-3)*

5. $\frac{7}{8}$ and $\frac{3}{4}$ ______ **6.** $\frac{11}{12}$ and $\frac{3}{8}$ ______ **7.** $\frac{3}{5}$ and $\frac{1}{4}$ ______ **8.** $\frac{5}{6}$ and $\frac{4}{5}$ ______

9. $\frac{1}{6}$ and $\frac{5}{8}$ ______ **10.** $\frac{5}{6}$ and $\frac{1}{2}$ ______ **11.** $\frac{1}{3}$ and $\frac{1}{5}$ ______ **12.** $\frac{1}{6}$ and $\frac{7}{9}$ ______

Mixed Review

Find the simplest form for each fraction.

13. *(7-5)* $\frac{6}{48}$ = ______ **14.** *(7-5)* $\frac{6}{16}$ = ______ **15.** *(7-5)* $\frac{8}{12}$ = ______ **16.** $\frac{20}{35}$ = ______

Write the name that best describes each figure.

17. *(6-4)*

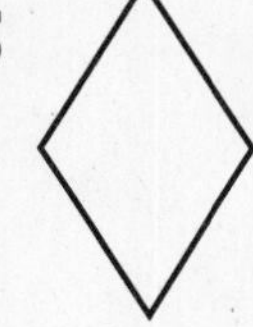

______

18. *(6-4)*

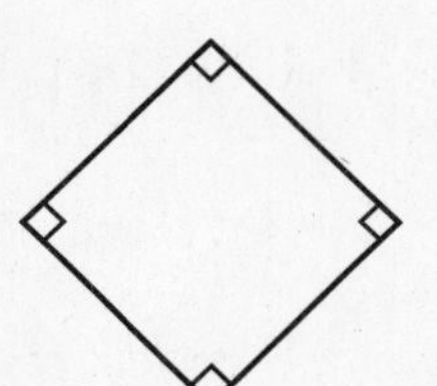

______

19. *(6-4)*

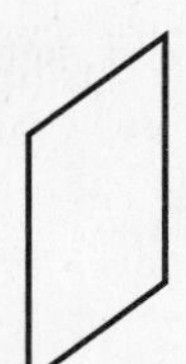

______

20. *(6-4)*

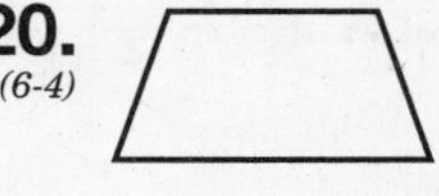

______

Use the figures to answer questions **21** and **22**.

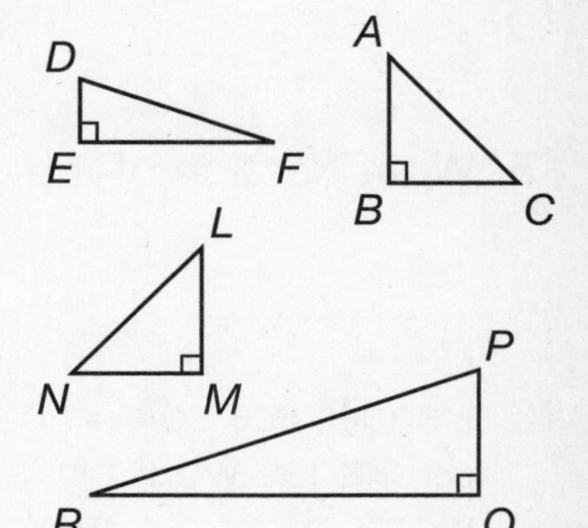

21. *(6-6)* Which triangle is congruent to triangle *ABC*?

______

22. *(6-6)* Which triangle is similar to triangle *DEF*?

______

Name ____________________

Daily Review 8-6

Daily Cumulative Review

Find each difference. You may use fraction strips or draw pictures to help. *(Lesson 8-5)*

1. $\frac{7}{8} - \frac{3}{4}$ ________

2. $\frac{3}{5} - \frac{1}{2}$ ________

3. $\frac{1}{3} - \frac{1}{5}$ ________

4. $\frac{1}{4} - \frac{1}{6}$ ________

Find each sum. Simplify. *(Lesson 8-4)*

5. $\frac{2}{9} + \frac{5}{6}$

6. $\frac{4}{5} + \frac{1}{2}$

7. $\frac{5}{8} + \frac{5}{12}$

8. $\frac{3}{5} + \frac{2}{7}$

Mixed Review

Divide and check.

9. *(5-10)* $12\overline{)\$98.76}$

10. *(5-10)* $15\overline{)\$92.10}$

11. *(5-10)* $28\overline{)5{,}688}$

Write $>$, $<$, or $=$ to complete.

12. *(7-6)* $\frac{5}{8}$ ◯ $\frac{7}{12}$

13. *(7-6)* $\frac{6}{9}$ ◯ $\frac{2}{3}$

14. *(7-6)* $\frac{3}{5}$ ◯ $\frac{6}{10}$

15. *(7-2)* What fraction of the glasses are full?

____

16. *(4-15)* Pencils are sold in paackages of 12. How many packages would Mrs. Cragin need to buy if she wants to give a pencil to each of her 29 students. ________

Name ____________________

Daily Review 8-7

Daily Cumulative Review

Find each difference. Simplify. *(Lesson 8-6)*

1. $\frac{7}{12} - \frac{3}{8} =$ ______ **2.** $\frac{7}{9} - \frac{2}{5} =$ ______ **3.** $\frac{7}{8} - \frac{5}{6} =$ ______

4. $\frac{3}{5} - \frac{2}{15} =$ ______ **5.** $\frac{5}{6} - \frac{2}{5} =$ ______ **6.** $\frac{5}{8} - \frac{1}{4} =$ ______

Find each difference. You may use fraction strips or draw pictures to help. *(Lesson 8-5)*

7. $\frac{1}{2} - \frac{1}{3} =$ ______ **8.** $\frac{3}{4} - \frac{1}{3} =$ ______ **9.** $\frac{7}{8} - \frac{1}{4} =$ ______

Mixed Review

Divide.

10. (4-7) 417 ÷ 4 = ______ **11.** (4-2) 6,400 ÷ 8 = ______

12. (5-1) 40,000 ÷ 20 = ______ **13.** (5-4) 315 ÷ 35 = ______

Write the mixed or whole number and improper fraction that name each shaded part.

14. (7-9) **15.** (7-9)

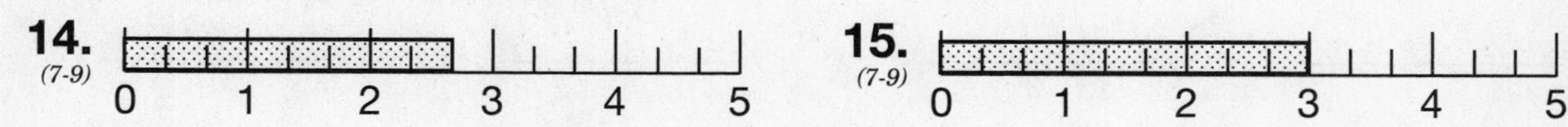

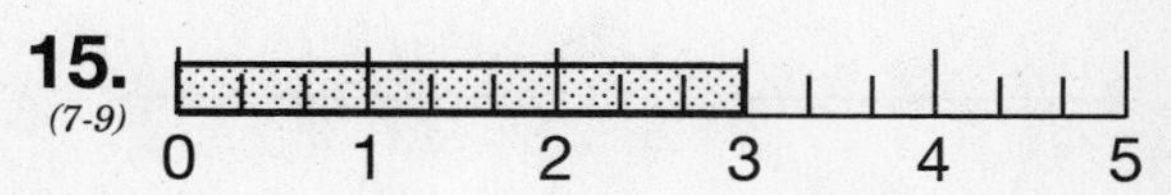

______ ______

16. (4-13) What are the factors of 48? ______

17. (4-14) Is 51 prime or composite? ______

18. (7-7) Jesse ate $\frac{1}{4}$ of a medium pizza. Salla ate $\frac{1}{3}$ of the same pizza. Who ate more pizza? ______

Name ______________________________

Daily Cumulative Review

Write if each problem has too much or too little information. Solve, if possible, or tell what is needed to solve. *(Lesson 8-7)*

1. Mrs. Edwards bought $\frac{1}{3}$ of a case of cookies. She received $12.65 in change from the store clerk. How much does a case of cookies cost?

____

____

2. There are 10 windows on each floor of an office building and $\frac{1}{5}$ of the windows on each floor face east. If there are 9 floors in the building, how many windows are in the building?

____

____

Find each difference. Simplify. *(Lesson 8-6)*

3. $\frac{5}{6} - \frac{1}{12}$ ________ **4.** $\frac{3}{4} - \frac{5}{8}$ ________ **5.** $\frac{7}{8} - \frac{5}{12}$ ________ **6.** $\frac{13}{14} - \frac{5}{6}$ ________

Mixed Review

Solve.

7. $85 ÷ 10 = ________ *(5-12)*

8. 22,212 ÷ 18 = ________ *(5-7)*

9. 53 − 7.89 = ________ *(2-18)*

10. 408 − 77 = ________ *(2-15)*

11. 3.8 + 9 = ________

12. 4.91 × 0.66 = ________

Compare. Use >, <, or = to complete.

13. $3\frac{2}{5}$ ◯ $3\frac{5}{8}$ *(7-11)*

14. 48 + 37 ◯ 90 *(2-14)*

15. 0.77 ◯ 0.7 *(2-11)*

16. 2,002 ◯ 2,020 *(2-5)*

Name ______________________________

Daily Review
8-9

Daily Cumulative Review

Find each sum or difference. Use fraction strips or drawings to help. Simplify. *(Lesson 8-8)*

1. $7\frac{5}{6} + 2\frac{1}{3}$

2. $6\frac{3}{5} - \frac{1}{10}$

3. $4 - 1\frac{1}{4}$

Write if each problem has too much or too little information. Solve, if possible, or tell what is needed to solve. *(Lesson 8-7)*

4. Alana collected shells at the beach. She gave $\frac{1}{2}$ of these to Shanara who gave $\frac{1}{3}$ of what she received to Chad. How many shells did Alana collect?

____

____

Mixed Review

Solve.

5. 3,248 + 5,733 *(2-15)*

6. 2 + 0.56 + 1.1 *(2-17)*

7. $\frac{2}{6} + \frac{2}{6} + \frac{2}{6}$ *(8-1)*

8. 6 × 8.5 *(3-10)*

9. 1.101 × 100 *(3-8)*

10. 63 ÷ 1,000 *(5-12)*

11. \$8.04 − \$4.66 *(2-18)*

12. 5 − 3.02 *(2-18)*

13. 7,238 ÷ 9 *(4-8)*

Name ______________________

Daily Cumulative Review

Estimate each sum or difference. *(Lesson 8-9)*

1. $4\frac{3}{8} + 3\frac{3}{5}$ ________

2. $2\frac{1}{2} + 6\frac{4}{7}$ ________

3. $5 - 3\frac{2}{3}$ ________

Find each sum or difference. Use fraction strips or drawings to help. Simplify. *(Lesson 8-8)*

4. $5\frac{3}{4} - 2\frac{5}{12}$

5. $7 - 3\frac{2}{9}$

6. $2\frac{3}{16} + 1\frac{5}{8}$

Mixed Review

Complete.

7. *(7-10)* $3 = \frac{\square}{7}$

8. *(7-10)* $5\frac{2}{3} = \frac{\square}{3}$

9. *(4-10)* ________ $\div 99 = 0$

10. *(4-2)* $21{,}000 \div 300 =$ ________

11. *(5-8)*

n	$n \div 3$
12	
21	
51	

12. *(5-8)*

n	$n - 22$
29	
22	
46	

13. *(4-12)* Find the length of a side of the square.

Perimeter = 10.24 cm

____

14. *(6-7)* Which of the figures shows [figure] turned? ________

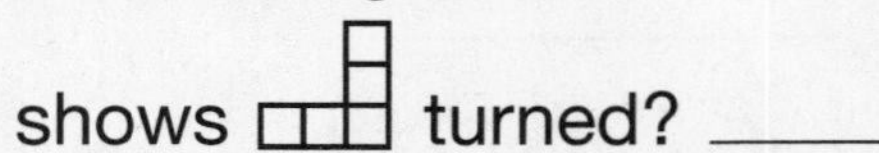

Name ______________________________

Daily Cumulative Review

Find each sum or difference. Simplify. *(Lesson 8-10)*

1. $4\frac{2}{5} + 3\frac{3}{10}$ ______

2. $10\frac{2}{3} - 7\frac{1}{5}$ ______

3. $4\frac{5}{6} - 2\frac{5}{8}$ ______

4. $9\frac{1}{4} + 2\frac{5}{8}$ ______

Estimate each sum or difference. *(Lesson 8-9)*

5. $4\frac{2}{9} + 5\frac{3}{7}$ ______

6. $6\frac{1}{2} - 3\frac{4}{5}$ ______

7. $1\frac{5}{11} + 2\frac{1}{9}$ ______

8. $7\frac{1}{5} - 2$ ______

Mixed Review

Find the greatest common factor for each pair.

9. 12 and 15 *(7-4)* ______

10. 16 and 28 *(7-4)* ______

11. 24 and 36 *(7-4)* ______

Find the LCD for each pair of fractions.

12. $\frac{3}{4}$ and $\frac{3}{10}$ *(8-3)* ______

13. $\frac{2}{3}$ and $\frac{4}{5}$ *(8-3)* ______

14. $\frac{5}{12}$ and $\frac{9}{21}$ *(8-3)* ______

Estimate the percent of each figure that is shaded.

15. *(7-12)* ______________________

16. *(7-12)* ______________________

Name ______________________________

Daily Cumulative Review

Find each sum. Simplify. *(Lesson 8-11)*

1. $2\frac{1}{10}$ + $1\frac{2}{5}$ + $3\frac{3}{10}$

2. $1\frac{3}{4}$ + $2\frac{1}{3}$ + $4\frac{1}{6}$

3. $5\frac{2}{9}$ + $2\frac{1}{6}$ + $\frac{2}{3}$

4. 5 + $\frac{3}{4}$ + $2\frac{1}{5}$

Find each sum or difference. *(Lesson 8-10)*

5. $6 + 3\frac{7}{8}$

6. $8\frac{9}{10} - 2\frac{1}{4}$

7. $4\frac{5}{6} - 1\frac{1}{8}$

8. $21\frac{1}{2} + 7\frac{2}{7}$

Mixed Review

Divide.

9. $36\overline{)490}$ *(5-6)*

10. $40\overline{)\$416.40}$ *(5-10)*

11. $0.4 \div 1000 =$ ______ *(5-12)*

Name each triangle by its sides and by its angles.

12. *(6-3)*

13. *(6-3)*

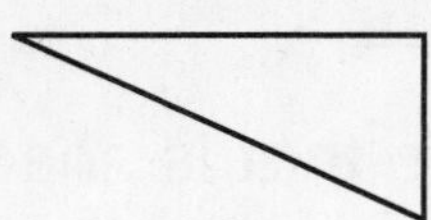

14. *(6-3)*

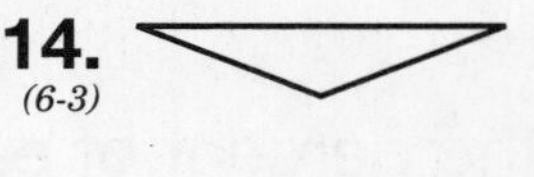

______________ ______________ ______________

______________ ______________ ______________

For each set, decide which does **not** belong.

15. *(7-12)* **A.** 50% **B.** $\frac{1}{2}$ **C.** 5 out of 1000 **D.** $\frac{5}{10}$ ______________

16. *(7-12)* **A.** 6% **B.** $\frac{60}{100}$ **C.** $\frac{6}{100}$ **D.** 6 out of 100 ______________

Name ______________________________

Daily Review 8-13

Daily Cumulative Review

Find each difference. Simplify. *(Lesson 8-12)*

1. $5\frac{5}{9} - 2\frac{8}{9}$

2. $7\frac{1}{10} - 5\frac{2}{10}$

3. $9\frac{9}{20} - 4\frac{3}{4}$

4. $9 - 6\frac{5}{6}$

Find each sum. Simplify if possible. *(Lesson 8-11)*

5. $1\frac{1}{8} + 4\frac{4}{5}$

6. $5\frac{3}{8} + 2\frac{1}{2}$

7. $3\frac{2}{5} + 6\frac{7}{10}$

8. $5\frac{7}{16} + 2\frac{1}{4}$

Mixed Review

Find equivalent fractions with a denominator of 6.

9. *(7-3)* $\frac{1}{2} = \frac{\square}{6}$

10. *(7-3)* $\frac{12}{36} = \frac{\square}{6}$

11. *(7-3)* $\frac{2}{3} = \frac{\square}{6}$

12. *(7-3)* $\frac{20}{24} = \frac{\square}{6}$

Write each improper fraction as a mixed number in simplest form, or as a whole number.

13. *(7-10)* $\frac{52}{6} =$ ________

14. *(7-10)* $\frac{42}{7} =$ ________

15. *(7-10)* $\frac{60}{8} =$ ________

16. *(7-10)* $\frac{55}{7} =$ ________

Use this circle graph to answer **17** and **18**.

17. *(7-12)* What fractional part of those surveyed preferred dogs?

____

Favorite Pet

Fish 10%
Bird 5%
Dog 45%
Cat 40%

18. *(7-14)* Which is the least favorite pet?

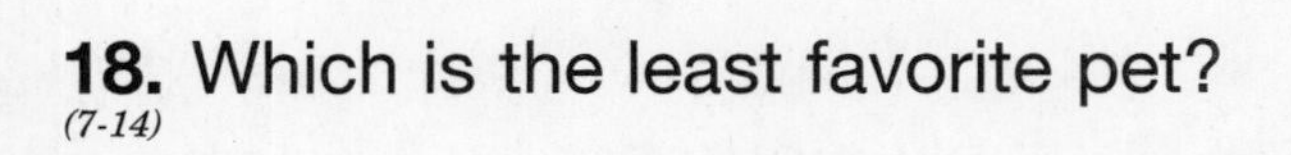

Name ______________________

Daily Review 8-14

Daily Cumulative Review

Work backward or draw a picture to solve the problem. *(Lesson 8-13)*

1. Mrs. York baked cookies and gave half to her neighbor, Mrs. Jensen. Mrs. Jensen gave $\frac{1}{3}$ of hers to Mr. Green. Mr. Green got 12 cookies. How many cookies did Mrs. York bake? ______

2. Regina and her dad biked west $\frac{5}{8}$ mile and then turned south and biked $1\frac{1}{2}$ miles. They turned northeast and biked $1\frac{3}{8}$ miles back to their starting point. How far did they bike in all? ______

Find each difference. Simplify. *(Lesson 8-12)*

3. $6 - 1\frac{7}{8}$

4. $4\frac{1}{4} - 2\frac{1}{3}$

5. $6\frac{1}{5} - 1\frac{3}{10}$

6. $20\frac{5}{6} - 7\frac{3}{8}$

Mixed Review

Find the simplest form of each fraction.

7. *(7-5)* $\frac{18}{24} =$ ______

8. *(7-5)* $\frac{24}{36} =$ ______

9. *(7-5)* $\frac{42}{48} =$ ______

10. *(7-5)* $\frac{20}{45} =$ ______

Write each as a fraction and a decimal.

11. *(7-13)* 20%

12. *(7-13)* 50%

13. *(7-13)* 4%

14. *(7-13)* 83%

Write each rule using a variable.

15. *(1-7)* 6.7 less than number

16. *(1-7)* Multiply a number by 11.

Name ______________________________

Daily Review 8-15

Daily Cumulative Review

Find the length to the nearest $\frac{1}{4}$-inch. *(Lesson 8-14)*

1. ____________

2. ____________

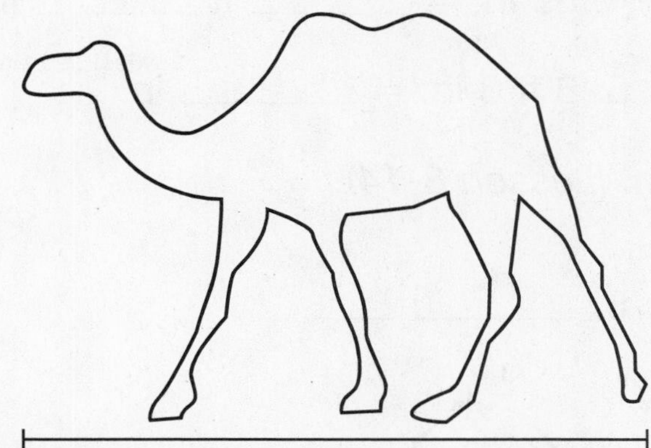

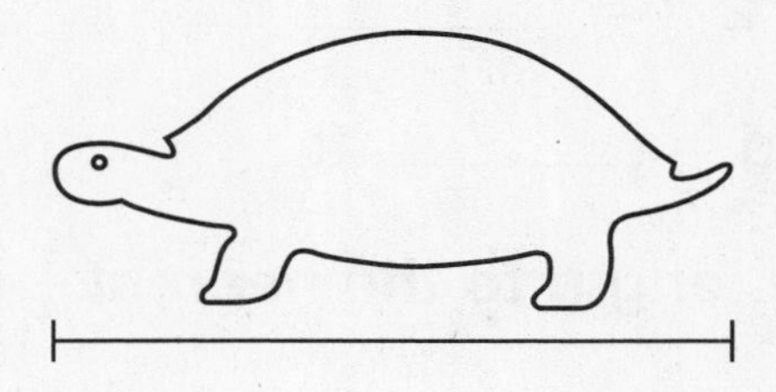

Work backward or draw a picture to solve the problem. *(Lesson 8-13)*

3. Farrad, Eli, and Sean worked on geometry projects over the weekend. Eli worked $\frac{1}{3}$ of the time that Farrad worked, and Farrad worked $\frac{3}{4}$ the time that Sean worked. Sean worked 4 hours. How long did the other boys work?

____

Mixed Review

Write >, <, or = to complete.

4. *(7-7)* $\frac{7}{10}$ ◯ $\frac{3}{4}$ **5.** *(7-11)* $3\frac{4}{8}$ ◯ $3\frac{6}{12}$ **6.** *(4-10)* 0 ◯ 99×0

Shade the drawing to show each fraction.

7. *(7-9)* $1\frac{3}{5}$

8. *(7-9)* $\frac{3}{2}$

9. *(7-9)* $\frac{8}{4}$

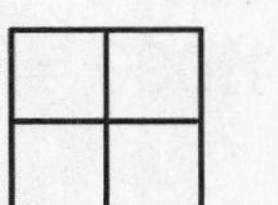

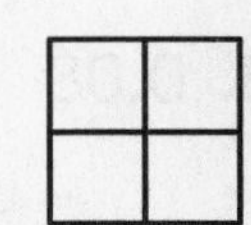

10. *(6-7)* Write the motion used to get from start to finish. ____________

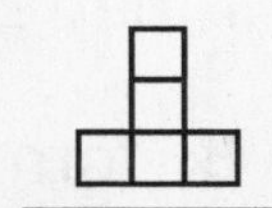

Name ______________________

Daily Review 8-16

Daily Cumulative Review

Complete. *(Lesson 8-15)*

1. 24 ft = ________ yd

2. 2 mi = ________ yd

3. 3 yd 2 ft = ________ ft

4. 69 in. = ________ ft ________ in.

5. 15 yd = ________ ft

6. 6 ft 3 in. = ________ in.

Find the length to the nearest $\frac{1}{4}$-inch. *(Lesson 8-14)*

7. ____________

8. 

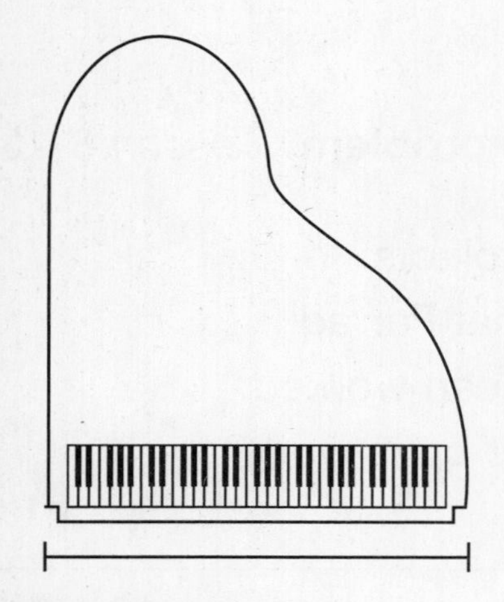

Mixed Review

Complete.

9. $4\frac{1}{6} = \frac{\square}{6}$ *(7-10)*

10. 900 ÷ ________ = 30 *(5-1)*

11. $\_\_\_\_\_\_\_\_^{5}$ = 100,000 *(2-3)*

12. 20,000,000 = twenty ________ *(2-4)*

13. 0.08 × 1,000 = ________ *(3-8)*

14. ________ × 60 = 600,000 *(3-1)*

15. Lines are parallel if they ________. *(6-1)*

A. never meet **B.** form a triangle **C.** intersect **D.** form angles

Name ______________________________

Daily Review
9-1

Daily Cumulative Review

Decide whether you need an exact answer or estimate. Solve. *(Lesson 8-16)*

1. Jason mows lawns during the summer. He can mow Mrs. Park's lawn in $2\frac{1}{2}$ hours. He can trim with a weed-eater in about $1\frac{1}{4}$ hours. If he starts at 8:00 A.M., can he finish by noon? Explain your answer.

____

2. Ryan wants to build a recycle cage for cans. He plans to cut metal rods for the frame and use wire mesh for the bottom and sides. Rods are 12 feet long and mesh comes in rolls that are 3 feet wide. Will 2 rods be enough to make a cage? Explain.

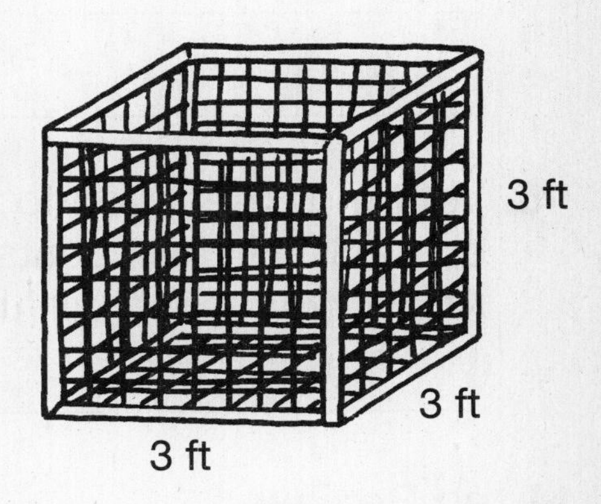

____

____

Complete. *(Lesson 8-15)*

3. a.

Number of inches					360	720
Number of yards	1	2	3	5		

b. To change from inches to yards, you must ________ the number of inches by 36.

c. To change from yards to inches, you must ________ the number of yards by 36.

Mixed Review

Find each sum.

4. $\frac{1}{4} + \frac{3}{8} + \frac{5}{16}$ (8-2)

5. $2\frac{2}{3} + 1\frac{5}{6}$ (8-8)

6. $7.3 + 0.86 + 2$ (2-16)

__________ __________ __________

Name ________________________

Daily Cumulative Review

Find each product. You may use counters to help. *(Lesson 9-1)*

1. $\frac{1}{4}$ of 24 ________ **2.** $\frac{1}{3}$ of 27 ________ **3.** $\frac{3}{4}$ of 16 ________

Decide whether you need an exact answer or estimate. Solve. *(Lesson 8-16)*

4. Ashley's car holds 12 gallons of gas and gets about 25 miles to the gallon. Can she make a 500 mile trip on two tanks of gas? Explain.

____

____

5. Your mom sent you to the store to get bread, milk, and eggs. Bread costs \$1.19, milk costs \$2.79, and eggs cost \$1.35. Tax is \$0.35. About how much will the total be?

____

Mixed Review

6. *(7-5)* Find the simplest form for $\frac{18}{45}$. ________

Find each difference.

7. *(8-12)* $6 - 1\frac{1}{4}$ ________

8. *(8-6)* $\frac{5}{9} - \frac{1}{3}$ ________

9. *(2-18)* \$10 − \$1.98 ________

10. *(2-15)* $\begin{array}{r} 407 \\ -\ 38 \\ \hline \end{array}$

Draw all lines of symmetry.

11. *(6-8)*

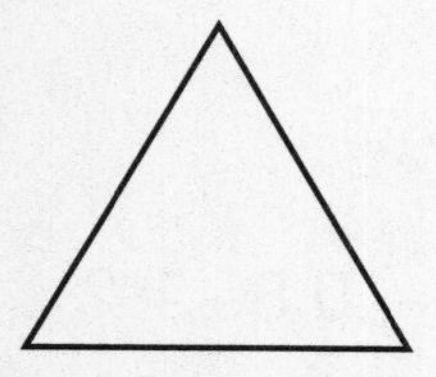

12. *(6-8)*

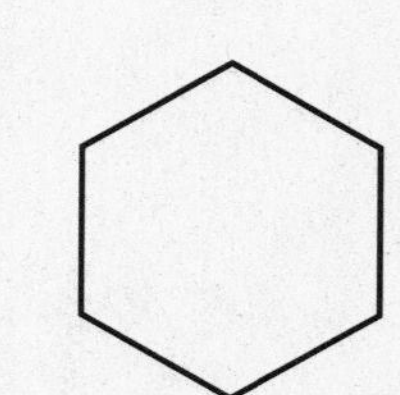

Name ______________________

Daily Review 9-3

Daily Cumulative Review

Find each product. Use mental math. *(Lesson 9-2)*

1. $\frac{1}{6}$ of 48 ________ **2.** $\frac{1}{7}$ of 21 ________ **3.** $\frac{1}{3}$ of 24 ________

4. $\frac{3}{10}$ of 30 ________ **5.** $\frac{5}{9}$ of 18 ________ **6.** $\frac{7}{8}$ of 56 ________

Find each product. You may use counters to help. *(Lesson 9-1)*

7. $\frac{1}{5}$ of 35 ________ **8.** $\frac{3}{4}$ of 16 ________ **9.** $\frac{2}{3}$ of 27 ________

10. $\frac{1}{3}$ of 90 ________ **11.** $\frac{5}{6}$ of 42 ________ **12.** $\frac{5}{8}$ of 16 ________

Mixed Review

13. Which of the figures is congruent to 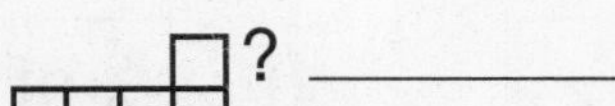? ________
(6-7)

A. 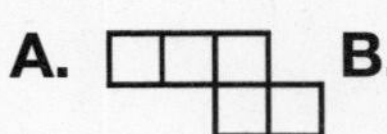 **B.** **C.** 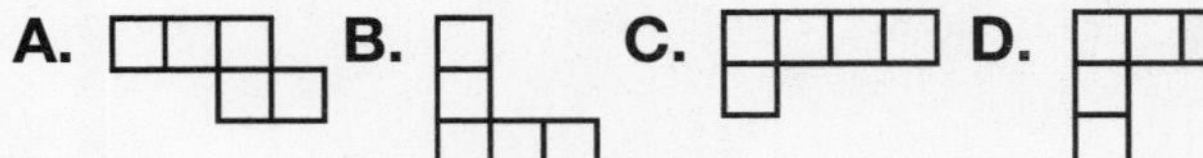 **D.** 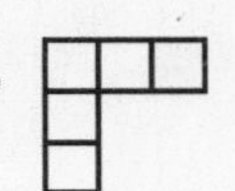

Write the name for each.

14. *(6-1)*

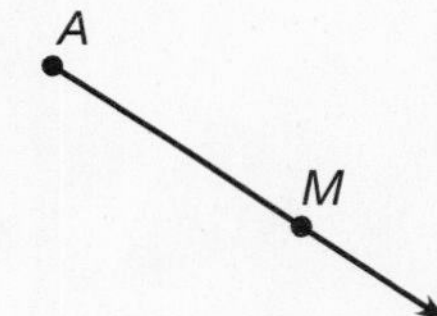

15. *(6-1)*

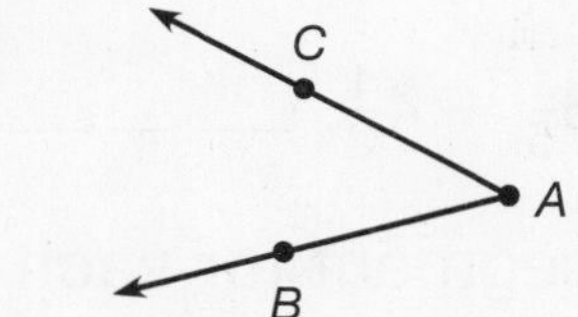

16. *(6-1)*

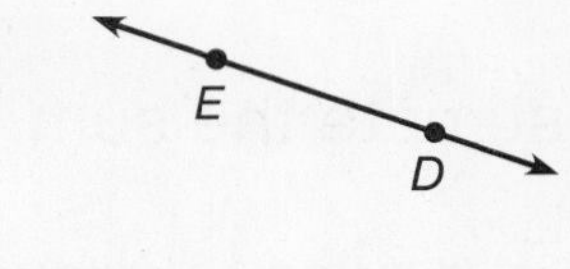

________________ ________________ ________________

17. Describe how you compare two fractions whose denominators are the same.
(7-6)

____

Use any strategy to solve.

18. Andrea can make 15 cloth angels in 2 days. How many can she make in 10 days? ________
(7-8)

Name ______________________________

Daily Cumulative Review

Use rounding, benchmark, or compatible numbers to estimate each product. *(Lesson 9-3)*

1. $\frac{7}{12} \times 8$ ________ 2. $4\frac{5}{6} \times 7$ ________ 3. $\frac{3}{5} \times 21$ ________

4. $\frac{11}{24} \times 12$ ________ 5. $2\frac{1}{20} \times 9$ ________ 6. $\frac{3}{4} \times 31$ ________

Complete the table. Use patterns to help you find each product. *(Lesson 9-2)*

	$\frac{1}{9}$ of 45	5
	$\frac{2}{9}$ of 45	10
7.	$\frac{3}{9}$ of 45	

8.	$\frac{4}{9}$ of 45	
9.	$\frac{5}{9}$ of 45	
10.	$\frac{6}{9}$ of 45	

11.	$\frac{7}{9}$ of 45	
12.	$\frac{8}{9}$ of 45	
13.	$\frac{9}{9}$ of 45	

Mixed Review

Find each difference. Simplify.

14. $\frac{7}{8} - \frac{3}{8} =$ ________ *(8-5)*
15. $\frac{2}{3} - \frac{1}{6} =$ ________ *(8-5)*
16. $\frac{7}{10} - \frac{1}{2} =$ ________ *(8-5)*

17. Estimate the sum. $6\frac{9}{10} + 3\frac{1}{5} + 4\frac{1}{2}$. ________ *(8-9)*

Use your ruler to draw a line segment for each length.

18. $1\frac{1}{2}$ in. *(8-14)*
19. $\frac{3}{4}$ in. *(8-14)*

Write each as a percent.

20. 0.04 *(7-13)* ________
21. $\frac{70}{100}$ *(7-13)* ________
22. 25 out of 100 *(7-13)* ________
23. 0.40 *(7-13)* ________

Round each answer to the nearest cent.

24. $6\overline{)\$14.07}$ *(4-11)*

25. $\$1.30 \times 0.325$ *(3-13)*

26. $\$0.13 \times 15$ *(3-10)*

Name ______________________

Daily Review 9-5

Daily Cumulative Review

Use each drawing to help you complete each sentence. *(Lesson 9-4)*

1. $\frac{2}{3}$ is shaded. $\frac{1}{4}$ of $\frac{2}{3}$ is ________

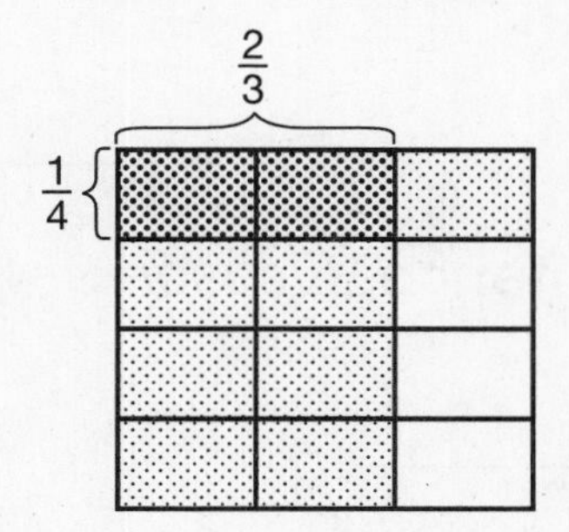

2. $\frac{1}{2}$ is shaded. $\frac{3}{5}$ of $\frac{1}{2}$ is ________

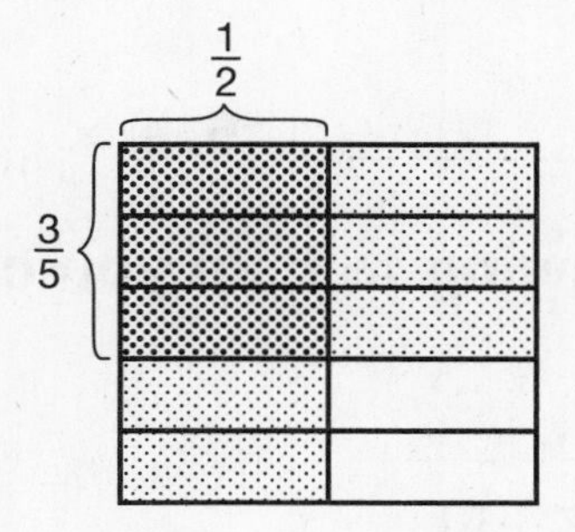

Use counting, benchmarks, or compatible numbers to estimate each product. Write the letter of the estimate that is closer to the actual product. *(Lesson 9-3)*

3. $\frac{5}{8} \times 57$ ________ **A.** less than 35 **B.** more than 35

4. $3\frac{8}{9} \times 12$ ________ **A.** less than 48 **B.** more than 48

Mixed Review

5. *(7-2)* Vicke accidentally dropped a carton of eggs. Write four fractions that describe how many eggs were broken

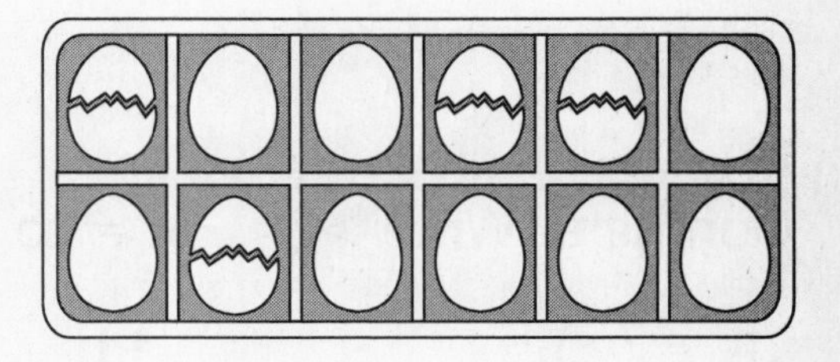

____

6. *(7-6)* Find the greatest common factor of 24 and 30. ________

7. *(5-3)* Estimate the quotient using compatible numbers.

22,000 ÷ 80 ________

8. *(8-3)* Why is the LCD of $\frac{5}{6}$ and $\frac{3}{8}$ not the product of 6 and 8?

____

9. *(8-15)* 153 in. = ________ ft ________ in.

Name ______________________________

Daily Cumulative Review

Find each product. Simplify. *(Lesson 9-5)*

1. $\frac{5}{7} \times \frac{1}{2} =$ ________ **2.** $\frac{3}{4} \times \frac{4}{9} =$ ________ **3.** $\frac{1}{7} \times \frac{2}{9} =$ ________

4. $\frac{2}{3} \times \frac{7}{8} =$ ________ **5.** $\frac{5}{6} \times \frac{1}{10} =$ ________ **6.** $\frac{9}{11} \times \frac{5}{6} =$ ________

Use each drawing to help you complete each sentence. *(Lesson 9-4)*

7. $\frac{1}{3} \times \frac{2}{5} =$ ________

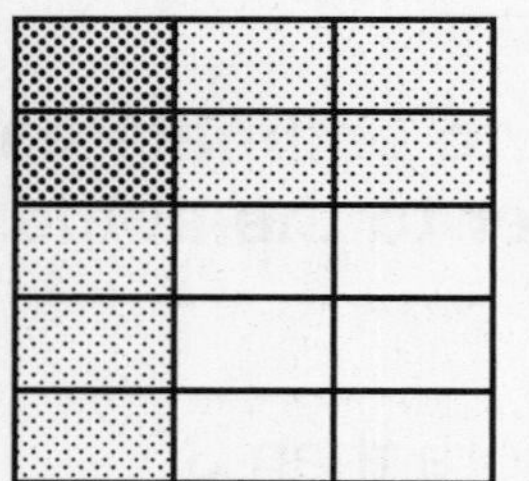

8. $\frac{5}{6} \times \frac{2}{3} =$ ________

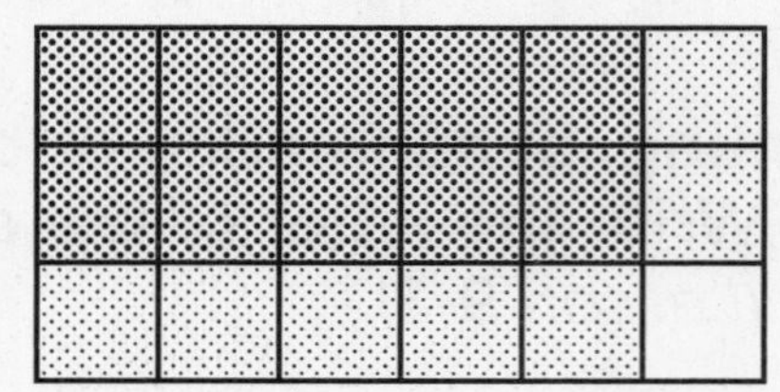

Mixed Review

9. *(8-6)* If $\frac{3}{4}$ is subtracted from $\frac{7}{8}$, will the difference be greater or less than $\frac{1}{4}$? Explain.

____

Compare. Write >, <, or = to complete.

10. *(7-6)* $\frac{2}{3}$ ◯ $\frac{2}{5}$ **11.** *(7-7)* $\frac{9}{10}$ ◯ $\frac{11}{12}$ **12.** *(7-11)* $1\frac{8}{12}$ ◯ $1\frac{4}{6}$

Divide. Check your answer.

13. *(4-11)* 3)$7.3 2 **14.** *(5-5)* 3 8)1,6 3 4 **15.** *(4-12)* 7)6.3 9 1

Name ____________________

Daily Review
9-7

Daily Cumulative Review

Overestimate or underestimate to solve the problem. *(Lesson 9-6)*

1. The art club has $240 in its treasury. They need supplies that cost $51.69, $39.98, $96.43, and $11.24. Do they have enough to buy all of the supplies?

a. Can the problem be solved with an estimate or does it require an exact answer? ____________

b. Should you overestimate or underestimate? Why?

____

____

c. Does the club have enough money? Explain.

____

____

d. If they need to spend $25 on contest entry fees, how can the club be sure it has enough? Explain.

____

____

Find each product. Simplify. *(Lesson 9-5)*

2. $\frac{2}{5} \times \frac{3}{16} =$ ________ **3.** $\frac{5}{6} \times \frac{8}{15} =$ ________ **4.** $\frac{3}{4} \times \frac{2}{5} =$ ________

5. $\frac{6}{7} \times \frac{5}{8} =$ ________ **6.** $\frac{1}{3} \times \frac{1}{3} =$ ________ **7.** $\frac{5}{7} \times \frac{2}{5} =$ ________

Mixed Review

Find each sum.

8. *(8-2)* $\frac{1}{3} + \frac{4}{9} + \frac{2}{9} =$ ________ **9.** *(8-8)* $3\frac{2}{7} + \frac{11}{14} =$ ________

Name ________________________________

Daily Review 9-8

Daily Cumulative Review

Complete. *(Lesson 9-7)*

1. $\frac{2}{5} \times 20 = \frac{\square}{5} =$ ________

2. $\frac{7}{8} \times 5 = \frac{\square}{8} =$ ________

3. $5 \times \frac{3}{7} = \frac{\square}{7} =$ ________

4. $4 \times \frac{5}{9} = \frac{\square}{9} =$ ________

Estimate to solve 5–6. Write whether you overestimated or underestimated. Explain your answer. *(Lesson 9-6)*

5. Cody makes ceramic whistles to sell in his mom's booth at a craft fair. Each whistle sells for $2.25. If 16 whistles sell, will he have enough to buy a $30 shirt at the next booth.

____

____

6. A recipe calls for $1\frac{3}{4}$ cups flour. Megan has $6\frac{1}{2}$ cups of flour. Does she have enough flour to triple the recipe?

____

Mixed Review

7. *(8-14)* Find the length of the toy truck to the nearest $\frac{1}{4}$-inch.

____

8. *(7-7)* Compare. Write $\frac{9}{11}$, $\frac{4}{5}$, $\frac{17}{22}$ in order from least to greatest.

____

9. *(7-9)* Make a drawing that shows the fraction $\frac{13}{5}$.

Name ______________________________

Daily Cumulative Review

Complete. *(Lesson 9-8)*

1. $2\frac{2}{3} \times 5 = \frac{\square}{3} \times 5 = \frac{\square}{3} = \square\frac{\square}{3}$

2. $1\frac{2}{7} \times 6 = \frac{\square}{7} \times 6 = \frac{\square}{7} = \square\frac{\square}{7}$

3. $3\frac{1}{2} \times 4\frac{1}{3} = \frac{\square}{2} \times \frac{\square}{3} = \frac{\square}{6} = \square\frac{\square}{6}$

4. $1\frac{1}{5} \times 2\frac{3}{4} = \frac{\square}{5} \times \frac{\square}{4} = \frac{\square}{20} = \square\frac{\square}{20} = \square\frac{\square}{10}$

Find each product. *(Lesson 9-7)*

5. $\frac{2}{3} \times 9 =$ __________

6. $\frac{8}{9} \times 18 =$ __________

7. $\frac{4}{7} \times 21 =$ __________

8. $\frac{5}{6} \times 24 =$ __________

Mixed Review

Find each sum or difference. Simplify if possible.

9. $\frac{7}{9} - \frac{1}{9} =$ __________ *(8-1)*

10. $6 + 1\frac{1}{2} + 2\frac{5}{8} =$ __________ *(8-11)*

11. $\frac{6}{11} - \frac{2}{5} =$ __________ *(8-6)*

12. $3 - 1\frac{2}{3} =$ __________ *(8-8)*

13. *(7-12)* Estimate the percent of the figure that is shaded.

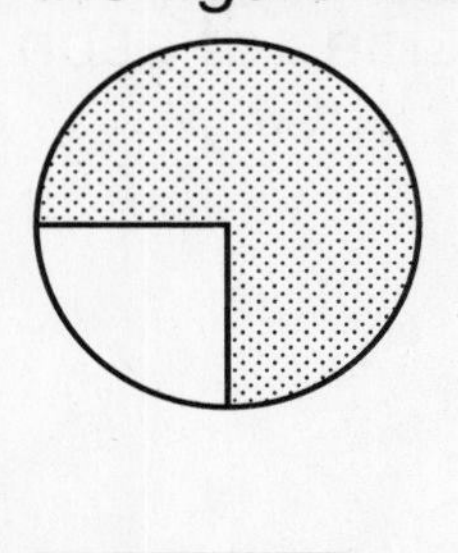

____

14. *(6-8)* Use the line of symmetry to complete the figure.

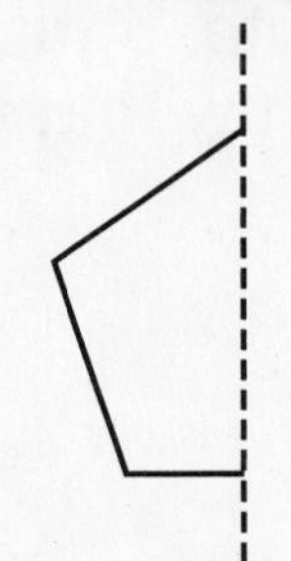

Name ______________________

Daily Review 9-10

Daily Cumulative Review

Use logical reasoning to solve the problem. *(Lesson 9-9)*

Sarah, Rachel, Halley, and Matthew won awards in math, history, reading, and science at the academic banquet. No student won an award in a subject that begins with the same letter as his or her name. Neither Sarah nor Halley won the math award. Matthew won his award for his report on the Revolutionary War. Which student won each award?

1.

	Math	History	Reading	Science
Sarah				
Rachel				
Halley				
Matthew				

2. Sarah: ______________

3. Rachel: ______________

4. Halley: ______________

5. Matthew: ______________

Find each product. Simplify. *(Lesson 9-8)*

6. $8\frac{2}{3} \times 3 =$ ______________

7. $5\frac{3}{4} \times \frac{1}{2} =$ ______________

Mixed Review

8. How do you simplify $5\frac{10}{8}$?
(8-10)

____

Identify each angle as acute, right, or obtuse. Extend the sides of each angle. Then measure each with a protractor.

9.
(6-2)

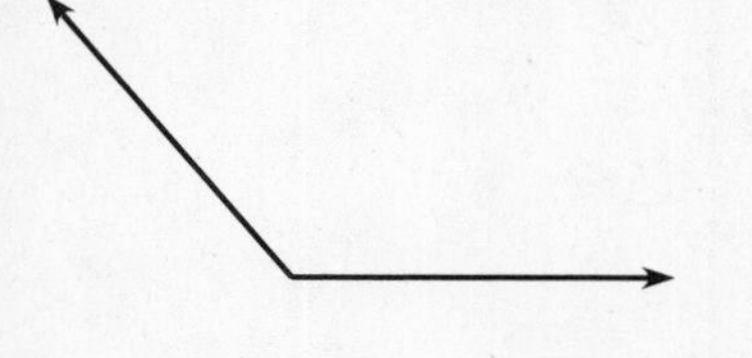

____

10.
(6-2)

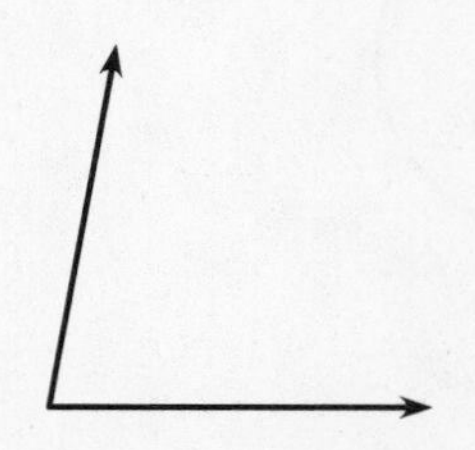

____

Name ______________________________

Daily Review 10-1

Daily Cumulative Review

Complete the drawings to find each quotient. *(Lesson 9-10)*

1. How many $\frac{1}{2}$'s are there in 5? ________

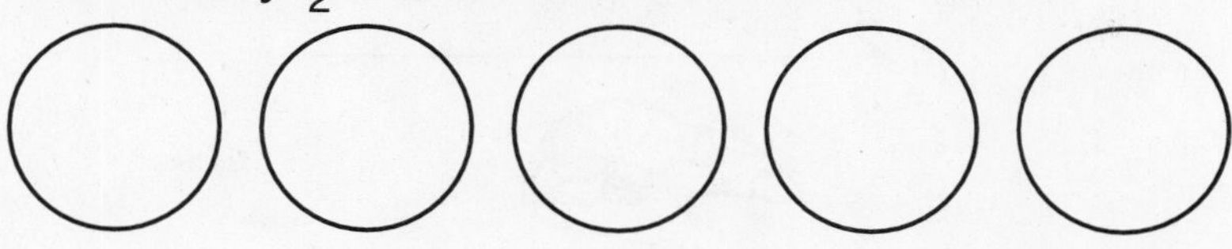

2. How many $\frac{1}{5}$'s are there in 3? ________

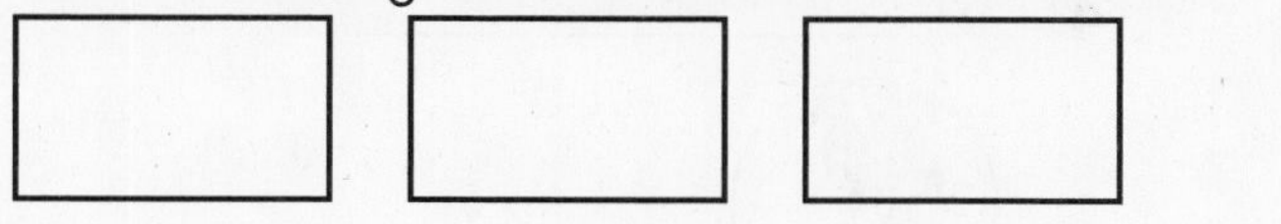

3. How many $\frac{1}{4}$'s are there in 2? ________

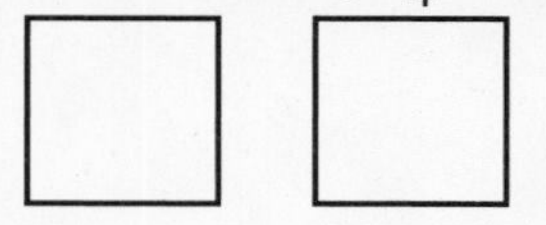

4. How many $\frac{1}{6}$'s are there in 4? ________

Use logical reasoning or any strategy to solve the problem.
(Lesson 9-9)

5. A certain type of bacteria doubles in number every 24 hours in a Petri dish. At the beginning of an experiment, there are 2 bacteria in the dish. It takes 10 days for the dish to be completely covered. On what day is it half covered? What strategy did you use?

____

Mixed Review

Find each product

6. *(3-13)* $\begin{array}{r} 5.06 \\ \times\ 0.45 \\ \hline \end{array}$

7. *(3-5)* $\begin{array}{r} 84 \\ \times\ 62 \\ \hline \end{array}$

8. *(9-1)* $\frac{2}{7} \times 21 =$ ________

Name ____

Daily Review 10-2

Daily Cumulative Review

Choose the most appropriate unit of measure to estimate the length or height of each. Write cm, dm, m, or km. *(Lesson 10-1)*

1. ________________

2. ________________

3. ________________

4. ________________

Find each quotient. *(Lesson 9-10)*

5. $6 \div \frac{1}{4} =$ ____________

6. $13 \div \frac{1}{3} =$ ____________

7. $5 \div \frac{1}{8} =$ ____________

8. $7 \div \frac{1}{9} =$ ____________

Mixed Review

You want to design an office building with 16 offices so that each office has a balcony on one wall and a window on another.

9. How many offices will be on each floor? ____________
(5-9)

10. How many floors will the building have? ____________
(5-9)

11. How many sets of curtains will you need for the windows and balcony doors? ____________
(5-9)

Write each as a fraction and a decimal.

12. 90%
(7-13)

____

____

13. 20%
(7-13)

____

____

14. 65%
(7-13)

____

____

Name ________________________

Daily Review 10-3

Daily Cumulative Review

Complete. *(Lesson 10-2)*

1. 15 mm = ________ cm

2. 30 m = ________ dm

3. 8,000 mm = ________ dm

4. 9,000 mm = ________ m

5. 20 dm = ________ cm

6. 3,000 cm = ________ m

Choose the most appropriate unit of measure to estimate the length or height of each. Write cm, dm, m, or km. *(Lesson 10-1)*

7. ________________

8. ________________

Mixed Review

9. What fraction of the set is square?
(7-1)

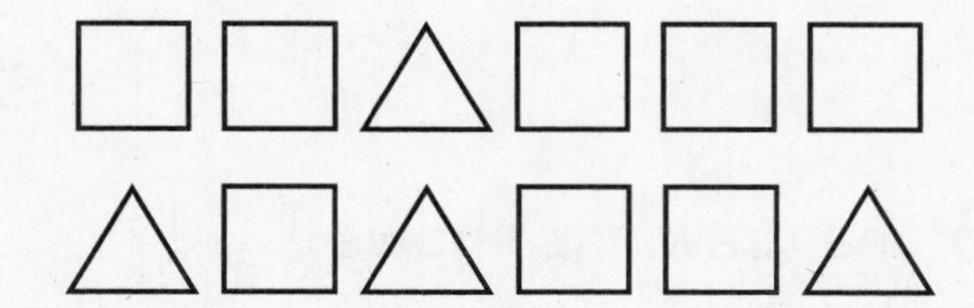

____

Find each quotient.

10. $8 \div \frac{1}{4} =$ ________
(9-10)

11. $5\overline{)\$50.45}$
(4-11)

12. $30\overline{)\$184.50}$
(5-10)

13. Jordan is planning an exercise schedule. He will start with 4 sit-ups. Every day, he will do 3 more sit-ups than he did the day before. On what day of his schedule will he do 40 sit-ups?
(7-3)

____

Name ______________________________

Daily Cumulative Review

Complete. *(Lesson 10-3)*

1. 740 cm = __________ m

2. 0.12 m = __________ cm

3. 10 cm = __________ m

4. 90 m = __________ cm

5. 3.6 m = __________ cm

6. 5.1 cm = __________ m

Complete. *(Lesson 10-2)*

7. 900 dm = __________ m

8. 20 cm = __________ dm

9. 700 mm = __________ dm

10. 50 dm = __________ cm

Mixed Review

11. *(8-14)* Find the length of the bird to the nearest $\frac{1}{4}$-inch.

____

12. *(9-4)* Which of the drawings shows $\frac{1}{6} \times \frac{1}{2}$? __________

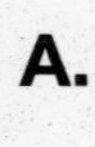

A. 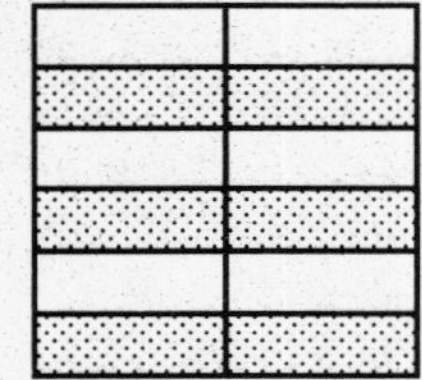

B. 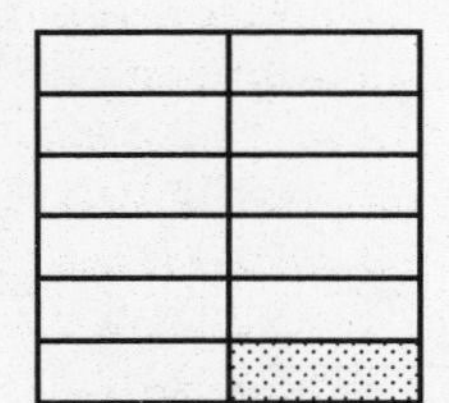

C. 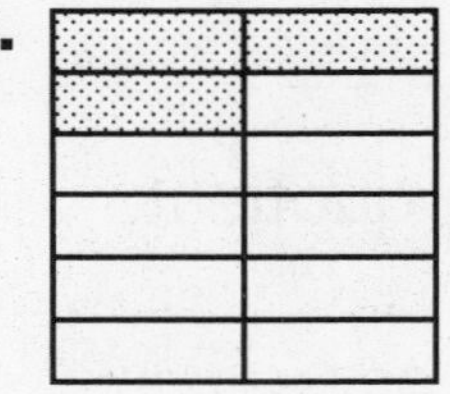

13. *(7-3)* Find a fraction equivalent to $\frac{5}{6}$ with a denominator of 24. __________

Compare. Write >, <, or = to complete.

14. *(7-13)* 60% ◯ $\frac{3}{5}$

15. *(2-14)* 327 + 133 ◯ 400

16. *(7-11)* $4\frac{7}{8}$ ◯ $6\frac{1}{3}$

17. *(7-7)* $\frac{3}{10}$ ◯ $\frac{1}{4}$

18. *(2-5)* two million, two hundred thousand ◯ 2,200,000

Name ______________________

Daily Review 10-5

Daily Cumulative Review

Complete. *(Lesson 10-4)*

1. 100 mm = __________ cm **2.** 48 mm = __________ cm

3. 18 m = __________ mm **4.** 538 cm = __________ m

5. 29 cm = __________ mm **6.** 9.6 m = __________ mm

Write each measurement, first in centimeters only and then in meters only. *(Lesson 10-3)*

7. 4 m 26 cm ______________________

8. 5 m 9 cm ______________________

9. 7 m 83 cm ______________________

Mixed Review

Find each sum or difference. Simplify.

10. *(8-1)* $\frac{5}{6} + \frac{5}{6}$ __________

11. *(8-6)* $\frac{7}{10} - \frac{3}{5}$ __________

12. *(8-10)* $7\frac{5}{9} - 4$ __________

Write if the problem has too much or too little information. Solve, if possible, or tell what is needed to solve.

13. *(8-7)* A tailor needs two pieces of fabric, $1\frac{2}{3}$ yards long and $1\frac{1}{2}$ yards long, and 3 spools of the thread. How much fabric should he buy?

____

Complete.

14. *(8-15)* 3 ft 7 in. = __________ in. **15.** 10 yd 2 ft = __________ ft

16. *(7-4)* Find the greatest common factor of 18 and 72. __________

17. *(4-13)* What are the factors of 42? ______________________

Name ______________________

Daily Review 10-6

Daily Cumulative Review

Write a multiplication number sentence describing the perimeter of each polygon. *(Lesson 10-5)*

1. 9 ft, 9 ft, 9 ft, 9 ft, 9 ft

2. 8 in., 8 in., 8 in.

3. 7 cm, 7 cm, 7 cm, 7 cm, 7 cm, 7 cm

______________ ______________ ______________

Complete. *(Lesson 10-4)*

4. Which length is the longest? __________
A. 840 mm **B.** 84 cm **C.** 8.4 m

5. Which length is the shortest? __________
A. 371 mm **B.** 3.71 cm **C.** 37.1 m

6. Which two lengths are equal? __________
A. 48.9 cm **B.** 4.89 m **C.** 4,890 mm

Mixed Review

Find each sum or difference. Simplify if possible.

7. *(8-11)* $4\frac{3}{10} + 1\frac{1}{2} + \frac{3}{5}$

8. *(8-8)* $6 - 3\frac{5}{6}$

9. *(8-5)* $\frac{5}{8} - \frac{3}{8}$

10. *(8-4)* $\frac{3}{4} + \frac{5}{6}$

11. *(4-15)* Work backward to solve the problem.

After doing some odd jobs during the week, Nick had $46. He cleaned Mrs. Helm's gutters for $8. He earned $5 per hour for 2 hours digging holes for Mrs. Walkers new rose bushes. He cleaned Mr. Howard's garage for 2 hours at $6 per hour.

How much did he have at the beginning of the week? __________

Name ______________________________

Daily Review
10-7

Daily Cumulative Review

Use the formula $P = 2 \times (l + w)$ to find the perimeter of each rectangle. Fill in the missing numbers. *(Lesson 10-6)*

1.

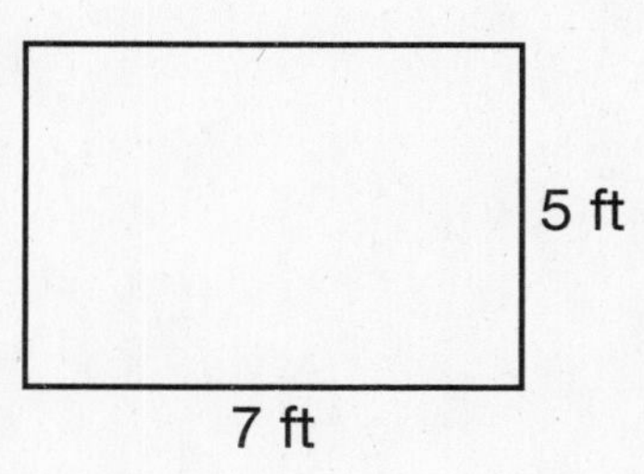

$P = 2 \times$ (___ + ___)

$P = 2 \times$ (___)

$P =$ ___ ft

2.

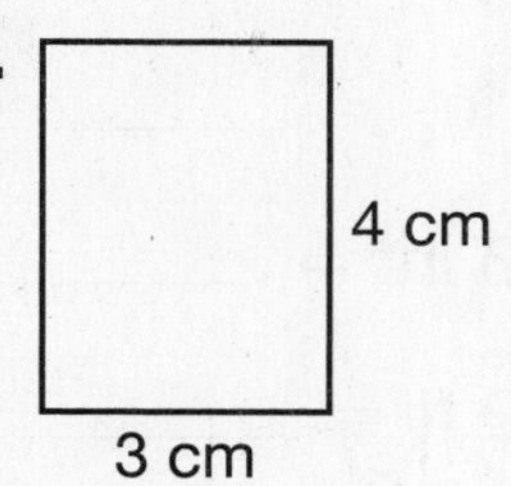

$P = 2 \times$ (___ + ___)

$P = 2 \times$ (___)

$P =$ ___ cm

Find each perimeter. *(Lesson 10-5)*

3.

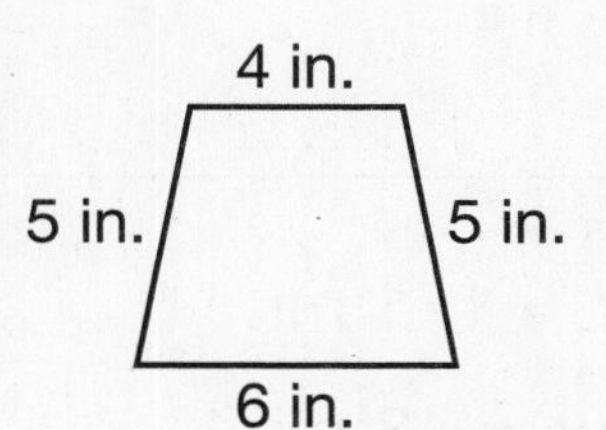

____

4.

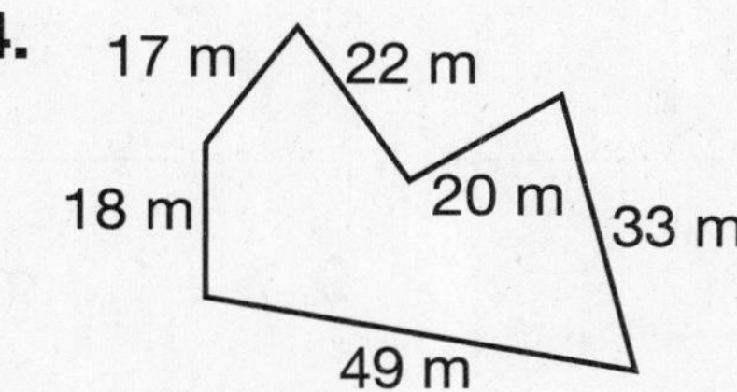

____

Mixed Review

Find each quotient or product.

5. 72,000 ÷ 80 = __________ *(5-1)*

6. 547 ÷ 24 = __________ *(5-5)*

7. 0.6 of 0.5 __________ *(3-12)*

8. $\frac{2}{3}$ of 24 __________ *(9-2)*

9. Use any strategy to solve the problem. *(8-13)*

Tyler is reading a book for a book report. Monday, he read $\frac{1}{4}$ of the book. Tuesday, he read $\frac{1}{6}$. Wednesday, he read $\frac{1}{3}$. On Thursday, he read 3 chapters and finished the book.

How many chapters did the book have? __________

Name ______________________

Daily Review
10-8

Daily Cumulative Review

Find each sum. *(Lesson 10-7)*

1. 5 yd 1 ft + 3 yd 2 ft = ______________

2. 7 ft 5 in. + 4 ft 7 in. = ______________

3. 6 ft 10 in. + 2 ft 3 in. = ______________

4. 8 yd 2 ft + 9 yd 2 ft = ______________

Find the perimeter of each rectangle. *(Lesson 10-6)*

5.
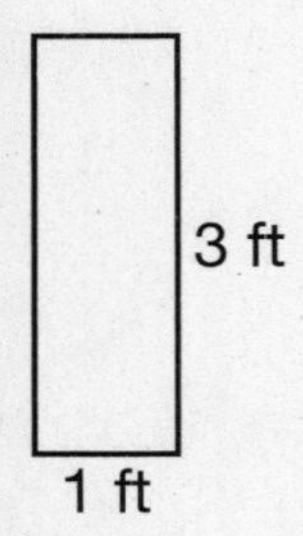

____

6.
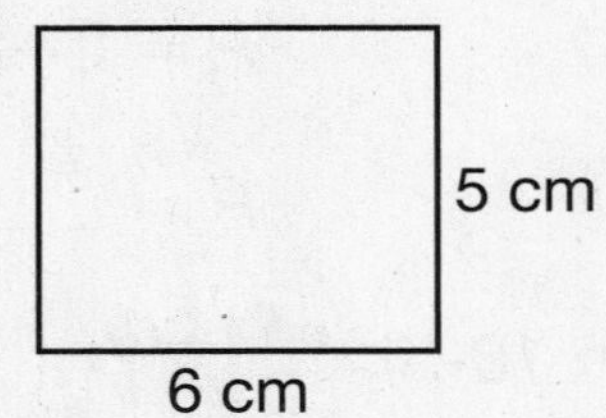

____

7.
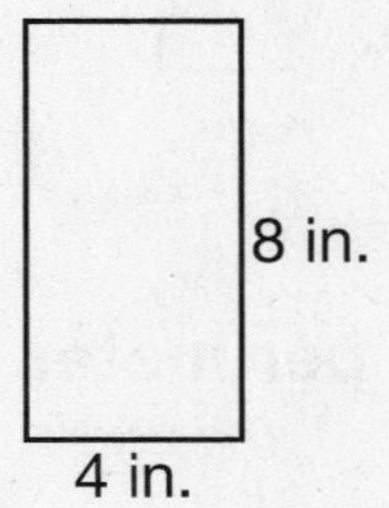

____

8. $l = 4$ in.
$w = 3$ in.
$P =$ ________

9. $l = 1.3$ m
$w = 0.7$ m
$P =$ ________

10. $l = 171$ mi
$w = 48$ mi
$P =$ ________

Mixed Review

Multiply.

11. *(9-5)* $\frac{2}{3}$ and $\frac{3}{3}$ ____________

12. *(9-5)* $\frac{6}{6}$ and $\frac{5}{6}$ ____________

13. *(9-3)* Estimate the product of $3\frac{2}{9}$ and 33.

____

14. *(7-8)* Theresa walks 7 blocks each day to school. Ryan walks 6 blocks. If Theresa has walked 56 blocks since the beginning of school, how many blocks has Ryan walked?

____

Name ______________________________

Daily Review 10-9

Daily Cumulative Review

Use the formula $A = l \times w$ to find the area of each rectangle. Fill in the missing numbers. *(Lesson 10-8)*

1.

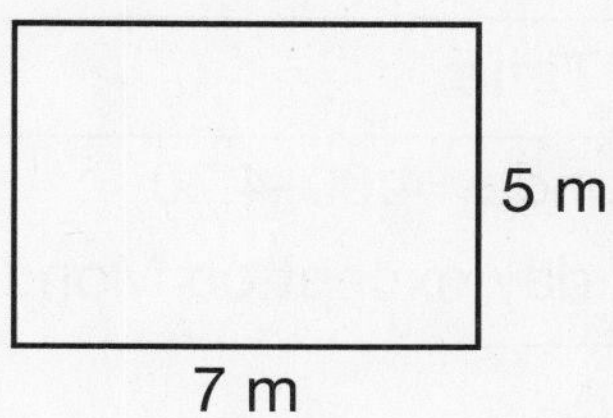

$A =$ _____ $\times$ _____

$A =$ _____ m^2

2.

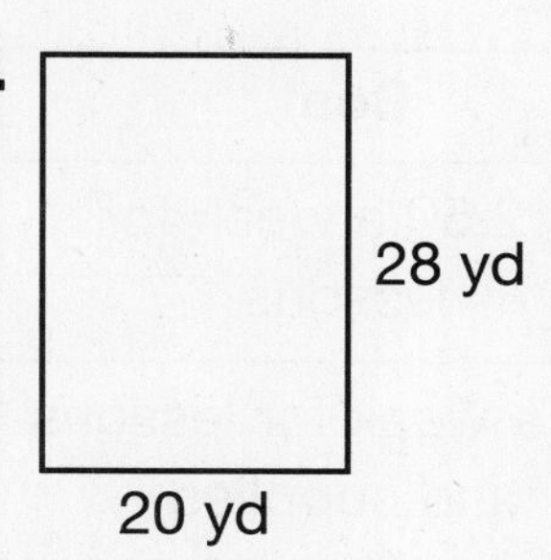

$A =$ _____ $\times$ _____

$A =$ _____ yd^2

Find each product. *(Lesson 10-7)*

3. 2×5 ft 7 in. = __________

4. 3×6 ft 9 in. = __________

5. 4×8 yd 1 ft = __________

6. 5×3 yd 2 ft = __________

Mixed Review

7. Make a drawing that shows $\frac{5}{3}$.
(7-9)

Complete.

8. $9\frac{5}{7} = \frac{\square}{7}$
(7-10)

9. $3 \times \frac{5}{6} =$ ________
(9-7)

10. 5 m 2 cm = _____ cm
(10-3)

11. If $n = 7$, what is $8 \times n$? _____
(5-8)

12. Find the mean, median, and mode for the set of data.
(4-9) \$4.10, \$5.60, \$1.80, \$1.80, \$7.70

__________, __________, __________

Name ______________________________

Daily Review 10-10

Daily Cumulative Review

Make a decision. You want to participate in music, art, and drama. The following is a list of things you might do. *(Lesson 10-9)*

Activity	Cost	Time
Piano Lessons	$12.50 a week for lessons	Lesson: Monday 4:00–4:30, Practice: $\frac{3}{4}$ hour a day except on Monday.
Art Lessons	$17 a week for lessons and supplies	Lesson: Tuesdays 4:00–6:00
Musical Play	$3 bus fare for each practice	Play practice: 6:00–7:30 Monday through Thursday for 4 weeks.

1. How much would it cost for 4 weeks for each activity?

____

2. How much time does each activity require in a 4-week period?

____

3. Which activity would you choose? Why?

____

____

Find the area of each rectangle. *(Lesson 10-8)*

4. $l = \frac{1}{2}$ ft
$w = 1\frac{1}{2}$ ft

$A =$ ________

5. $l = 4.6$ m
$w = 2.5$ m

$A =$ ________

6. $l = 9$ in.
$w = 8$ in.

$A =$ ________

Mixed Review

Use >, <, or = to complete.

7. 0.3 ◯ 0.30
(2-11)

8. $\frac{8}{3}$ ◯ $\frac{9}{4}$
(7-11)

9. 8 m 5 cm ◯ 850 cm
(10-3)

Name ______________________

Daily Cumulative Review

Find each area. *(Lesson 10-10)*

1.

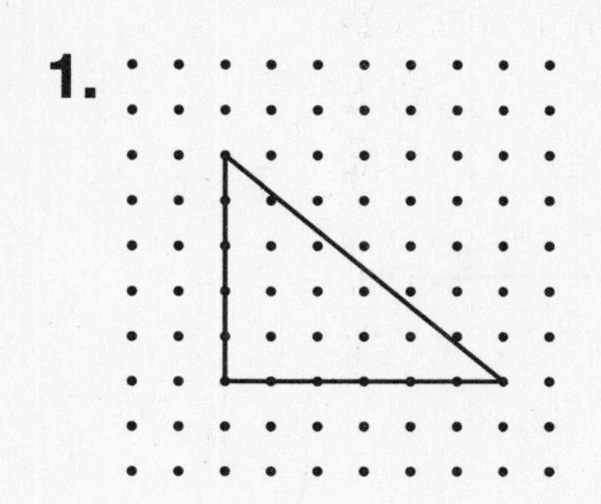

____

2.

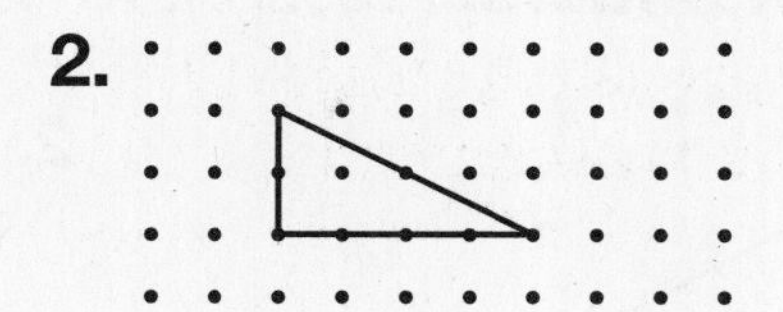

____

Make a decision. You have $75 to spend on new summer clothes. You find the following items that you like on sale. *(Lesson 10-9)*

Item	Cost	Item
Shirt A	$15	will only go with solid color shorts
Shirt B	$18	will go with any pair of shorts
Shirt C	$22	will go with any pair of shorts
Shorts A	$12	will go with only solid color shirts
Shorts B	$15	will go with any shirt
Sandals	$23	will go with casual or dress clothes
Running Shoes	$36	will go with casual clothes

3. Which items would you buy? Explain your decision.

____

____

Mixed Review

Find each sum or difference.

4. $\frac{1}{2} + \frac{2}{5}$ *(8-2)*

____

5. $7.9 - 1.3$ *(2-16)*

____

6. $6 + 1\frac{3}{4} + 2\frac{1}{7}$ *(8-11)*

____

Name ______________________________

Daily Review 10-12

Daily Cumulative Review

Use the formula $A = \frac{1}{2} \times (b \times h)$ to find the area of each triangle. Fill in the missing numbers. *(Lesson 10-11)*

1.

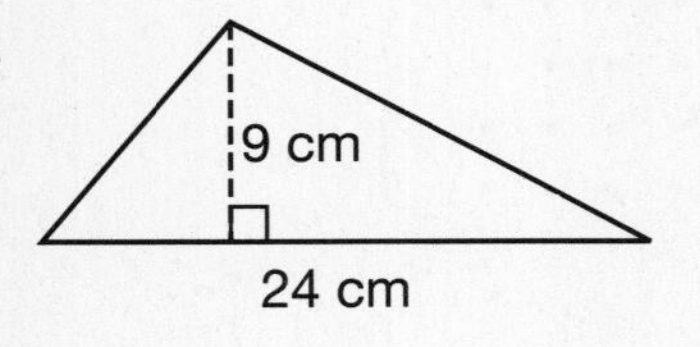

$A = \frac{1}{2} \times (\_\_\_\_ \times \_\_\_\_)$

$A = \frac{1}{2} \times (\_\_\_\_)$

$A = \_\_\_\_$ cm^2

2.

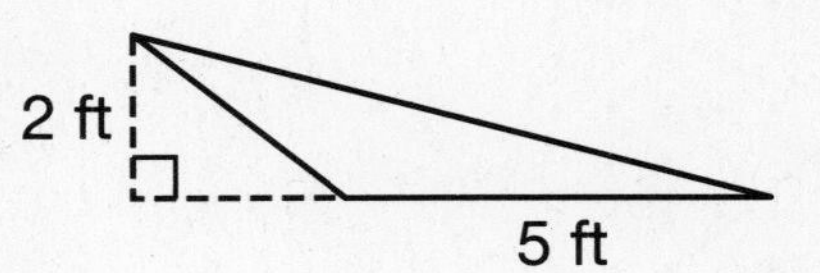

$A = \frac{1}{2} \times (\_\_\_\_ \times \_\_\_\_)$

$A = \frac{1}{2} \times (\_\_\_\_)$

$A = \_\_\_\_$ ft^2

Find each area. *(Lesson 10-10)*

3.

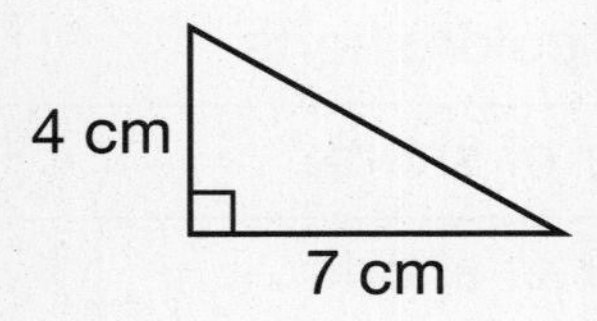

____

4.

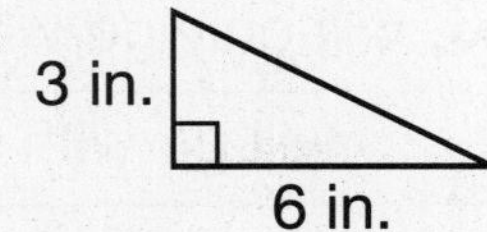

____

5.

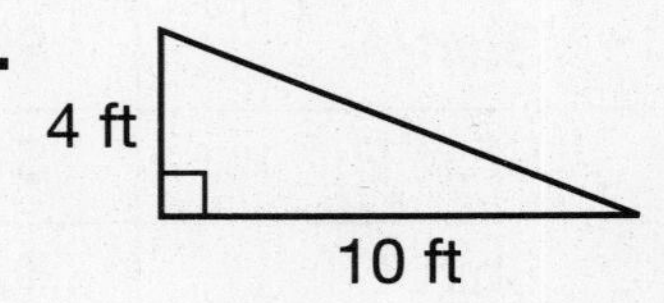

____

Mixed Review

Estimate to solve. Tell whether you overestimated or underestimated. Explain your reasoning.

6. *(9-6)* Michi is making ham sandwiches for a party. If each of the 56 guests eats one sandwich that has 1 slice of ham and there are about 12 slices to a pound of ham, how many pounds of sliced ham should she buy?

____

____

Estimate. Then find each product.

7. *(9-8)* $4\frac{7}{8} \times 3\frac{1}{5}$ ______________

8. *(9-3)* $3\frac{1}{7} \times 28$ ______________

9. *(3-10)* $6.90 × 19 ______________

Name ______________________

Daily Review 10-13

Daily Cumulative Review

Find each area. *(Lesson 10-12)*

1.

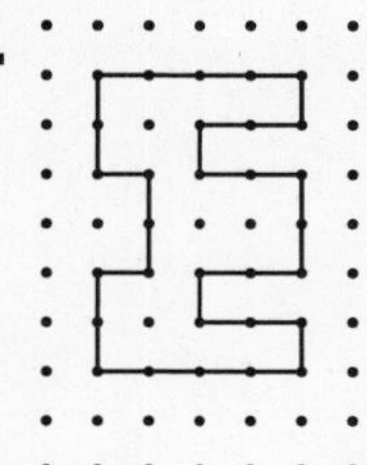

2.

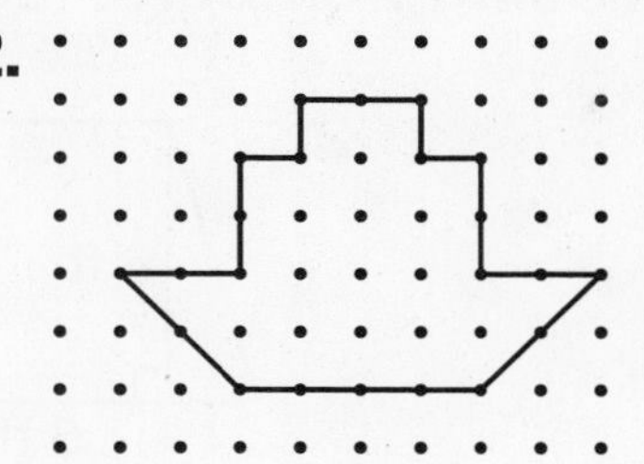

3.

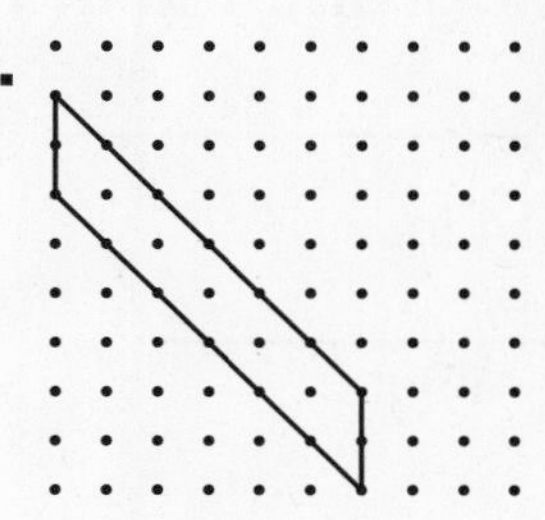

______ ______ ______

Find each area. *(Lesson 10-11)*

4.

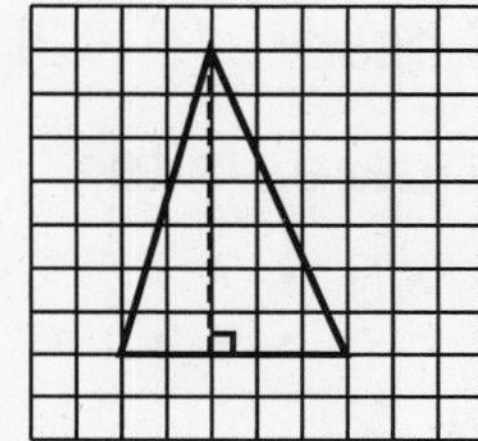

5.

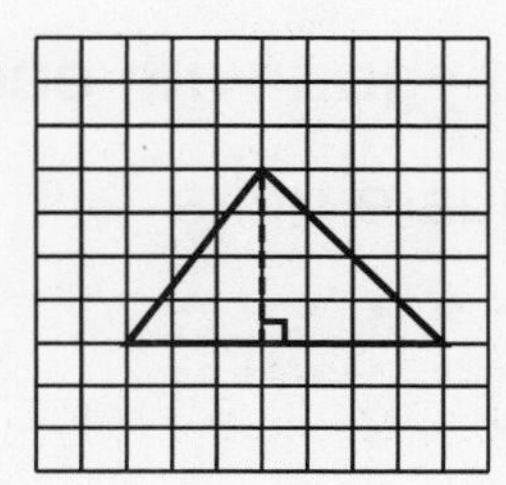

6.

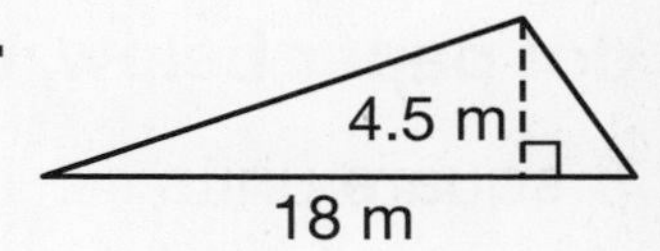

A = ______ *A* = ______ *A* = ______

Mixed Review

7. Is $\frac{1}{6}$ greater than or less than $\frac{1}{12}$? Explain.
(7-6)

____

8. Regan and her 3 friends ordered large pizzas cut into 12 pieces. Regan can eat 4 pieces. Her friends usually eat 6 pieces each. Are 2 large pizzas enough? Explain.
(7-10)

____

9. Devon plans to go to bed at 9:00 P.M. He practices the piano for 45 minutes every day. He plans to work on his geometry project for 2 hours. Vacuuming the living room takes 15 minutes and dinner takes 30 minutes. He wants to watch $1\frac{1}{2}$ hours of TV. A shower takes 15 minutes. What time should he start doing all these things? ______
(9-9)

Name ______________________________

Daily Review 10-14

Daily Cumulative Review

Use the formula $A = b \times h$ to find the area of each parallelogram. Fill in the missing numbers. *(Lesson 10-13)*

1.

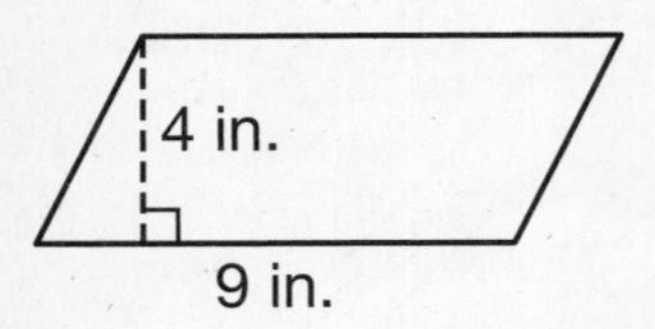

$A =$ ______ $\times$ ______

$A =$ ______ in^2

2.

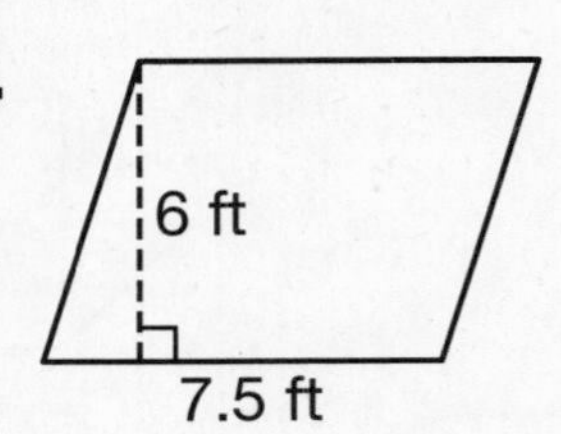

$A =$ ______ $\times$ ______

$A =$ ______ ft^2

On dot paper below, draw a polygon with each area. *(Lesson 10-12)*

3. 8 square units **4.** 5 square units **5.** $6\frac{1}{2}$ square units

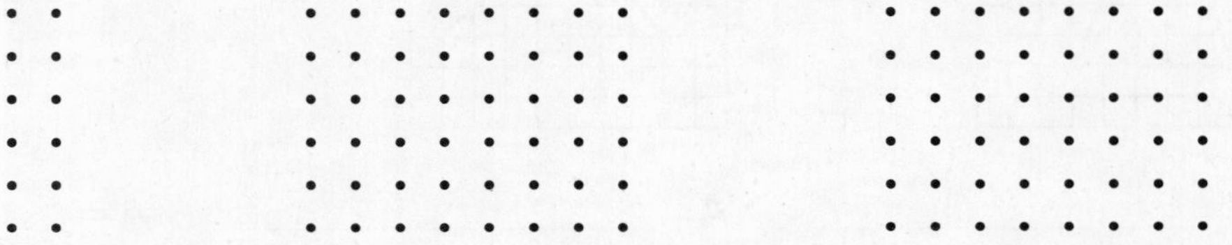

Mixed Review

6. Kelsey's pencil is 16.5 cm long. Andrew's pencil is 135 mm long. Who has the longer pencil? *(10-2)*

____

7. Decide which does *not* belong to the set. ________ *(7-12)*

A. 60% **B.** $\frac{6}{10}$ **C.** 0.06 **D.** 60 out of 100

Find the simplest form for each fraction.

8. $\frac{6}{40}$ ________ *(7-5)*

9. $\frac{9}{24}$ ________ *(7-5)*

10. $\frac{16}{36}$ ________ *(7-5)*

11. Dawn said she would share half a bag of candy with Ian. Ian got $\frac{13}{26}$ of the bag. Did Ian get half? Explain. *(7-2)*

____

Name ______________________________

Daily Review 10-15

Daily Cumulative Review

Find the number of counters in each envelope. Fill in the missing numbers. *(Lesson 10-14)*

1.

$n + 3 = 11$ $n = 8$

a. $n + 3 -$ ____ $= 11 -$ ____

b. $n =$ ____

c. check ____ $+ 3 = 11$

2.

$4 \times n = 20$ $n = 5$

b. $(4 \times n) \div$ ____ $= 20 \div$ ____

b. $n =$ ____

c. check $4 \times$ ____ $= 20$

Find each area. *(Lesson 10-13)*

3.

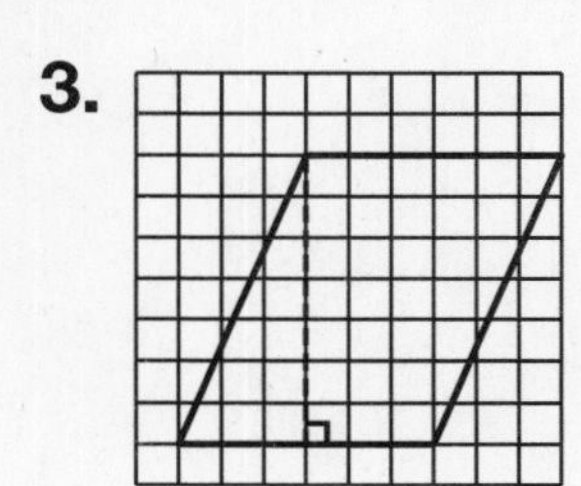

4.

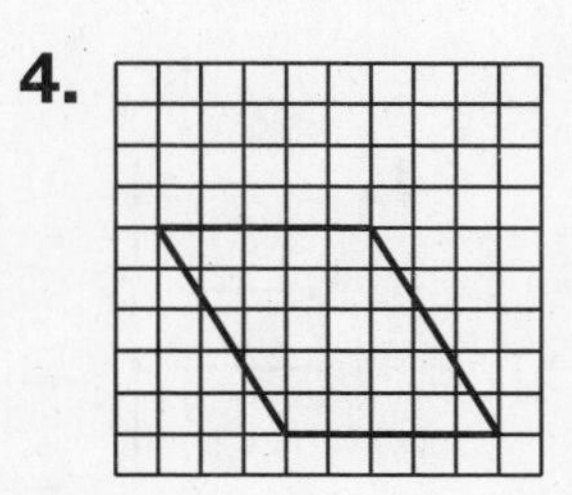

5.

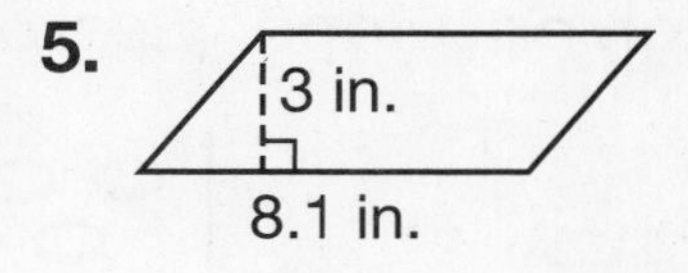

______________ ______________ ______________

Mixed Review

6. (6-8) Write whether you would flip, turn, or slide the figures to show they are congruent. ____________

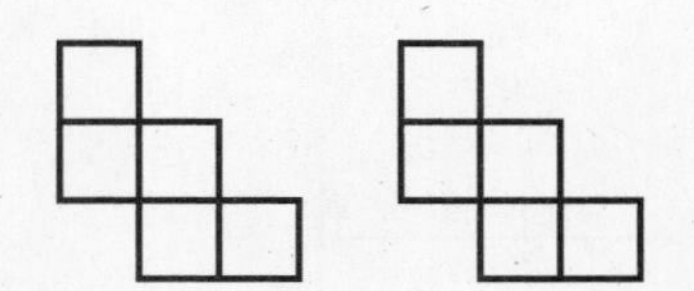

Complete.
Write acute, straight, obtuse, or right.

7. (6-2) An angle with measure 180° is ____________.

8. (6-2) An angle with measure 91° is ____________.

9. (6-2) An angle with measure 90° is ____________.

Name ______________________

Daily Review 10-16

Daily Cumulative Review

Look for a pattern to solve the problem. *(Lesson 10-15)*

1. During school, Jasmine wakes up at 6:30 A.M. She has been sleeping until 10:00 A.M. all summer. School starts in about a month. Jasmine plans to get up 15 minutes earlier every day until she is back on schedule for school. How many days before school starts should she begin her plan?

____

2. For an awards banquet, 2 tables will be placed at the foot of the room for the speakers. Other tables will be placed end to end as shown. How many more tables need to be added to seat a total of 52 people?

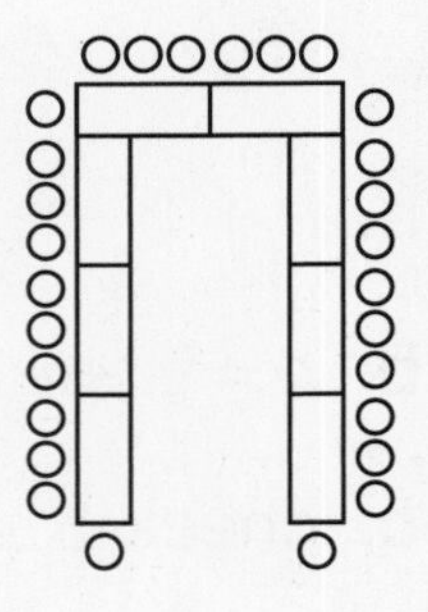

____

Use counters to find the number of counters in each envelope. *(Lesson 10-14)*

3.

$5 + n = 9$

$n =$ ________

4.

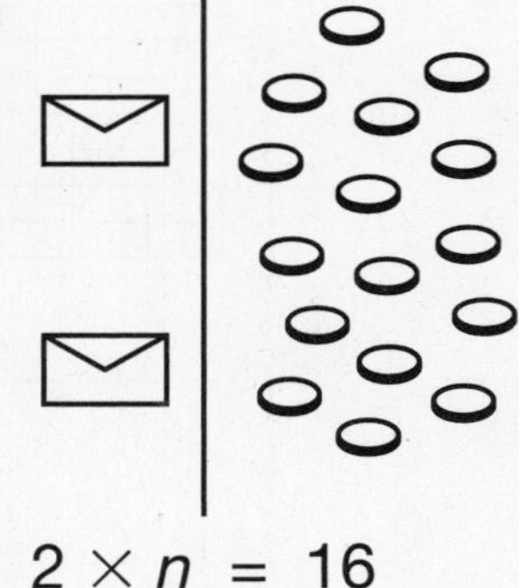

$2 \times n = 16$

$n =$ ________

Mixed Review

Estimate each product or quotient using compatible numbers.

5. $638 \div 81$ (5-4)

____

6. $\frac{5}{6} \times 25$ (9-3)

____

7. $4\frac{7}{9} \times 3\frac{1}{6}$ (9-8)

____

Name ______________________________

Daily Review 11-1

Daily Cumulative Review

Use the formula $C = \pi \times d$ to find the circumference of each circle. Fill in the missing numbers. *(Lesson 10-16)*

1.

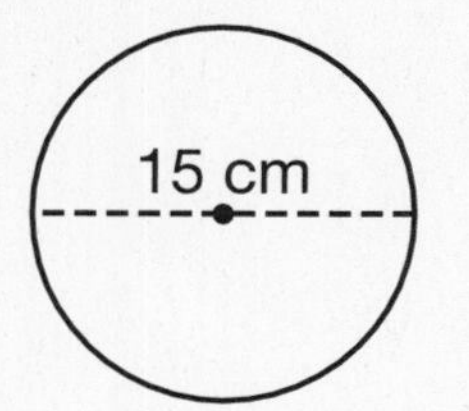

$C = 3.14 \times$ ______

$C =$ ________ cm

2.

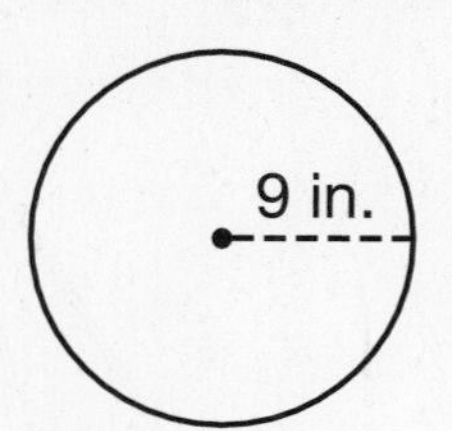

$C = 3.14 \times$ ___ $\times$ ___

$C =$ ____________ in.

3.

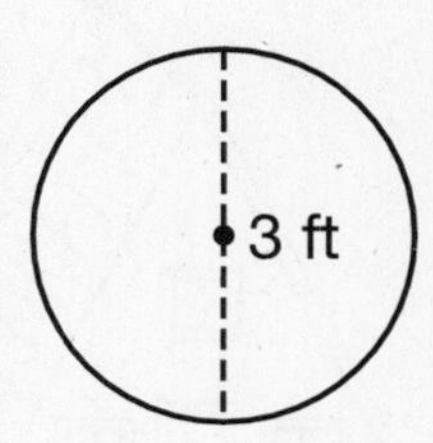

$C = 3.14 \times$ ______

$C =$ __________ ft

Look for a pattern or use any strategy to solve each problem. *(Lesson 10-15)*

4. Stacey's mom is packing for a 6-day business trip. She packs 3 blouses (white, pink, and gray) and 2 skirts (black and white). Each blouse goes with each skirt. Will she have enough clothes to have a different outfit each day? Explain.

____

____

5. The weatherman noted that the high temperature on Monday was 1 degree cooler than on Sunday, Tuesday was 2 degrees cooler than Monday, and Wednesday was 3 degrees cooler than Tuesday. The pattern continued through Saturday. If the high temperature on Sunday was 78°F, what was the high temperature on the following Saturday? __________

Mixed Review

Complete.

6. *(10-3)* 0.08 m = ______ mm

7. *(8-15)* 6 ft 3 in. = ______ in.

8. *(9-4)* $\frac{1}{4}$ of $\frac{1}{2}$ = ______

9. *(7-3)* $\frac{5}{7} = \frac{\square}{21} = \frac{30}{\square}$

Name ______________________________

Daily Review 11-2

Daily Cumulative Review

Write the name of the solid suggested in each drawing. *(Lesson 11-1)*

1.

____

2.

____

Find each circumference. Use 3.14 for π. *(Lesson 10-16)*

3.

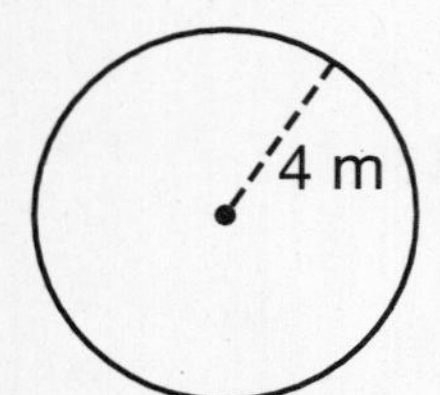

$C =$ ______________________

4.

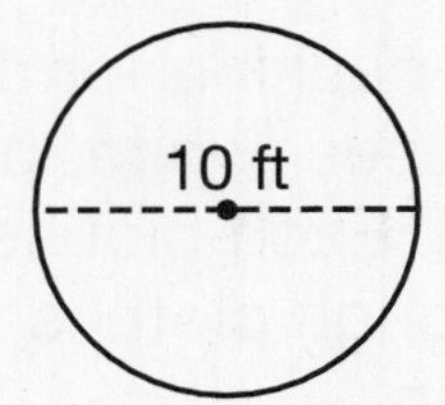

$C =$ ______________________

Mixed Review

Find each perimeter.

5. a square with sides of 1.5 m ______________________
(10-5)

6. a regular pentagon with sides of 3 ft ______________________
(10-5)

7. Choose the most appropriate unit of measure to estimate the height of a building. ______________
(10-1)

A. cm **B.** dm **C.** m **D.** km

Find each product.

8. $5\frac{7}{9} \times 1\frac{1}{4}$
(9-8)

9. 6.25×8.4
(3-13)

10. 50×40
(3-1)

______________ ______________ ______________

Name ______________________

Daily Cumulative Review

Complete the table. *(Lesson 11-2)*

	Edges of Base	Number of Vertices	Total Number of Edges	Name of Solid
1.				
2.				

Write the name of the solid suggested in each drawing. *(Lesson 11-1)*

3.

____

4.

____

Mixed Review

5. Which length is the shortest? ______
(10-4)

A. 7,103 mm **B.** 7.103 m **C.** 71.03 cm

Use logical reasoning to solve the problem.

6. Beth, Mick, Terri, and Cathy are ages 10, 12, 14, and 16. Beth is neither the oldest nor youngest. Terri is 4 years older than Cathy. Mick is 4 years older than Beth. What are their ages?
(9-9)

	10	12	14	16
Beth				
Mick				
Terri				
Cathy				

____

____

Name ________________________________

Daily Review 11-4

Daily Cumulative Review

Name the figure that would be formed by each net. *(Lesson 11-3)*

1. ____________________

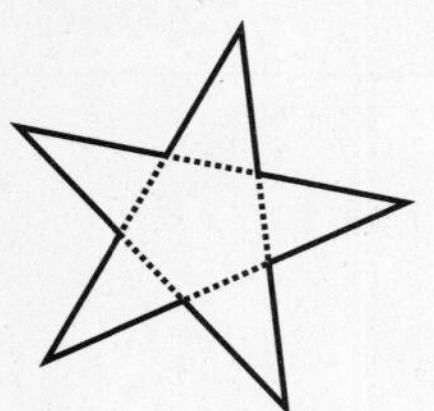

2. ____________________

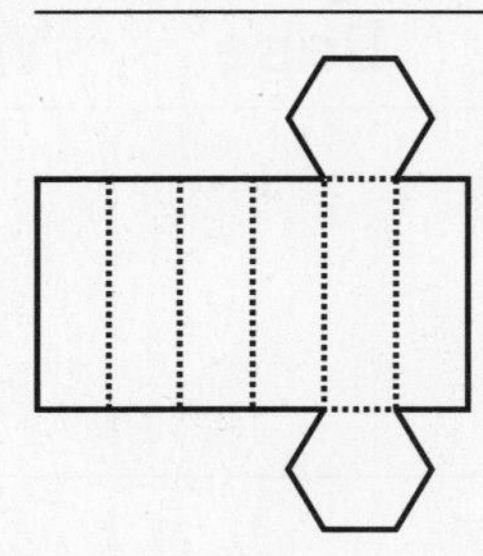

Decide if each statement is true or false. *(Lesson 11-2)*

3. A triangular prism has 9 edges. ________

4. A pentagonal prism has 5 faces. ________

5. A rectangular prism has 8 vertices. ________

6. The number of edges of one base of a prism is half the number of vertices of the prism. ________

Mixed Review

Find each area.

7. *(10-13)*

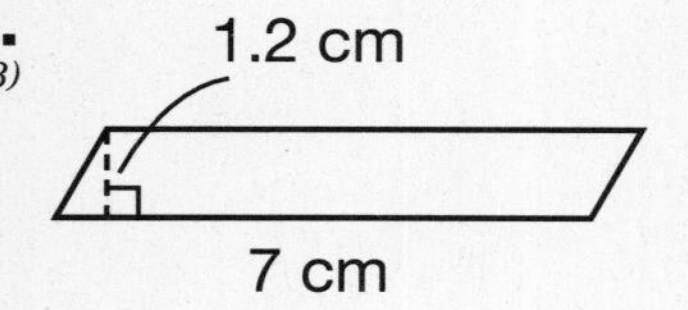

____

8. *(10-10)*

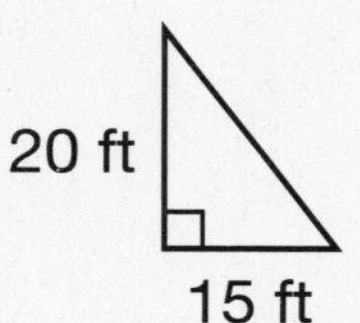

____

9. *(10-8)*

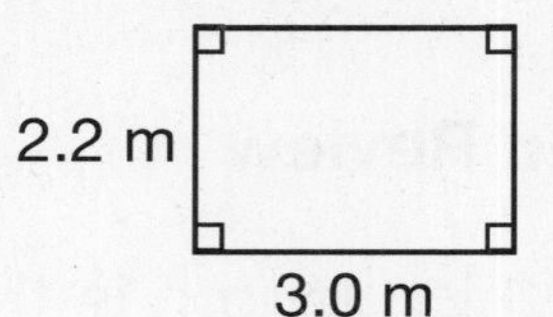

____

Find each quotient.

10. $4 \div \frac{1}{12}$ *(9-10)* ____________

11. $16\overline{)\$24.00}$ *(5-10)*

12. 60,000 ÷ 30 *(5-1)* ____________

13. Write the missing factors. 1, ☐, ☐, ☐, ☐, 20 *(4-14)*

Name ______________________

Daily Review 11-5

Daily Cumulative Review

Use a calculator to find the surface area of each figure. *(Lesson 11-4)*

1.

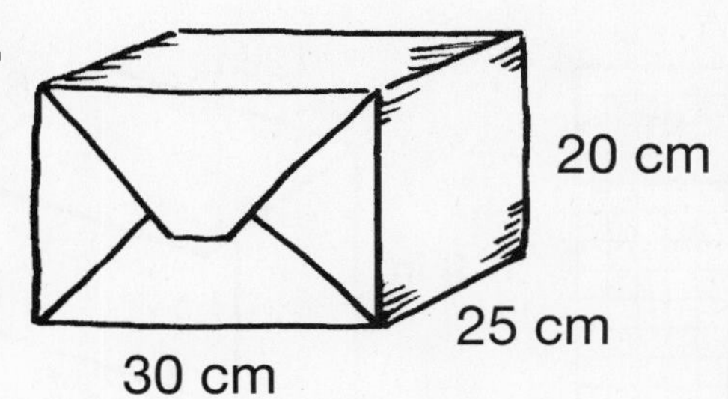

____

2.

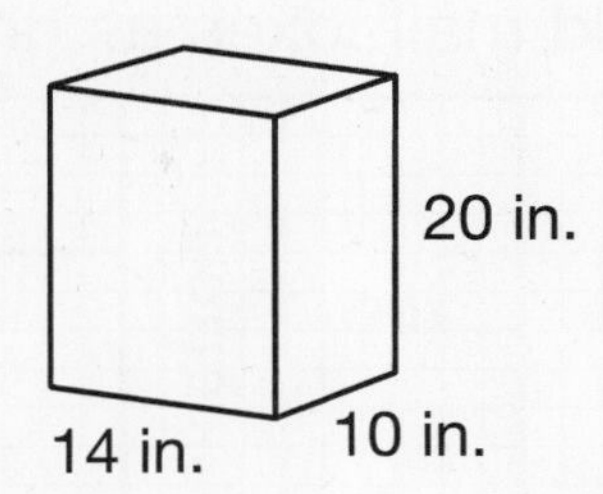

____

Draw a net for the solid shown. *(Lesson 11-3)*

3. triangular prism

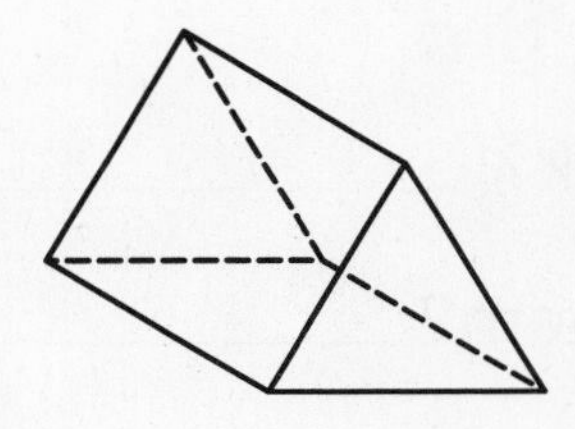

Mixed Review

Find each perimeter.

4. *(10-6)* rectangle:
$l = 2$ in.
$w = 6$ in.

____

5. *(10-5)* equilateral triangle:
side = 1.7 m

____

6. *(10-7)* square:
side = 3 ft 2 in.

____

Decide whether you need an exact answer or an estimate. Solve.

7. *(8-16)* Your body weight is a measure of the force of gravity. Jupiter's gravitational pull is about 2.5 times that of Earth. Amy's dad weighs about 160 pounds on Earth. How much would he weigh on Jupiter?

____

Name ______________________________

Daily Review 11-6

Daily Cumulative Review

Plan and solve. *(Lesson 11-5)*

You want to build mailboxes as gifts.

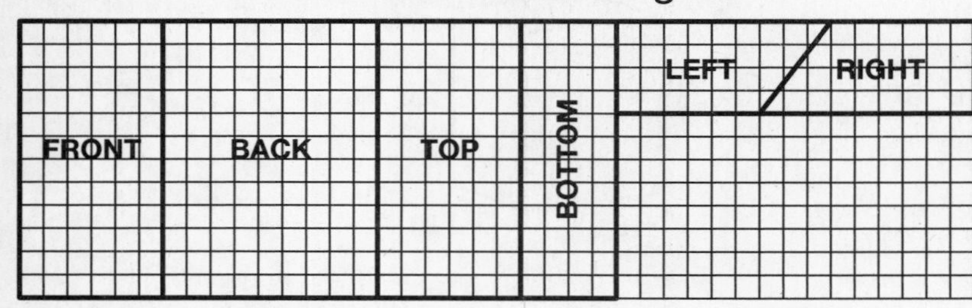

Scale: 1 square = 1 in^2

You can buy a 1-ft by 12-ft board for $12.

1. Into what geometric figures will the board be cut?

____

What length of board will you need for:

2. the front? ____________ **3.** the back? ____________

4. the top? ____________ **5.** the bottom? ____________

6. the left and right sides cut as shown? ____________

7. How many mailboxes could be made from one 12-foot board? (Hint: There is room for another pair of sides in the plan above.) ______

Use a calculator to find the surface area. Solve. *(Lesson 11-4)*

8. Kyoko's bedroom is 11 ft wide, 13 ft long, and 8 ft high. A gallon of paint covers about 400 ft^2. How many gallons of paint does Kyoko need for 2 coats of paint on the walls and ceiling? ____________

Mixed Review

Complete.

9. 8 m = ________ cm *(10-2)*

10. $\frac{4}{5} \times 3 = \frac{\square}{5}$ = ________ *(9-7)*

11. 43 in. = ____ ft ____ in. *(8-15)*

12. 527 ÷ ________ = 5.27 *(5-12)*

Name ____________________

Daily Review 11-7

Daily Cumulative Review

Complete. Check the reasonableness of your answer. *(Lesson 11-6)*

1. 3 lb = ______ oz

2. 4 T = ______ lb

3. 64 oz = ______ lb

4. 56 oz = ______ lb ______ oz

5. 6 T 500 lb = ______ lb

6. 9,000 lb = ______ T

Plan and solve. *(Lesson 11-5)*

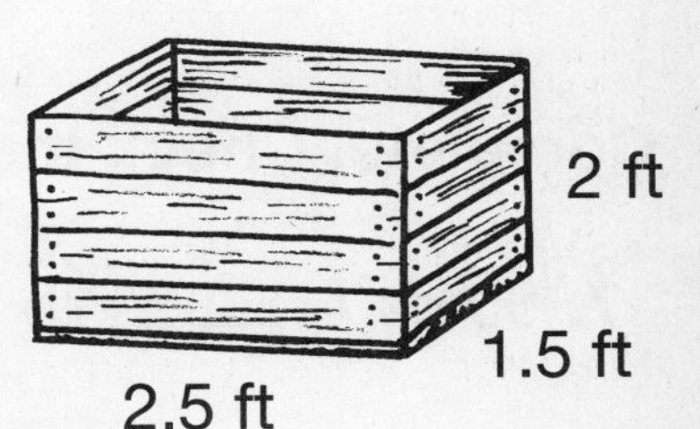

You plan to make a toy bin from 6-in. wide boards. The bin has no top.

What is the total length of board needed to make:

7. the front? ______

8. the back? ______

9. the bottom? ______

10. the left side? ______

11. the right side? ______

12. the entire bin? ______

13. How many 12-ft boards should you buy? ______

Mixed Review

Find each area.

14. *(10-12)*

15. *(10-8)*

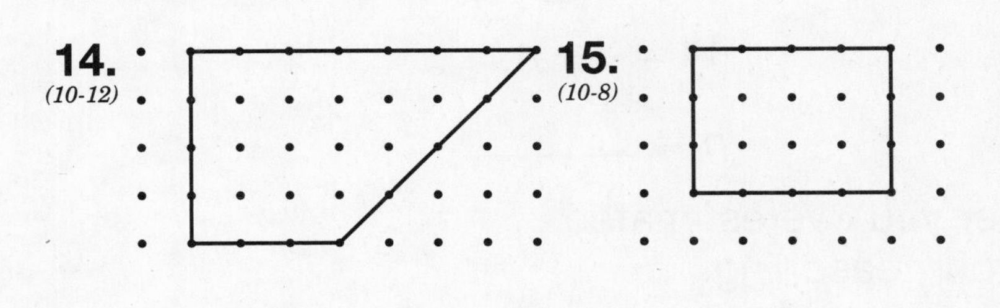

16. *(10-11)*

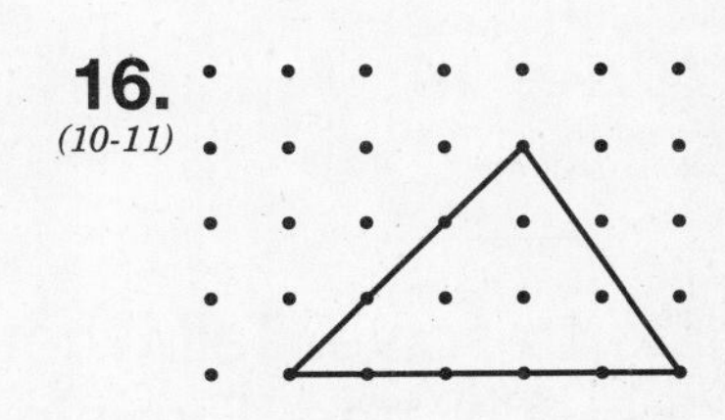

______ ______ ______

Find each product or quotient. Simplify.

17. *(9-5)* $\frac{5}{9} \times \frac{9}{9} =$ ______

18. *(9-7)* $\frac{2}{9} \times 45 =$ ______

19. *(9-2)* $\frac{4}{5}$ of $20 =$ ______

20. *(9-10)* $4 \div \frac{1}{5} =$ ______

21. *(9-8)* $2\frac{3}{4} \times \frac{2}{3} =$ ______

22. *(9-10)* $1 \div \frac{1}{8} =$ ______

Name ______________________________

Daily Cumulative Review

Use mental math to change to kilograms or grams. *(Lesson 11-7)*

1. 4.7 kg = ________ g

2. 4,900 g = ________ kg

3. 0.5 kg = ________ g

4. 300 g = ________ kg

5. 30 g = ________ kg

6. 6,000 g = ________ kg

Complete. Check the reasonableness of your answer. *(Lesson 11-6)*

7. 90 oz = ______ lb ______ oz

8. 2,000,000 lb = ________ T

9. 17 oz = ______ lb ______ oz

10. 30 lb = ________ oz

11. 0.01 T = ________ lb

12. 5 lb = ________ oz

Mixed Review

Find the number of counters in each envelope.

13. *(10-14)*

$2 \times n = 14$

$n =$ ________

14. *(10-14)*

$11 = 3 + n$

$n =$ ________

Estimate to solve. Tell whether you overestimated or underestimated. Explain your reasoning.

15. *(9-6)* Zelda has $15 to buy school supplies. Notebooks cost $4.98 each, glue costs $1.19, pencils cost 10¢ each, and a package of 6 pens costs $1.29. Does she have enough to buy 2 notebooks, 1 bottle of glue, 10 pencils, and a package of pens?

____

____

Name ______________________________

Daily Review 11-9

Daily Cumulative Review

Write each temperature in Celsius and Fahrenheit. *(Lesson 11-8)*

1.

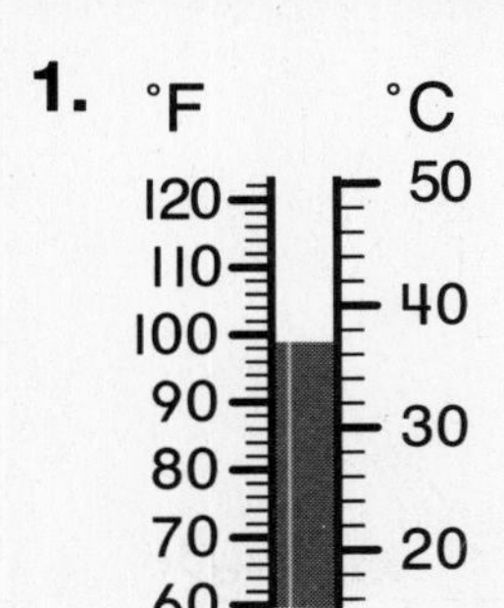

____

2.

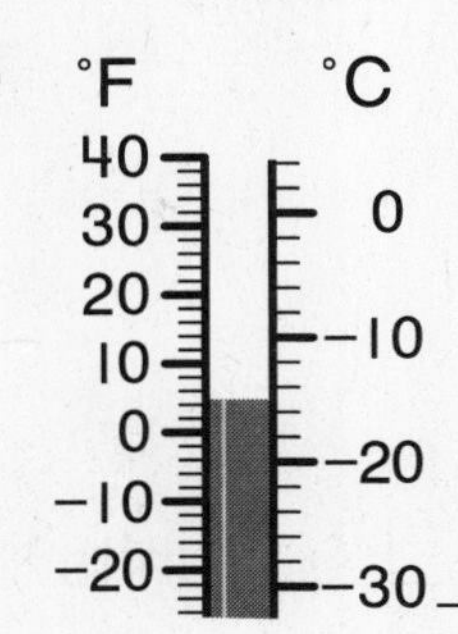

____

Use mental math to change to kilograms or grams. *(Lesson 11-7)*

3. How many kilograms?

425 g

____

4. How many grams?

1.81 kg

____

Mixed Review

Estimate each product, quotient, sum, or difference.

5. *(9-3)* $6\frac{6}{7} \times 21$ __________

6. *(8-9)* $4\frac{7}{8} + 9\frac{1}{10}$ __________

7. *(5-2)* $551 \div 90$ __________

8. *(3-14)* 3.9×5.12 __________

9. *(8-9)* $16\frac{1}{8} - 8\frac{11}{12}$ __________

10. *(5-10)* $\$2.10 \div 40$ __________

Write if the problem has too much or too little information.
Solve if possible, or tell what is needed to solve.

11. *(8-7)* Chelsea finished $\frac{2}{3}$ of her math assignment in one hour. She did 4 more problems in the next 15 minutes. How many more problems does she still need to complete?

____

____

Name ______________________________

Daily Review 11-10

Daily Cumulative Review

Find each volume. *(Lesson 11-9)*

1.

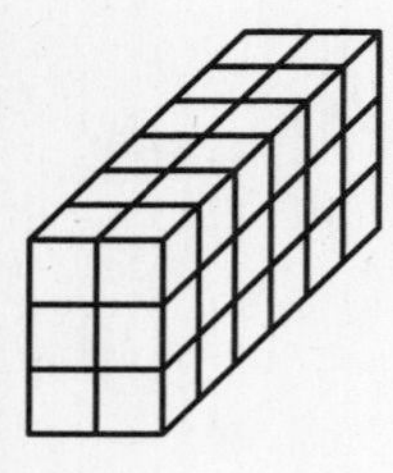

______ units^3

2.

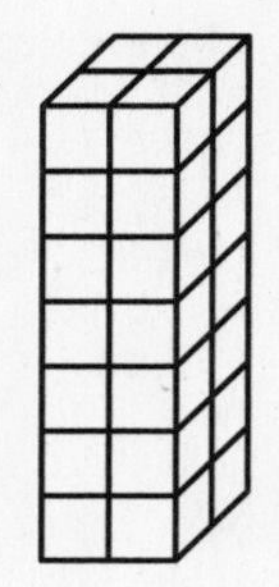

______ units^3

Write each temperature in Celsius and Fahrenheit. *(Lesson 11-8)*

3.

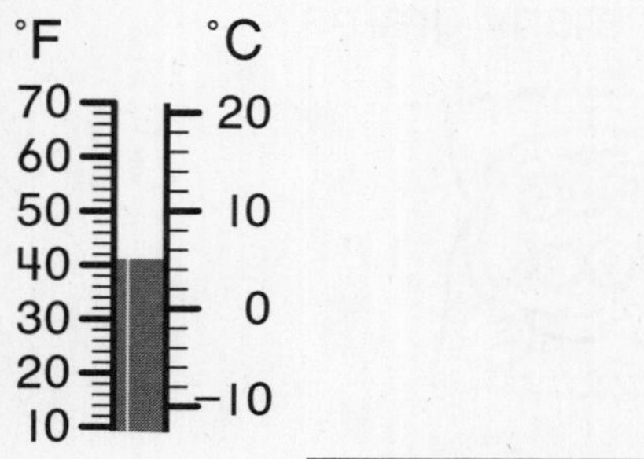

____

4.

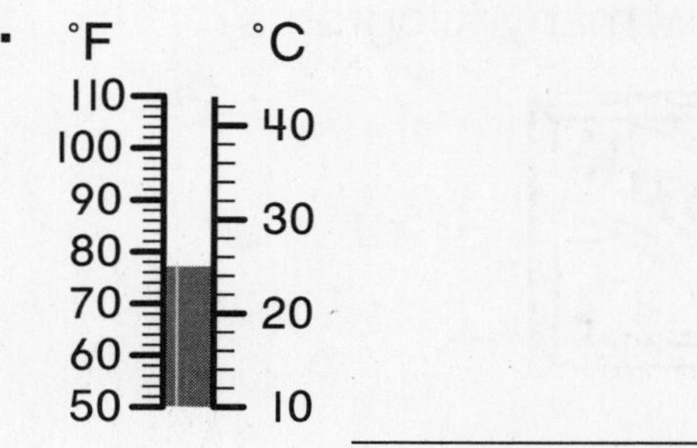

____

Mixed Review

Find the diameter of each circle to the nearest hundredth. Use 3.14 for π.

5. $C = 314$ cm *(10-16)*

$d =$ ______________

6. $C = 75$ in. *(10-16)*

$d =$ ______________

7. $C = 4.7$ m *(10-16)*

$d =$ ______________

8. Find the length to the nearest $\frac{1}{4}$-inch. *(8-14)*

____

Find each sum or difference.

9. $3\frac{1}{6} + 2\frac{5}{12}$ *(8-8)*

10. $\frac{5}{6} - \frac{2}{3}$ *(8-6)*

11. $\frac{1}{3} + \frac{2}{3} + \frac{1}{3}$ *(8-1)*

______________ ______________ ______________

Name ______________________

Daily Cumulative Review

Complete. *(Lesson 11-10)*

1. 34 fl oz = ________ c

2. $\frac{1}{4}$ c = ________ tbsp

3. 1 gal = ________ c

4. $3\frac{1}{2}$ qt = ________ pt

Find each volume. *(Lesson 11-9)*

5.

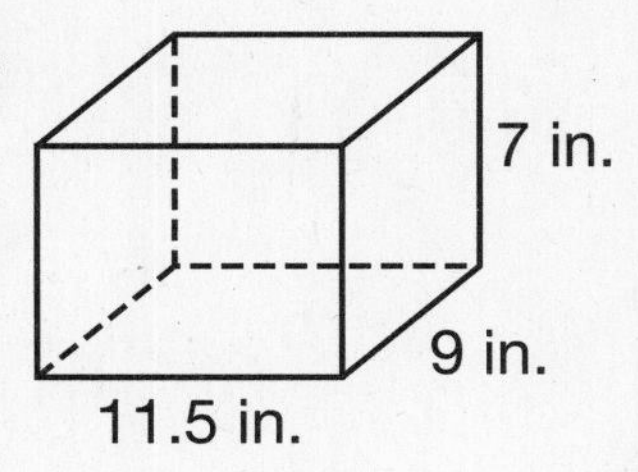

____

6.

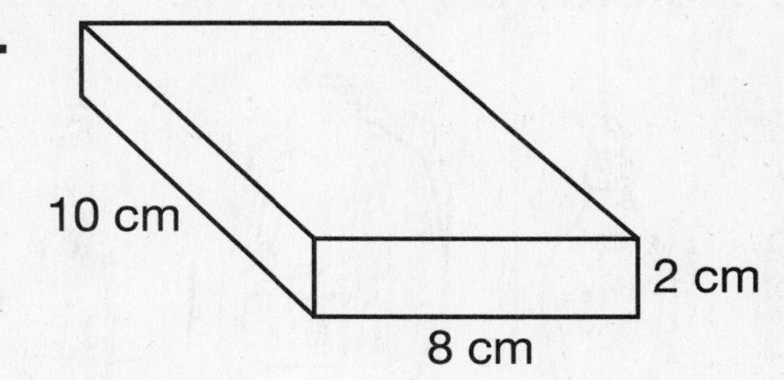

____

7. $l = 6$ cm, $w = 5$ cm, $h = 4$ cm

$V =$ ________________

8. $l = 1.5$ m, $w = 2$ m, $h = 7$m

$V =$ ________________

Mixed Review

Find each sum or difference.

9. $\frac{3}{5} + \frac{7}{10}$ *(8-2)* ________

10. $\frac{10}{11} - \frac{13}{22}$ *(8-5)* ________

11. $9 - 3\frac{3}{7}$ *(8-8)* ________

12. *(7-13)* Write 1% as a fraction and a decimal. ________________

13. *(7-4)* Find the greatest common factor of 48 and 32. ________________

14. *(6-4)* Jordan is drawing a sketch of a baseball diamond. There is a right angle at each base and the distances between the bases are the same.

What shape should he use? ________________

Name ______________________________

Daily Review 11-12

Daily Cumulative Review

Complete. *(Lesson 11-11)*

1. 500 mL = ________ L

2. 6.25 L = ________ mL

3. 46 mL = ________ L

4. 0.01 L = ________ mL

5. 0.2 L = ________ mL

6. 20,050 mL = ________ L

Use the drawing to answer 7–12. *(Lesson 11-10)*

4 fl oz | 3 c | 1 gal | 10 fl oz | $\frac{3}{4}$ pint | 8 fl oz

7. ________ c of shoe polish

8. ________ qt chocolate syrup

9. ________ qt of milk

10. ________ tbsp soy sauce

11. ________ c balsamic vinegar

12. ________ c baby formula

Mixed Review

Use the diagram at the right.

13. *(6-5)* For exercise, Ruthie walks to Tasher Pond and back every day. How many different routes can she take to the pond and back home again?

____

14. *(7-11)* List the paths from shortest to longest.

____

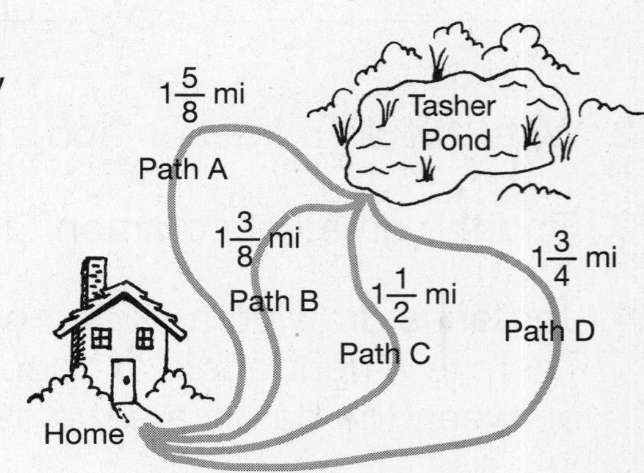

Name ________________________________

Daily Review
11-13

Daily Cumulative Review

Complete the table. *(Lesson 11-12)*

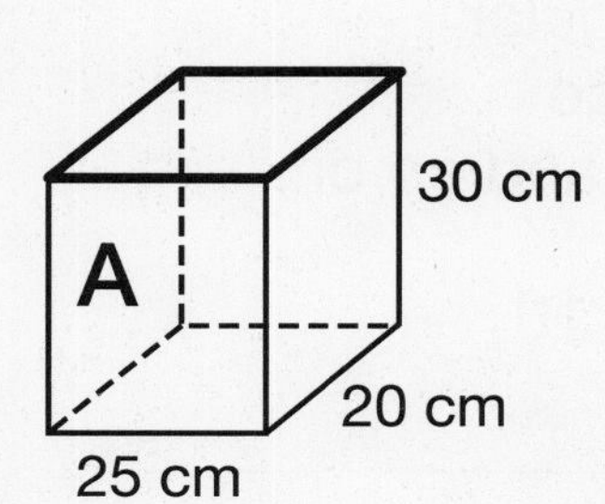

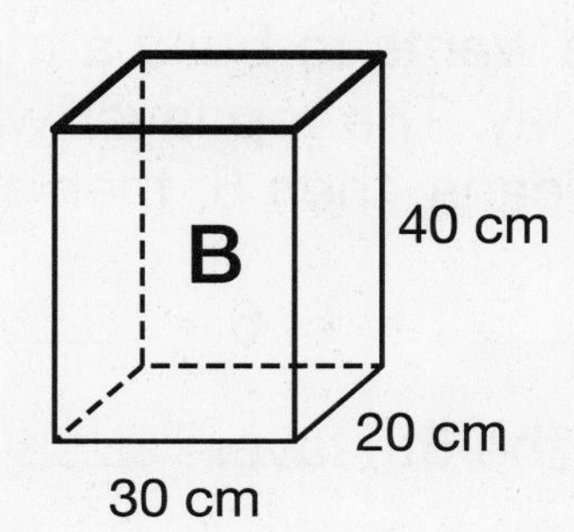

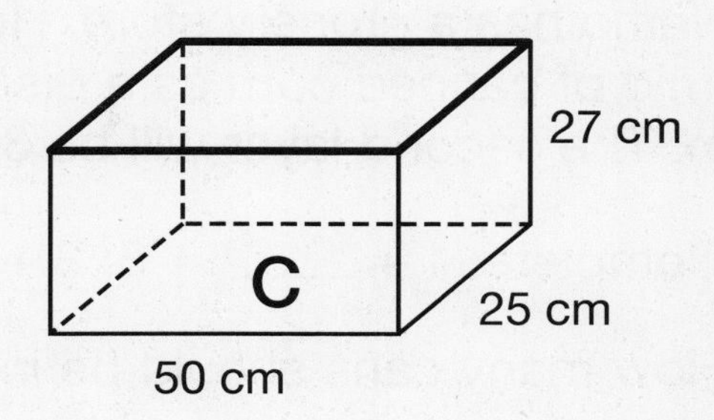

	Aquarium	Volume (cm^3)	Amount of Water (L)	Amount of Water (mL)	Mass of Water (kg)	Mass of Water (g)
1.	A					
2.	B					
3.	C					

Complete. *(Lesson 11-11)*

4. 0.21 L = ________ mL

5. 250 mL = ________ L

6. 9.5 L = ________ mL

7. 40 mL = ________ L

8. 2,800 mL = ________ L

9. 0.005 L = ________ mL

Mixed Review

10. Which polygon is congruent to the first one in the row? ________
(6-6)

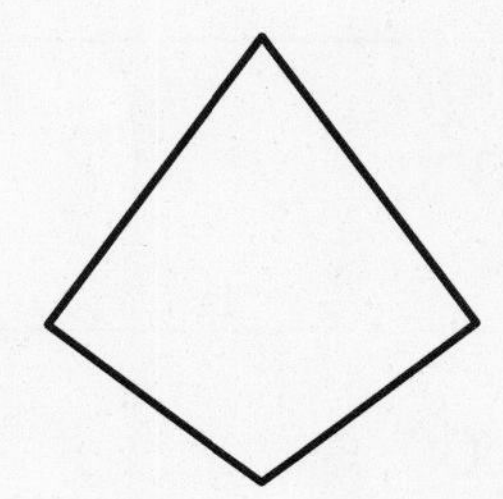

A.

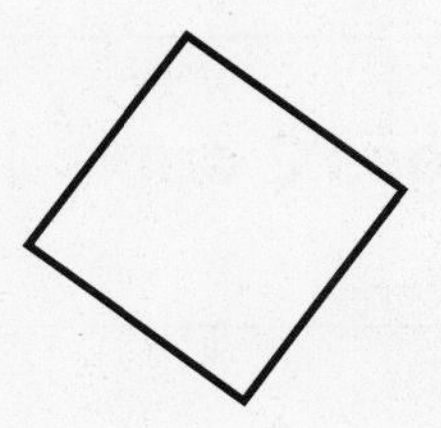

B.

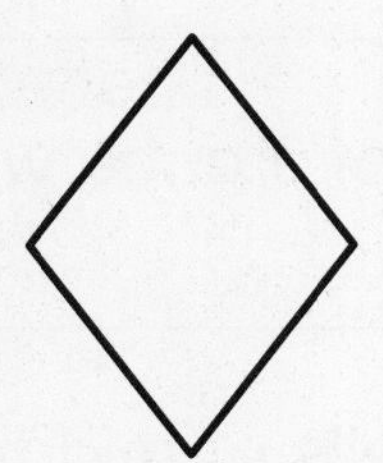

C.

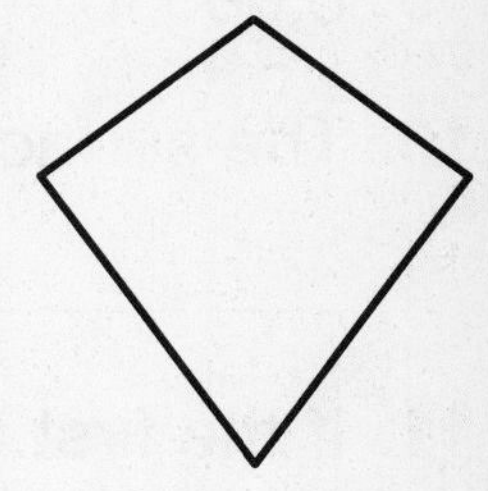

11. What is the measure of a straight angle? ____________
(6-2)

Name ______________________________

Daily Review 12-1

Daily Cumulative Review

Solve a simpler problem to solve the problem below. *(Lesson 11-13)*

Mr. Nemo has a grocery store. He wants to build a triangular pyramid of canned corn as a display. The top layer will be 1 can. The second layer will be 3 cans, then 6, then 10, and so on.

1. Complete. 1 + ____ = 3; 3 + ____ = 6; 6 + ____ = 10

2. How many cans should be in the 5th layer? ______________

3. What is the total number of cans in a triangular pyramid with 6 layers? Explain.

____

Write the number for each. *(Lesson 11-12)*

4. 3,000 mL of water would fill a ______ cm^3 container.

5. 1.5 kg of water would fill a ______ mL container.

6. 4.2 L of water would have a mass of ______ kg.

7. A 580 cm^3 container can hold ______ L.

Mixed Review

Decide if each statement is true or false. If false, write what would make the statement true.

8. A triangular pyramid has 4 edges. ______________
(11-2)

9. 6,000 lb = 3 T ______________
(11-6)

10. The surface area of a cube with edges 2 cm is 18 cm^2.
(11-4)

____

11. If the first three bells of middle school ring at 8:10, 9:00, and 9:50, the fourth bell should ring at 10:30.
(10-15)

____

Name ________________________________

Daily Cumulative Review

Write each ratio in three ways. Simplify. *(Lesson 12-1)*

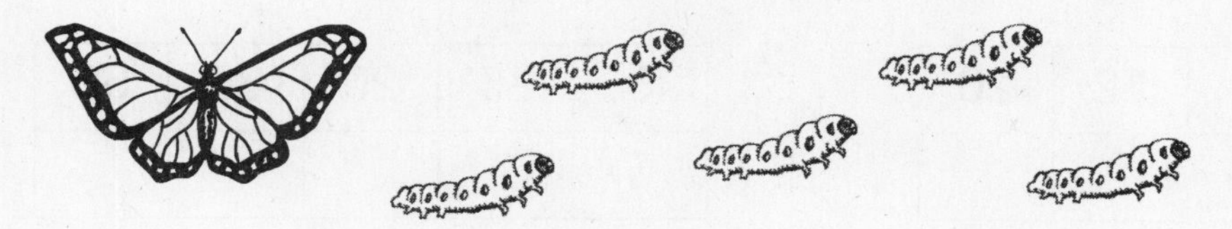

1. butterflies to caterpillars ________ ________ ________

2. adult mice to baby mice ________ ________ ________

Use any strategy to solve. *(Lesson 11-13)*

3. Miss Eliza's quilt is made of 16 large squares. Each square is made of 4 smaller squares, and each smaller square is made of 2 colored triangles and 2 white triangles. How many white triangles are in her quilt? ________

Mixed Review

Decide if each statement is *always*, *sometimes*, or *never* true.

4. A pyramid has two bases. *(11-1)* ____________

5. The net for a rectangular prism consists of 6 squares *(11-3)* ____________

6. The volume of a rectangular prism with length 10 cm and width 10 cm is 100 cm^3. *(11-9)* ____________

7. The measure of an obtuse angle is between 90° and 180°. *(6-2)* ____________

Name ____________________

Daily Review 12-3

Daily Cumulative Review

Complete each ratio table. *(Lesson 12-2)*

1.

4	8		12	20
5		20		

2.

5	15	20	30	50
6				

3.

2	6	8	20	
	27			81

4.

		15		
7	21	35	28	49

Write each ratio in three ways. Simplify. *(Lesson 12-1)*

5. adult skunks to baby skunks

________ ________ ________

6. adult turtles to baby turtles

________ ________ ________

Mixed Review

Complete.

7. 6 lb = ________ oz *(11-6)*

8. 160 mL = ________ L *(11-11)*

Find each change in temperature.

9. 72°F to 88°F ________ *(11-8)*

10. 20°F to −5°F ________ *(11-8)*

11. −5°C to 5°C ________ *(11-8)*

12. 100°C to 37°C ________ *(11-8)*

13. *(8-13)* Daria has 10 notebooks. One fifth of them are red and $\frac{1}{2}$ of them are blue. The rest are green. How many green notebooks does she have? ________

Name ______________________________

Daily Review 12-4

Daily Cumulative Review

Complete. *(Lesson 12-3)*

1. This graph shows two ordered pairs of equal ratios. Name each ratio.

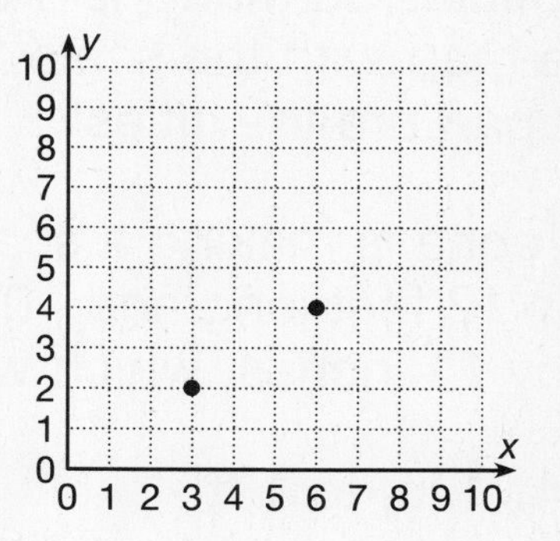

____

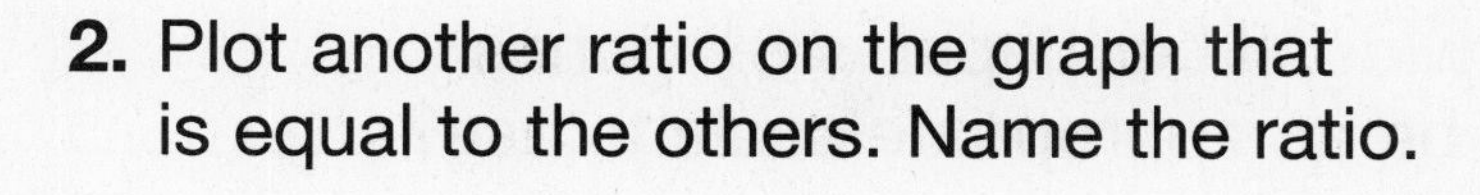

2. Plot another ratio on the graph that is equal to the others. Name the ratio.

____

Complete each ratio table. *(Lesson 12-2)*

3. Jolon found his favorite ice cream on sale, 2 cartons for $5. How much would it cost to buy 4, 6, 8, or 10 cartons?

Boxes of Ice Cream	2	4			
Price	$5				

4. Each of Miss Horne's art students will need 4 brushes. How many brushes will be needed for 6, 12, 18, 20, or 22 students?

Number of Students	6	12			
Number of Brushes					

Mixed Review

Complete.

5. 29 ft = _____ yd _____ ft *(8-15)*

6. 0.9 m = ________ mm *(10-4)*

7. 36,000 ÷ ________ = 90 *(4-2)*

8. 7 m 30 cm = ________ m *(10-3)*

9. Identify 5 as prime or composite. ______________ *(4-14)*

10. Which is cheaper: 4 for $7 or $1.70 each? ______________ *(5-11)*

11. How many lines of symmetry does a square have? ______________ *(6-8)*

Name ____________________

Daily Review 12-5

Daily Cumulative Review

Solve each problem. *(Lesson 12-4)*

1. Berlin, Germany, is 4 cm from Stockholm, Sweden on a map with the scale 1 cm to 200 km. About how far apart are the cities? ________

2. Teona is making a scale drawing of her room. The room is 12 feet long and 10 feet wide. If her paper is $8\frac{1}{2}$ inches by 11 inches, which would be an appropriate scale to use? ________

A. 1 in. to 1 ft **B.** 1 in. to 2 ft **C.** 2 in. to 1 ft

Use grid paper. Plot the ordered pairs from each ratio table on the graph and draw a straight line through each set of points. *(Lesson 12-3)*

3.

4	8	12	16	20
2	4	6	8	10

4.

3	9	12	15	18
1	3	4	5	6

y
10
9
8
7
6
5
4
3
2
1
0
0 2 4 6 8 10 12 14 16 18 20
x

5. If the lines are extended, what ordered pair represents the point where the lines cross? ________

Mixed Review

Complete.

6. 5 kg of water would fill a ________ mL container.
(11-12)

7. 20.4 g = ________ kg
(11-7)

8. 2.5 mm = ________ cm
(10-4)

9. 4.1 − ________ = 0.9
(2-18)

10. ________ − 2.15 = 4.08
(2-18)

11. Find the mode, median, and range for 10,15, 25, 30, 30.
(1-4)

____

Name ______________________________

Daily Review 12-6

Daily Cumulative Review

Complete the table. Look for patterns. *(Lesson 12-5)*

1.	Thirds					
2.	Ninths	$\frac{1}{9}$	$\frac{2}{9}$	$\frac{3}{9}$		
3.	Percents	$11\frac{1}{9}\%$	$22\frac{2}{9}\%$	$33\frac{3}{9}\%$	$44\frac{4}{9}\%$	

Solve each problem. *(Lesson 12-4)*

4. A scale drawing of a house floor plan is 10 in. by 8 in. The real house is 75 ft by 60 ft. What does 1 in. represent in the drawing? __________

5. A picture of a monument uses the scale 1 cm to 4 m. If the monument is actually 20 m tall, how tall is it in the picture? __________

Mixed Review

6. *(11-13)* Chiara made a secret code where the 1st letter of the alphabet is exchanged with the 14th letter, the 2nd letter with the 15th, and so on.

What letter is exchanged with the letter G? __________

7. *(11-3)* Name the solid formed by the net.

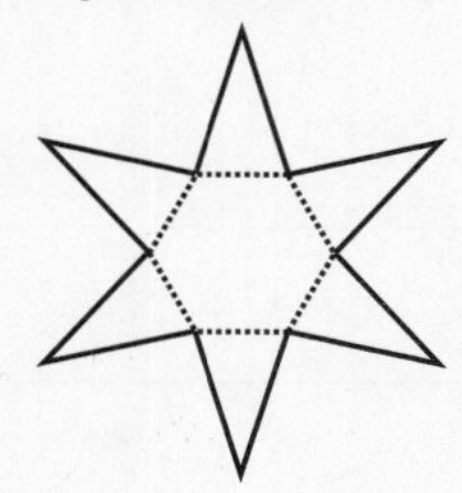

____

8. *(11-4)* Find the surface area of the figure.

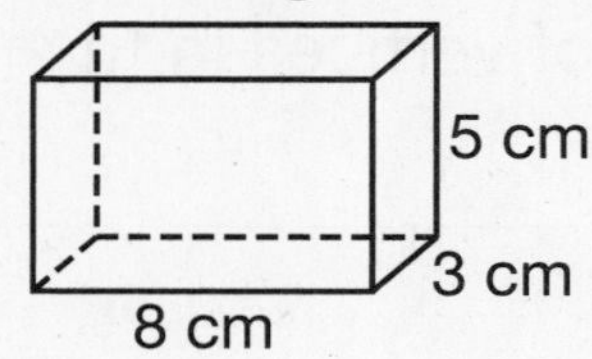

____

9. *(11-2)* How many vertices does the figure in Exercise 8 have? __________

Name ______________________

Daily Review
12-7

Daily Cumulative Review

Estimate. *(Lesson 12-6)*

1. 49% of 500 ________ **2.** 24% of 200 ________

3. 11% of 99 ________ **4.** 33% of 1,200 ________

5. 5% of 700 ________ **6.** 65% of 60 ________

Complete each pattern. *(Lesson 12-5)*

7. $\frac{1}{40}$ = ________% **8.** $\frac{1}{25}$ = ________%

$\frac{2}{40}$ = ________% $\frac{2}{25}$ = ________%

$\frac{3}{40}$ = ________% $\frac{3}{25}$ = ________%

$\frac{4}{40}$ = ________% $\frac{4}{25}$ = ________%

$\frac{5}{40}$ = ________% $\frac{5}{25}$ = ________%

Mixed Review

Tell which is greater. Explain.

9. 5 lb 11 oz or 90 oz ______________________
(11-6)

10. the number of vertices in triangular pyramid or
(11-2) the number of vertices in triangular prism

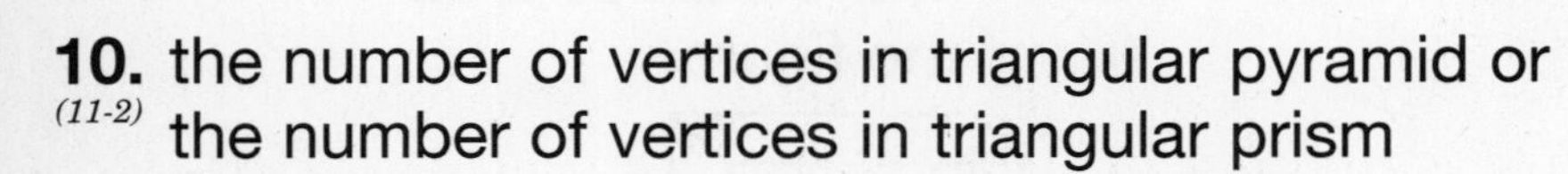

11. the perimeter of rectangle *A*
(10-6) or the perimeter of rectangle *B*

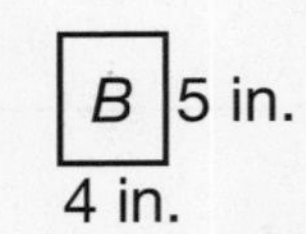

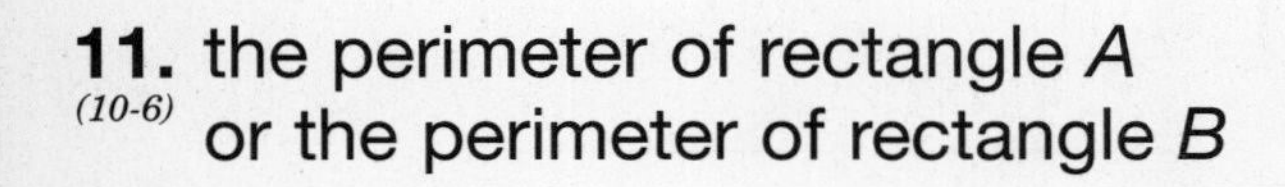

Name ______________________

Daily Review 12-8

Daily Cumulative Review

Choose a method. Find the percent of each. *(Lesson 12-7)*

1. 12% of 30 = ________ **2.** 40% of 90 = ________

3. 62% of $210 = ________ **4.** 55% of $40 = ________

5. 8% of $60 = ________ **6.** 25% of $75 = ________

Estimate. *(Lesson 12-6)*

7. 34% of 900 ________ **8.** 76% of 240 ________

9. 26% of 81 ________ **10.** 49% of 66 ________

Mixed Review

11. *(10-16)* Find the circumference. Use 3.14 for π.

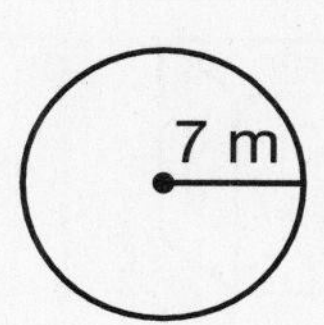

____

12. *(10-14)* Find the value of n. Use counters to help.

$n + 7 = 11$

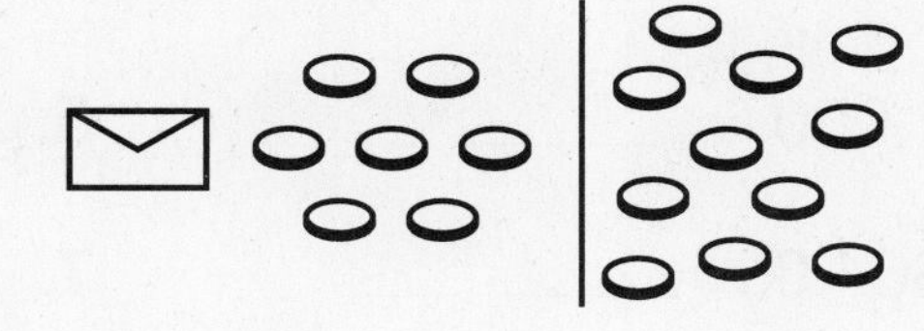

n = ________

Find each product or quotient.

13. *(9-8)* $7\frac{2}{5} \times 3$ = ________ **14.** *(9-10)* $11 \div \frac{1}{6}$ = ________

15. *(5-1)* 8,000 ÷ 20 = ________ **16.** *(3-10)* $72.31 × 8 = ________

17. *(5-5)* $17\overline{)105}$ **18.** *(5-5)* $41\overline{)12{,}560}$

Name ______________________________

Daily Review 12-9

Daily Cumulative Review

Complete the table. Tell if the probabilities of the outcomes are equally likely or not. If the probabilities are not equal, tell which outcome is more likely. Then decide if the situation is fair or unfair. *(Lesson 12-8)*

	Situation	Probability of Outcome	Fairness
1.	Spin the spinner. Outcomes: A, B, C, or D		
2.	Draw a marble. Outcomes: Red (R), Blue (B), or Yellow (Y)		
3.	Throw a number cube. Outcomes: 1, 2, 3, 4, 5, 6		

Choose a method. Find the percent of each. *(Lesson 12-7)*

4. 48% of 7,000 = ________

5. 2% of $5.00 = ________

6. 15% of $64.00 = ________

7. 60% of $82.00 = ________

Mixed Review

8. *(4-12)* Find the length of the side of the square.

Perimeter 12.24 m

____

9. *(4-15)* The tag shows the price has been lowered twice. What was the original price?

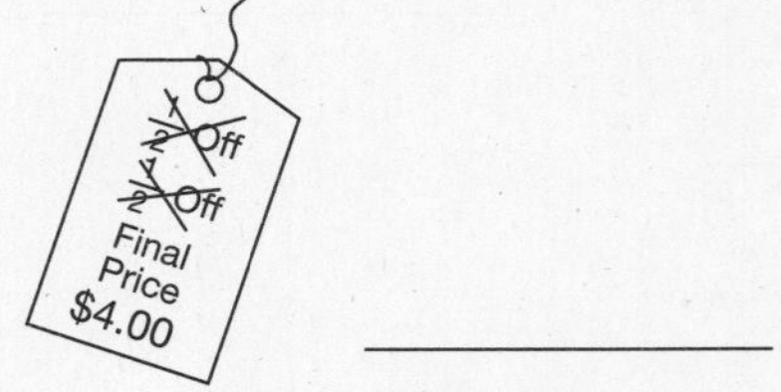

____

10. *(4-13)* Find all the factors of 54. ______________________________

Name ______________________

Daily Review 12-10

Daily Cumulative Review

Predict from the sample. *(Lesson 12-9)*

A bag of candy-coated chocolates contains yellow, red, blue, green, brown, and orange chocolates.
How many of each color were in the samples?

Sample	Count	Color
Sample 1	4	Blue
	1	Orange
	3	Red
	2	Yellow
Sample 2	3	Blue
	1	Orange
	2	Red
	2	Yellow
	2	Brown
Sample 3	2	Blue
	2	Red
	3	Yellow
	2	Orange
	1	Green

1. blue ______ **2.** orange ______

3. red ______ **4.** yellow ______

5. brown ______ **6.** green ______

7. Predict the most common color candy.

____

8. If sample 3 were the only sample, what color candy would you predict to be the most common? ______________________

Tell if the situation is fair or unfair. *(Lesson 12-8)*

9. Spin the spinner.

______

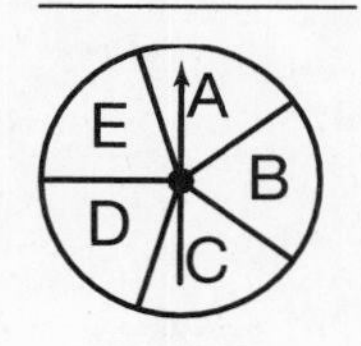

10. Draw a number.

______

11. Draw card X or card Y.

______

Mixed Review

Add or subtract.

12. *(8-12)* $9 - 2\frac{1}{3}$

13. *(8-10)* $3\frac{5}{6} + 1\frac{2}{3}$

14. *(10-7)* 6 yd 2 ft + 7 yd 2 ft

Name ______________________________

Daily Review
12-11

Daily Cumulative Review

Predict from the experiment. *(Lesson 12-10)*

If you spin the spinner 10 times,
State how many times you would
expect the outcome would be:

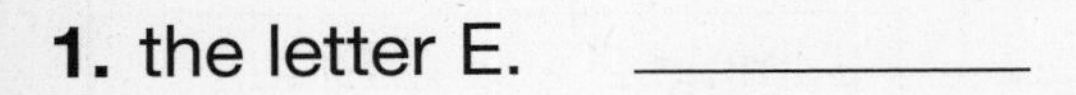

1. the letter E. __________
2. a vowel. __________
3. a consonant. __________

Predict from the samples. *(Lesson 12-9)*

You are playing a word game with a friend.
You draw 6 letters at a time.

4. How many letters were drawn in the 5 samples? __________
5. How many vowels were drawn in the 5 samples? __________
6. Predict how many vowels are in a bag of 75 tiles. __________

Sample	Vowels
1	3
2	3
3	4
4	1
5	1

Mixed Review

Complete.

7. *(7-10)* $11\frac{3}{4} = \frac{\square}{4}$ **8.** *(9-2)* $\frac{1}{3}$ of 36 = ______ **9.** *(12-5)* $\frac{7}{20}$ = ______%

10. *(11-7)* 413 g = ______ kg **11.** *(7-13)* 0.07 = ______% **12.** *(8-15)* 5 mi = ______ ft

13. *(7-10)* $\frac{26}{6} = 4\frac{\square}{3}$ **14.** *(10-3)* 1.4 m = ______ cm **15.** *(7-5)* $\frac{18}{27} = \frac{\square}{3}$

16. *(7-6)* Do you get the same sum when you use 12 rather than 6 as a common denominator for $\frac{2}{3}$ and $\frac{1}{2}$? Explain.

____

Name ______________________________

Daily Review
12-12

Daily Cumulative Review

Use an organized list to solve. *(Lesson 12-11)*

1. Tony has math, science, history, and language homework to do. Make an organized list of the order in which he can do the assignment if he does:

a. math first. ______________________________

b. science first. ______________________________

c. history first. ______________________________

d. language first. ______________________________

e. In how many different ways can he do his homework? ________

2. a. Angela, Brian, and Cash are going to have their picture taken together. Write a list of all the ways they can line up for the picture.

____

b. How many ways can they line up? ______________

Use any strategy to solve. *(Lesson 12-10)*

3. A wooden top with 4 sides has the numbers 1, 2, 3, and 4 on the sides. The top is spun twice and the numbers that come up are added. List all of the different sums that can occur.

____

Mixed Review

Find the percent of each.

4. 3% of 500 ______ *(12-7)*

5. 60% of 20 ______ *(12-7)*

6. 15% of 20 ______ *(12-7)*

7. Write the ratio of As to Bs in three ways. *(12-1)*
A A B B B B A

______ ______ ______

Name ___________________________

Daily Review 12-13

Daily Cumulative Review

Each spinner is spun once. The numbers from each spinner are added. Make tree diagrams to show possible outcomes. Give the probability of each outcome as a fraction. Simplify. *(Lesson 12-12)*

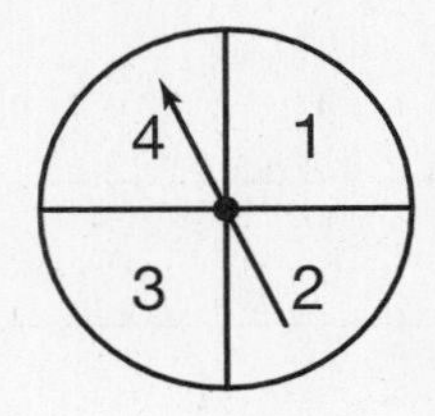

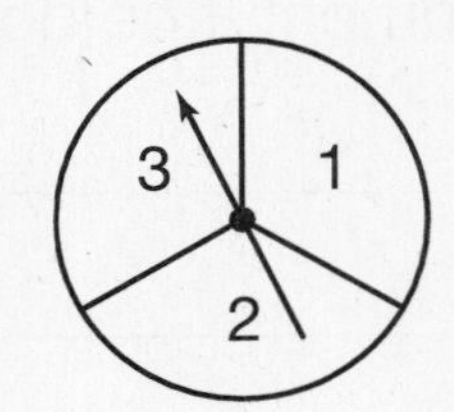

1. Sum of 1 __________

2. Sum of 2 __________

3. Sum of 3 __________

4. Sum of 4 __________

5. Sum of 5 __________

6. Sum of 6 __________

7. Sum of 7 __________

8. Sum of 8 __________

Use an organized list to solve. *(Lesson 12-11)*

9. Jarred has whole wheat and white bread, 3 kinds of meat (ham, turkey, roast beef), and 2 kinds of cheese (cheddar and Swiss). How many different sandwiches can he make with 1 bread, 1 meat, and 1 cheese? __________

Mixed Review

Complete.

10. $\frac{9}{50}$ = __________% *(12-5)*

11. 900 mL = __________ L *(11-11)*

12. 13% of 40 = __________ *(12-7)*

13. 0.0001 kg = __________ g *(11-7)*

14. Circle the triangle congruent to the first one. *(6-6)*

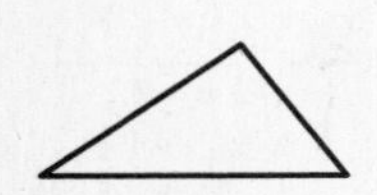

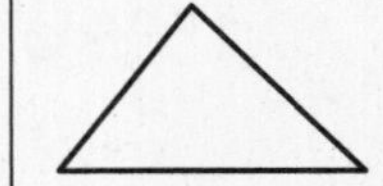

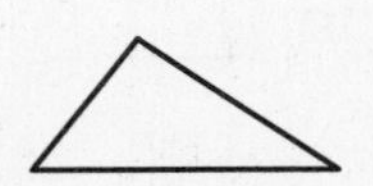

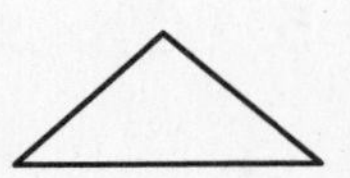

15. Use a protractor to measure the angle. __________ *(6-2)*

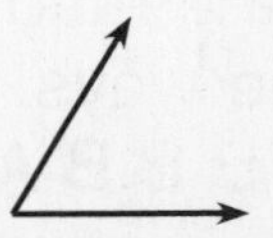

Name ______________________

Daily Review 1-1

Daily Cumulative Review

Mixed Review *(From Last Year)*

Write the word name for each number.

1. 380,109
   Three hundred eighty thousand, one hundred nine
2. 8,705,042
   Eight million, seven hundred five thousand, forty-two

Estimate each sum or difference. Round to the nearest hundred.

3. 639 + 279 **900**
4. 191 + 568 **800**
5. 412 − 219 **200**

Find each product.

6. $7 \times 5 = $ **35**
7. $9 \times 2 = $ **18**
8. $6 \times 8 = $ **48**
9. $4 \times 0 = $ **0**
10. $3 \times 8 = $ **24**

Classify each angle as right, acute, or obtuse.

11. **obtuse** 12. **right** 13. **acute**

14. Thea and Chris went to the pool at 2:05 P.M. and and left at 4:28 P.M. How long were they there? **2 hrs 23 min**
15. Shaquille has 56 basketball cards in his collection. His sister Lindsey has 47 cards in her collection. How many cards do they have in all? **103 cards**

Name ______________________

Daily Review 1-2

Daily Cumulative Review

Use the graph to answer 1–3. *(Lesson 1-1)*

1. Which is the largest of the Great Lakes? **Superior**
2. Which lake has an area of about 10,000 square miles? **Erie**
3. About how many square miles is Lake Huron? **23,000**

Area of Great Lakes

Area (square miles): 0, 5,000, 10,000, 15,000, 20,000, 25,000, 30,000, 35,000

Great Lakes: Superior, Michigan, Erie, Huron, Ontario

Mixed Review *(From Last Year)*

Compare. Write >, <, or =.

4. 735 **>** 537
5. 29,803 **<** 29,820
6. 5,213 **>** 5,212

Find each sum or difference.

7. $83 - 26 = $ **57**
8. $31 + 47 = $ **78**
9. $56 + 29 = $ **85**
10. $45 - 37 = $ **8**

Find each quotient.

11. 14 ÷ 7 **2**
12. 32 ÷ 8 **4**
13. 45 ÷ 9 **5**

Write a fraction for each part of the rug.

14. The part with a design. $\frac{3}{5}$
15. The plain part. $\frac{2}{5}$

16. A triangle has sides that are 36 feet, 25 feet, and 47 feet long. What is the perimeter of the triangle? **108 feet**

Name ______________________

Daily Review 1-3

Daily Cumulative Review

Use the line graph to answer 1–3. *(Lesson 1-2)*

1. How many years can a female born in 1970 expect to live? **75 years**
2. Between which two years was the increase in life expectancy the greatest? **1940 and 1950**
3. Write the coordinates that represent the life expectancy of a girl born in 1990. **(1990, 79)**

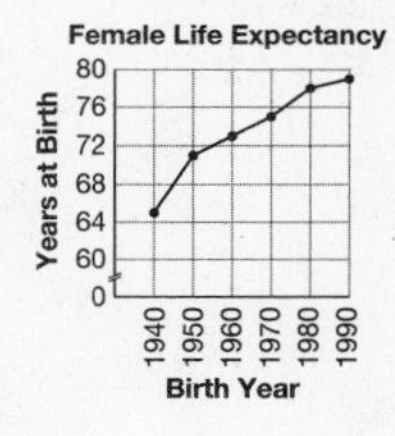

Use the pictograph to answer 4–6. *(Lesson 1-1)*

4. Which two eggs have the same incubation time? **Goose and duck**
5. Which egg will hatch in the fewest number of days? **Pigeon**
6. What is the incubation time for a chicken egg? **21 days**

Egg Incubation Time

Chicken	⬯⬯⬯⬯⬯⬯⬯
Goose	⬯⬯⬯⬯⬯⬯⬯⬯⬯⬯
Turkey	⬯⬯⬯⬯⬯⬯⬯⬯◖
Duck	⬯⬯⬯⬯⬯⬯⬯⬯⬯⬯
Pigeon	⬯⬯⬯⬯⬯⬯

⬯ = 3 days

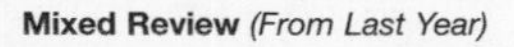

Mixed Review *(From Last Year)*

7. \$8.47 − 2.51 = **\$5.96**
8. \$3.78 + 5.95 = **\$9.73**
9. \$56.07 + 12.49 = **\$68.56**
10. \$82.05 − 36.19 = **\$45.86**

Compare. Write >, < or =.

11. $\frac{1}{3}$ **>** $\frac{1}{6}$
12. $\frac{4}{5}$ **>** $\frac{2}{5}$
13. $\frac{3}{10}$ **<** $\frac{1}{2}$

14. A Walk-A-Thon course is 2,846 yards long. How many feet is it? **8,538 feet**

Name ______________________

Daily Review 1-4

Daily Cumulative Review

Use the stem-and-leaf plot to answer 1–3. *(Lesson 1-3)*

The plot shows the number of points Jeri scored in games this basketball season.

Stem	Leaf
1	0 1 2 2 4 8 8 8 9
2	1 6 6 8
3	3

1. In how many games did Jeri score more than 20 points? **5**
2. What number of points did Jeri score most often? **18**
3. Jeri scored in every game she played. How many games did she play? **14**

Use the line graph to answer 4–6. *(Lesson 1-2)*

The graph shows average tuition and required fees for full-time students for in-state 4-year colleges and universities in the United States.

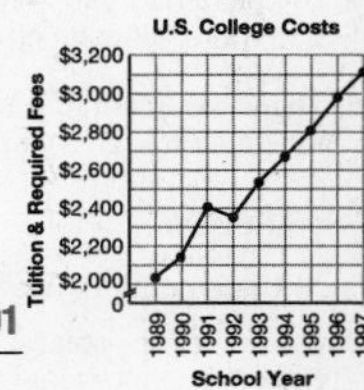

4. What has happened to tuition and required fees since 1992? **They have increased.**
5. Between which school years was the increase in fees the greatest? **1990, 1991**
6. Between which years did tuition and required fees decrease? **1991, 1992**

Mixed Review

7. (Gr. 4) 3 × 20 **60**
8. (Gr. 4) 6 × 40 **240**
9. (Gr. 4) 8 × 60 **480**
10. (Gr. 4) Tina's dog had 6 puppies. Two of them had brown fur. What fraction of the puppies had brown fur? Write the fraction in simplest form. $\frac{1}{3}$

Name ______________________

Daily Review 1-5

Daily Cumulative Review

Use the line plot to answer 1 and 2. *(Lesson 1-4)*

Number of Stories in Tall Buildings in Dallas

48 50 52 54 56 58 60 62 64 66 68 70 72 74

1. For the above data, give the:

   a. range 24 **b.** mode 50 **c.** median 52

2. Are about half of the tallest buildings 52 stories or taller? Explain.

   Yes, because the median is 52 stories.

Use the stem-and-leaf plot to answer 3–5. *(Lesson 1-3)*

3. What was the difference in the smallest number of newspapers brought in for recycling and the greatest number?

   18 newspapers

Number of Newspapers Brought for Recycling

Stem	Leaf
0	5 6 7 7 9
1	0 2 2 5 5 5
2	1 3

4. What number of newspapers was recycled most often?

   15 newspapers

5. How many different bundles of newspapers were recycled? 13

Mixed Review

6. $\frac{1}{6} + \frac{2}{3}$ $\frac{5}{6}$ (Gr. 4) **7.** $\frac{3}{5} - \frac{3}{10}$ $\frac{3}{10}$ (Gr. 4) **8.** $\frac{3}{8} + \frac{1}{4}$ $\frac{5}{8}$ (Gr. 4)

9. Shari spends $\frac{1}{3}$ of her time sleeping and $\frac{1}{4}$ of her time in school. Does she spend more time sleeping or in school? (Gr. 4)

   sleeping

Name ______________________

Daily Review 1-6

Daily Cumulative Review

Use the data in the bar graph to answer 1–2. *(Lesson 1-5)*

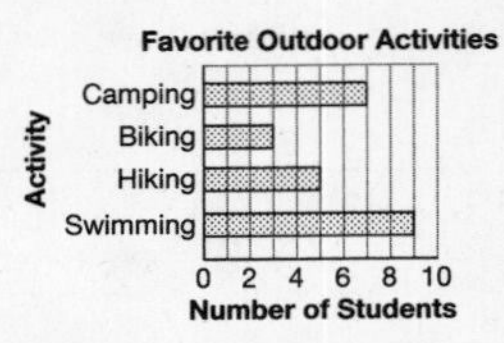

1. How many more students preferred swimming over hiking?

   4 students

2. What operation did you use to solve the problem?

   Subtraction

Find the range, median, and mode for each set of numbers in 3–4. *(Lesson 1-4)*

3. 10, 15, 10, 12, 11

   a. range 5 **b.** median 11 **c.** mode 10

4. 22, 13, 20, 25, 20, 31

   a. range 18 **b.** median 21 **c.** mode 20

Mixed Review

5. 4.7 + 0.16 = 4.86 (Gr. 4) **6.** 6.4 − 3.16 = 3.24 (Gr. 4)

7. Order the decimals from least to greatest. 11.25, 11.2, 11.5, 11.05 (Gr. 4)

   11.05, 11.2, 11.25, 11.5

Use the line graph to answer **8–9**.

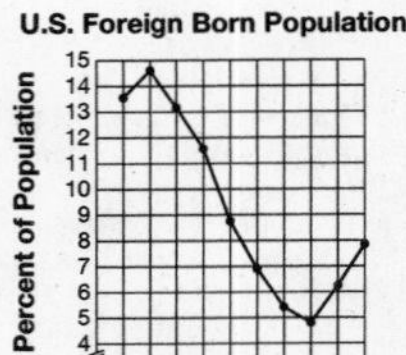

8. What was the foreign-born population trend from 1910 to 1970? (1-2)

   decreasing

9. What was the trend from 1970 to 1990? (1-2)

   increasing

Name ______________________

Daily Review 1-7

Daily Cumulative Review

Write the operation needed for each problem. Then solve each problem. *(Lesson 1-6)*

1. A dinner for two at the Chicken King costs $6.98. If Jim and Maria split expenses evenly, how much will each pay? Division $3.49

2. In five hours, the temperature fell from 45 degrees Fahrenheit to only 20 degrees Fahrenheit. How much did the temperature fall? Subtraction 25°F

3. A theater sold 150 tickets at $4 each. How much did the theater receive? Multiplication $600

Use any strategy to answer 4–5. *(Lesson 1-5)*

4. Rebekah had $90 in her account before she deposited $15 more. How much money is in her account now? $105

5. There are 3 feet in a yard. The I-610 Ship Channel Bridge in Houston is 210 yards long. How many feet is this? 630 ft

Mixed Review

Use the line graph to answer **6–7**.

6. During which month did the club have the most money? (1-2)

   January

7. How much money was in the club treasury in April? (1-2)

   $25

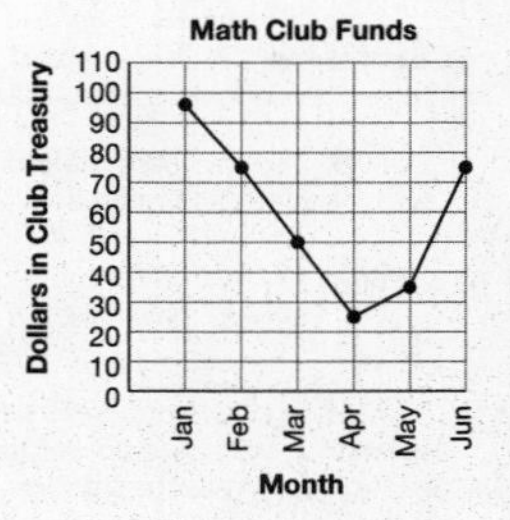

Name ______________________

Daily Review 1-8

Daily Cumulative Review

Find the rule for each table. Give the rule using words and a variable. *(Lesson 1-7)*

1.

A	B
0	0
1	3
4	12
6	18

Multiply by 3

$n \times 3$

2.

A	B
1	0
5	4
9	8
13	12

Subtract 1

$n - 1$

3.

A	B
1	6
4	9
8	13
10	15

Add 5

$n + 5$

Choose the operation for each problem. Then solve each problem. *(Lesson 1-6)*

4. Rika has finished all but 2 of her math problems. Her teacher had assigned 15 problems. How many problems has she completed?

   Subtraction 13 problems

5. Shawn earned $3.75 an hour working for a neighbor. How much did he earn in 4 hours?

   Multiplication $15

Mixed Review

Use the bar graph to answer **6–7**.

1995 Earnings (U.S.)

Annual Salary (thousands of dollars): 0 10 20 30 40 50 60

Education: Did not finish high school; High school graduate; Some college; Bachelor's degree; Advanced degree

6. About how much more did a high school graduate earn per year than someone who did not finish high school? (1-1)

   About $7,000 per year

7. About how much more does someone with a bachelor's degree earn per year than a high school graduate? (1-1)

   About $16,000 per year

Name ______________________

Daily Cumulative Review

Choose a scale and make a bar graph of the data in the table. *(Lesson 1-8)*

Normal Annual Precipitation to Nearest Inch			
Barrow, AK	5	Houston, TX	46
Phoenix, AZ	8	Duluth, MN	30

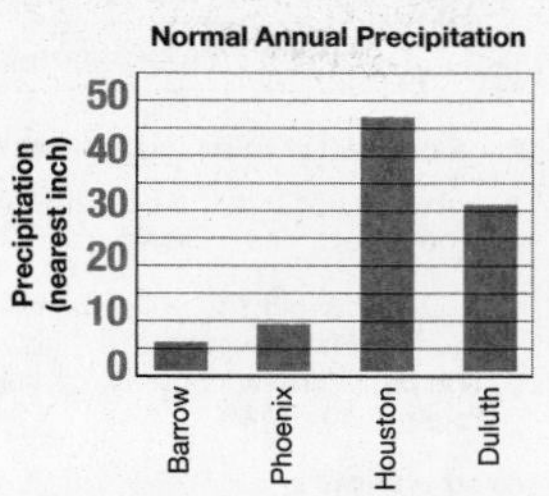

1. What scale did you use? **Possible answer: 5 in.**
2. What is the range of the data? **41 inches**

Find the rule for each table. Give the rule using words and a variable. *(Lesson 1-7)*

3.

A	B
15	3
20	4
25	5
30	6

Divide by 5

$n \div 5$

4.

A	B
6	4
9	7
12	10
15	13

Subtract 2

$n - 2$

5.

A	B
3	7
7	11
11	15
15	19

Add 4

$n + 4$

Mixed Review

The stem-and-leaf plot shows the minutes Kim spent practicing her flute each day.

Use the plot to answer **6–7**.

Stem	Leaf
2	5 5 7
3	0 0 2 5
3	5

6. (1-3) What is the least amount of time Kim practiced? **25 minutes**
7. (1-3) How many days did she practice? **8 days**

Name ______________________

Daily Review
1-10

Daily Cumulative Review

Use this table to make a line graph. *(Lesson 1-9)*

United States Computer Sales

Year	1987	1988	1989	1990	1991	1992	1993	1994	1995	1996
Dollars (Millions)	3.1	3.5	3.9	4.0	3.9	4.9	5.9	6.7	8.4	9.4

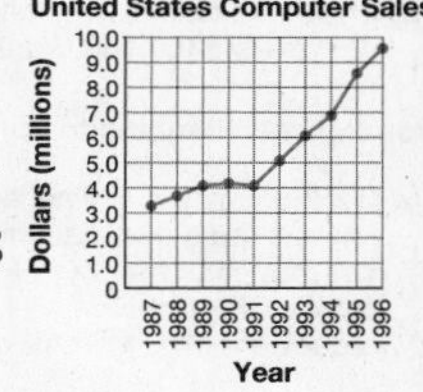

1. Between which years did computer sales decrease? **1990, 1991**
2. Between which years did sales increase the most? **1994, 1995**
3. If the trend from 1995 to 1996 continued, how many computers were sold in 1997? **About 10.4 million**

Use the graph to answer 4–5. *(Lesson 1-8)*

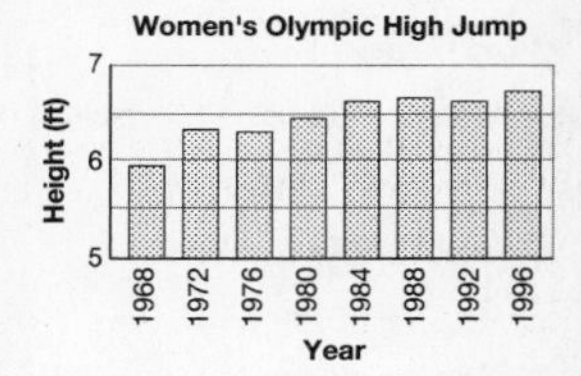

4. What is the scale on the graph? **1 foot**
5. What would make the graph easier to read? **Graph would be easier to read with 1 in. scale.**

Mixed Review

6. (1-4) Use the line plot to give the
   a. range **5**
   b. mode **2, 4**
   c. median **2**

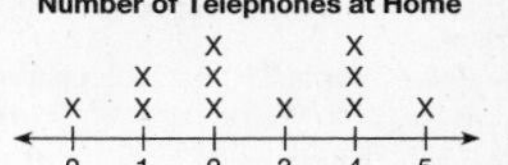

Name ______________________

Daily Cumulative Review

Make a stem-and-leaf plot for the height data. *(Lesson 1-10)*

Heights of Vollyball Team Members (inches)				
57	59	64	61	59
59	60	58	57	62
60	65	59	61	59

Stem	Leaf
5	7 7 8 9 9 9 9 9
6	0 0 1 1 2 4 5

1. What is the most common height on the volleyball team? **59 inches**
2. What is the median height on the team? **59 inches**

Use the table to answer 3–4. (Hint: Make a line graph.) *(Lesson 1-9)*

Number of Teams in the NBA			
Year	Teams	Year	Teams
1960	8	1980	22
1970	14	1990	27

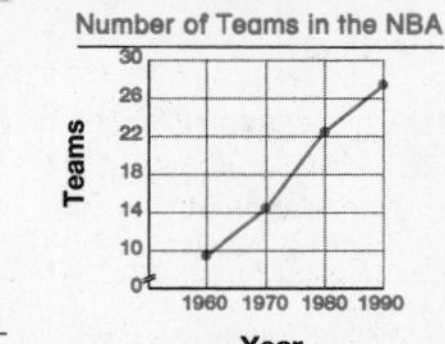

3. How many teams were in the NBA in 1970? **14 teams**
4. What trend does the data show? **Number of teams is increasing.**

Mixed Review

5. (1-7) Complete the table. Write its rule using a variable.

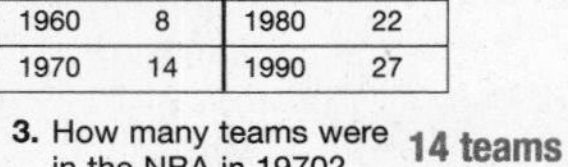

A	5	10	15	20	25	30
B	7	12	17	**22**	**27**	**32**

Rule: **$n + 2$**

6. (1-5) Marc bought 3 gallons of gasoline for his lawn mower. The gas cost $1.09 per gallon. How much did Marc pay for the gasoline? **$3.27**

Name ______________________

Daily Review
2-1

Daily Cumulative Review

Use any strategy to solve each problem. *(Lesson 1-11)*

1. At a clearance sale, shorts cost $9 each and shirts cost $15 each. How many shorts and shirts did Julie buy if she spent $63? **2 shorts and 3 shirts**
2. Angela has 35 cents in dimes and nickels. She has more nickels than dimes. How many nickels and dimes does she have? **3 nickels and 2 dimes or 5 nickels and 1 dime**

Make a stem-and-leaf plot for the distance data. *(Lesson 1-10)*

3.

Miles to School			
6	9	5	15
12	15	20	14
15	10	4	9

Stem	Leaf
0	4 5 6 9 9
1	0 2 4 5 5 5
2	0

4. What is the median number of miles? **11**
5. How many students were surveyed? **12**

Mixed Review

6. (1-5) Lee and his sister bought a computer game for $89. His sister paid $46. How much did Lee pay? **$43**

Use the bar graph to answer **7–9**.

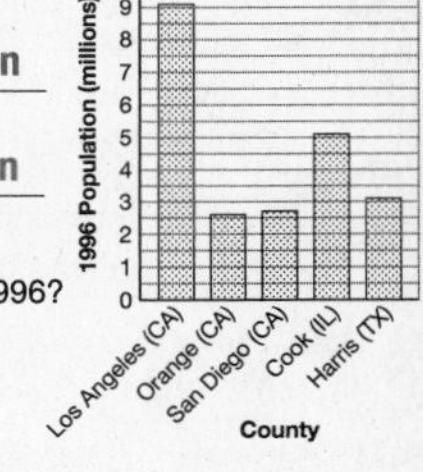

7. (1-1) How many people lived in Los Angeles County in 1996? **9.1 million**

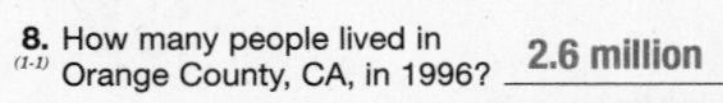

8. (1-1) How many people lived in Orange County, CA, in 1996? **2.6 million**
9. (1-1) About how many more people lived in Cook County than in Harris County in 1996? **2 million**

Name ______________________

Daily Cumulative Review

Use patterns to answer 1–2. *(Lesson 2-1)*

1. If a textbook has 500 pages, how many pages are in:

a. 10 textbooks? 5,000 **b.** 20 textbooks? 10,000

c. 200 textbooks? 100,000 **d.** 2,000 textbooks? 1,000,000

2. If you had one million dollars in $100 bills, how many $100 bills would you have? 10,000

Use logical reasoning to solve. *(Lesson 1-11)*

3. Connor, Emily, Caroline, and Andy are Mrs. Martin's children. Emily is the oldest daughter and Caroline is the youngest child. The names of her two youngest children start with the same letter of the alphabet. Her oldest child is not a girl. In what order were Mrs. Martin's children born?
Andy, Emily, Connor, Caroline

Mixed Review

4. (1-7) Write the rule using a variable: a number less 5.6 $n - 5.6$

Use the line plot to answer **5–8**.

Service Calls Per Day

Day	0	1	2	3	4	5	6	7	8
		X		XX	XXX	X			XX

5. (1-4) Give the range. 7

6. (1-4) Give the mode. 5

7. (1-4) Give the median. 5

8. (1-4) How many days had fewer than 5 service calls? 3

9. (1-8) Jeffrey earns $90 each week for mowing lawns. How much will he earn for mowing in 3 weeks? $270

Name ______________________

Daily Cumulative Review

Write each number in word form. *(Lesson 2-2)*

1. 2,030,005 Two million, thirty thousand, five

2. 87,000,540 Eighty-seven million, five hundred forty

Use a calculator to answer 3 and 4. *(Lesson 2-1)*

3. 1 mile = 5,280 feet. About how many miles would be in one million feet? About 189 miles

4. If Mr. Miser hid $1,000 in his mattress every month of his daughter's life, how old would she be when the mattress contained one million dollars? 83 years old

Mixed Review

Use the line graph to answer **5** and **6**.

Heat Index for 85° F

Apparent Temperature (°F): 0°, 78°, 81°, 84°, 87°, 90°, 93°, 96°, 99°, 102°, 105°, 108°

Relative Humidity (percent): 0 10 20 30 40 50 60 70 80 90 100

5. (1-2) If the relative humidity is 60%, how hot does 85°F feel? 90°F

6. (1-2) What is the relative humidity if the air temperature is 85°F but it feels like 93°F? 70%

Use the bar graph to answer **7** and **8**.

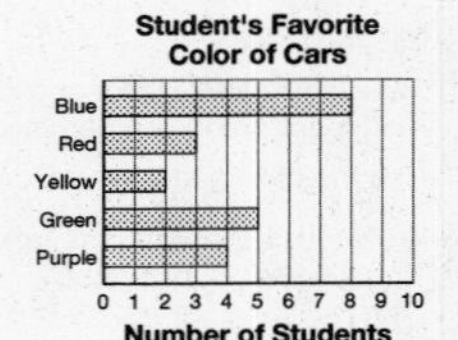

7. (1-5) How many students preferred blue or green? 13

8. (1-5) After the survey, 6 students changed their favorite color. How many did not? 16

Name ______________________

Daily Cumulative Review

Write each number using exponents. *(Lesson 2-3)*

1. 10,000 10^4 **2.** 10,000,000 10^7

3. $10 \times 10 \times 10 \times 10 \times 10$ 10^5 **4.** $10 \times 10 \times 10$ 10^3

Write each number in standard form. *(Lesson 2-2)*

5. Ten million, three hundred five thousand, six 10,305,006

6. Five hundred thirty million, forty-five thousand, two hundred
530,045,200

7. 60,000,000 + 50,000 + 300 + 70 60,050,370

Mixed Review

8. (1-11) Robbie, Jetta, Anna, and Kara are best friends. In a spelling bee, they won the top 4 prizes. Jetta did not win fourth prize. Anna placed just above Jetta. Kara placed just under Robbi. In what order, from first to fourth, did the four friends place?
Anna, Jetta, Robbi, Kara

Use the stem-and-leaf plot to answer each question.

Minutes of Long Distance Calls

Stem	Leaf
0	5 6 6 6
1	0 0 2 7
2	1 4 8
3	3

9. (1-3) How many long distance calls were made?
12

10. (1-3) What was the median length of the calls?
11 minutes

11. (1-3) What was the range of the length of the calls?
28

12. (1-3) Rose made the longest call. How long did she talk?
33 minutes

Name ______________________

Daily Review
2-5

Daily Cumulative Review

Write each number in standard form. *(Lesson 2-4)*

1. Six hundred fifty billion, seven million 650,007,000,000

2. Ten billion, five hundred thousand, thirty 10,000,500,030

3. Three billion, three hundred thousand, two 3,000,300,002

Insert the missing exponent. *(Lesson 2-3)*

4. $10^{\boxed{2}} = 100$ **5.** $10^{\boxed{7}} = 10,000,000$

6. $10^{\boxed{9}} = 1,000,000,000$ **7.** $10^{\boxed{4}} = 10,000$

Mixed Review

8. (1-9) Make a line graph. Use the data in the table.

Attendance at the Spring Festival	
1996	250
1997	325
1998	275

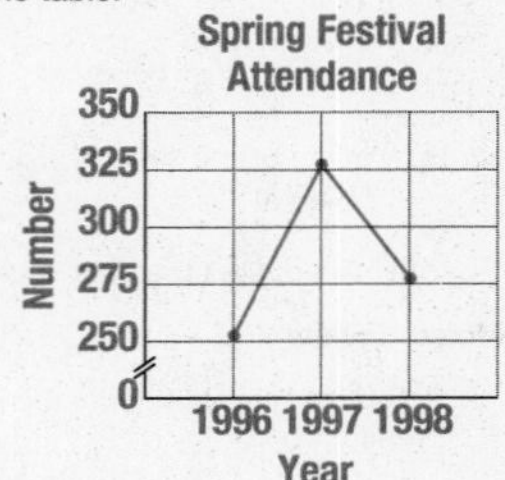

9. (1-7) Complete the table. Write its rule using a variable.

A	2	6	8	10	16	18
B	1	3	4	5	8	9

Rule: $n \div 2$

Name ____________________

Daily Review 2-6

Daily Cumulative Review

Write >, <, or = to complete. *(Lesson 2-5)*

1. 647,900 (<) 674,200
2. 10,510 (>) 10,501
3. Twelve thousand (>) 1,200
4. 85,678 (>) sixty thousand
5. Four million, one hundred (=) 4,000,100

Complete. *(Lesson 2-4)*

6. 260,030,515 = two hundred sixty __million__, thirty __thousand__, five __hundred__ fifteen
7. 800,080,008 = eight __hundred million__, eighty __thousand__, eight
8. How many 1,000s in 500,000? __500__
9. How many 100s in 80,000? __800__

Mixed Review

10. Choose a scale and make a horizontal bar graph of the data in the table. (1-8)

Source of Reference Material for Reports	
Encyclopedia	18
Dictionary	8
Internet	4
Magazine	12

Source of Reference Material

Reference Material: Encyclopedia, Dictionary, Internet, Magazine

0 4 8 12 16 20

Number of Reports

11. What is the value in dollars of 500,000 dimes? (2-1) __$50,000__
12. Complete. (2-3) __6,500__ × 100 = 650,000

Name ____________________

Daily Review 2-7

Daily Cumulative Review

Round to the nearest hundred thousand. *(Lesson 2-6)*

1. 6,452,371 __6,500,000__
2. 479,200 __500,000__
3. 57,200 __100,000__
4. 39,749,098 __39,700,000__

Order the numbers from least to greatest. *(Lesson 2-5)*

5. 734,261 743,425 697,998 699,035
   __697,998; 699,035; 734,261; 743,425__
6. 1,643,000 1,570,000 2,090,117 2,087,200
   __1,570,000; 1,643,000; 2,087,200; 2,090,117__

Mixed Review

7. (1-11) A store owner anticipates needing 2 salespeople for every 5 aisles of merchandise during a sale. There are 20 aisles in the store. How many sales people should he schedule to work during the sale?
   __8__
8. (1-8) Mary charges $6 per office for vacuuming and dusting. A company has 16 offices in their building. How much does Mary earn each time she cleans for this company?
   __$96__
9. (2-2) Look at these numbers. 76,000 4,006,000 506,000
   a. How are the three numbers alike? __They all have a six in the thousands place. They all end with three zeros.__
   b. How are the three numbers different? __Possible answer: They have different digits. They have different values.__
   c. Write each number in word form. __seventy-six thousand; four million, six thousand; five hundred six thousand__

Name ____________________

Daily Review 2-8

Daily Cumulative Review

Write each decimal shown. *(Lesson 2-7)*

1. __2.13__
2. __0.52__

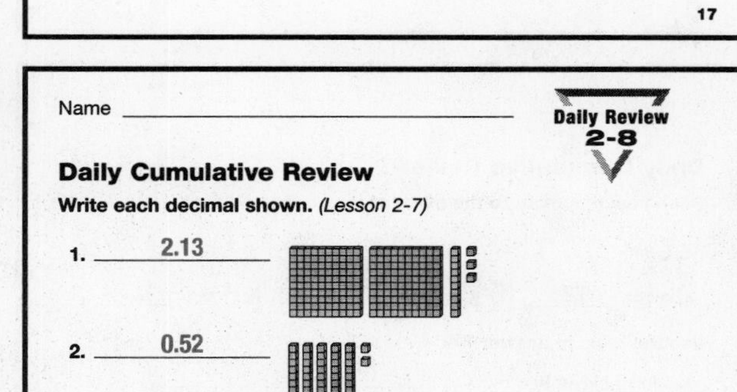

Use the table to answer 3 and 4. *(Lesson 2-6)*

3. Which airport had passenger arrivals and departures closest to 40,000,000?
   __San Francisco__
4. Which two airports had the same number of passenger arrivals and departures if rounded to the nearest 100,000?
   __Dallas/Ft. Worth and Los Angeles__

Traffic at U.S. Airports, 1996	
Airport	**Passenger Arrivals and Departures**
Chicago-O'Hare	69,133,189
Atlanta	63,344,730
Dallas/Ft. Worth	58,034,503
Los Angeles	57,974,559
San Francisco	39,247,308
Miami	33,504,579

Mixed Review

5. (2-3) How many 10,000s make 1,000,000?
   __100__
6. (1-4) Find the range, mode, and median for 18, 19, 16, 10, 19.
   range: __9__ mode: __19__ median: __18__
7. (1-6) David had 34 stuffed animals. He needed more space in his room so he gave Gayle 19 of them. How many stuffed animals does David have now? __15__

Name ____________________

Daily Review 2-9

Daily Cumulative Review

Write two decimals that name each shaded part. *(Lesson 2-8)*

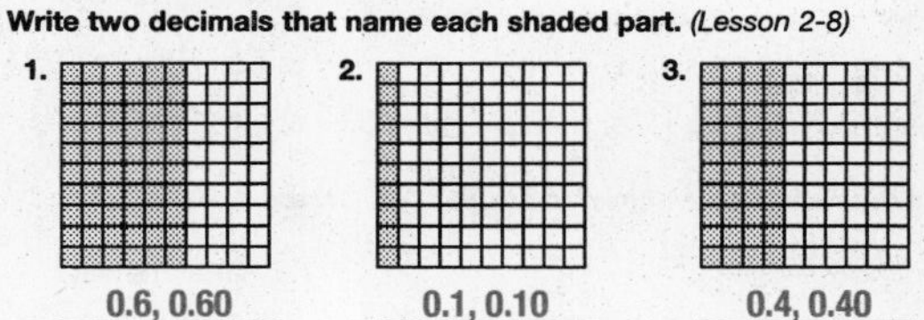

1. __0.6, 0.60__
2. __0.1, 0.10__
3. __0.4, 0.40__

Write each number in decimal form. *(Lesson 2-7)*

4. 5 hundredths __0.05__
5. 6 tenths __0.6__
6. 7 __7.0__
7. one and forty hundredths __1.40__

Mixed Review

Write the place-value position for each digit of 10,793,258,000.

8. (2-4) 2 __hundred thousands__
9. (2-4) 9 __ten millions__
10. (2-4) 8 __thousands__
11. (2-4) 7 __hundred millions__
12. (2-4) 1 __ten billions__
13. (2-4) 5 __ten thousands__
14. (2-1) A spring flows at a rate of 75 gallons per minute. About how many hours does it take to produce 1,000,000 gallons?
    __About 222 hours__
15. (1-10) Make a stem-and-leaf plot for the fund-raiser data.

Gift Wrap Sets Sold for Fund-Raiser			
12	2	6	15
21	14	15	4
26	18	11	15
8	12	14	15

Stem	Leaf
0	2 4 6 8
1	1 2 2 4 4 5 5 5 5 8
2	1 6

Name ______________________

Daily Review 2-10

Daily Cumulative Review

Write each number in decimal form. *(Lesson 2-9)*

1. 6 hundredths 0.06 **2.** 6 6.0 **3.** 6 thousandths 0.006

4. four and five thousandths 4.005 **5.** seven and sixty thousandths 7.060

Write each as an equivalent decimal using hundredths. *(Lesson 2-8)*

6. 0.3 0.30 **7.** 0.1 0.10 **8.** 0.7 0.70 **9.** 4 4.00

Mixed Review

Write >, <, or = to complete.

10. *(2-5)* 400,512 (>) 400,152 **11.** *(2-5)* 101,609 (<) 101,906

12. *(2-3)* A number has a 4 in the hundredths place. You multiply it by 10. Where will the 4 be in the product?

tenths place

13. *(1-11)* Elise, Felicia, Luke, and Heather have started a band, but they are having problems. The drummer and her trumpet-playing brother have to practice outside because of the noise. The drummer and keyboard players names are each 7 letters and too long for their name tags. Heather does not play the keyboard. Which instrument does each band member play if the fourth instrument is a guitar?

Elise: guitar, Felicia: keyboard, Luke: trumpet, Heather: drums

Name ______________________

Daily Review 2-11

Daily Cumulative Review

Complete the number line. *(Lesson 2-10)*

1. 6.73 6.74 6.75 6.76 6.77 6.78 6.79 6.8

2. Name two numbers between 6.75 and 6.8.

Possible answers: 6.76, 6.77, 6.78, 6.79

Write each number in decimal form. *(Lesson 2-9)*

3. two and three hundred sixty thousandths 2.360

4. nine and seventy-five thousandths 9.075

Mixed Review

5. *(1-9)* Use the table to make a line graph.

Year	1990	1991	1992	1993	1994	1995	1996
Wins	19	22	25	18	20	24	23

Team Wins

6. *(1-9)* Between which years shown on the graph did the number of wins decrease?

1992–1993, 1995–1996

7. *(2-2)* Write in word form: 370,105,246 three hundred seventy million, one hundred five thousand, two hundred forty-six

8. *(2-4)* Write in standard form: four hundred twenty-eight billion, sixty million, three hundred thousand

428,060,300,000

9. *(2-1)* A roll of pennies holds 100 pennies. How many pennies are in 10,000 rolls?

1,000,000

Name ______________________

Daily Review 2-12

Daily Cumulative Review

Write >, <, or = to complete. *(Lesson 2-11)*

1. 3.05 (<) 3.50 **2.** 0.7 (=) 0.70 **3.** 1.5 (>) 1.09

4. 6.15 (<) 6.25 **5.** 9.90 (>) 8.90 **6.** 2.1 (=) 2.10

Use the number line shown to answer 7–8. *(Lesson 2-10)*

3.0 3.5 4.0

7. Name two numbers between 3.1 and 3.6. Possible answers: 3.2, 3.3, 3.4, 3.5

8. Name two numbers between 3.6 and 4.0. 3.7, 3.8, 3.9

Mixed Review

9. *(1-6)* If there are an average of 250 words on one typewritten page, how many words are on 12 typewritten pages?

About 3,000

10. *(1-8)* Why is a graph with a scale of 10 easier to read than a graph with a scale of 25?

Possible answer: the smaller scale makes comparisons easier

Write each number in decimal form.

11. *(2-7)* three and sixty hundredths 3.60

12. *(2-7)* four and four hundredths 4.04

13. *(2-7)* five tenths 0.5

Write each number in standard form.

14. *(2-4)* three billion, fifty million 3,050,000,000

15. *(2-4)* forty billion, seven hundred thousand 40,000,700,000

16. *(2-4)* two billion, six hundred 2,000,000,600

Name ______________________

Daily Review 2-13

Daily Cumulative Review

Round each number to the place of the underlined digit. *(Lesson 2-12)*

1. 2.945 3 **2.** 3.05 3.1 **3.** 4.497 4.50

4. 9.706 9.71 **5.** 6.052 6.05 **6.** 0.749 0.7

Use the table to answer 7–9. *(Lesson 2-11)*

1996–1997 NBA Free Throw Leaders		
Player	**Team**	**Free Throw Percentage**
Elie	Houston	0.896
Brandon	Cleveland	0.902
Hornacek	Utah	0.899
Pierce	Denver/Charlotte	0.897
Price	Golden State	0.906

7. Which player had the highest free throw percentage? Price

8. Which of these players had the lowest free throw percentage? Elie

9. Order the players from highest to lowest free throw percentage. Price, Brandon, Hornacek, Pierce, Elie

Mixed Review

Write two decimals that name each shaded part.

10. *(2-8)* 0.7, 0.70 **11.** *(2-8)* 0.2, 0.20 **12.** *(2-8)* 0.5, 0.50

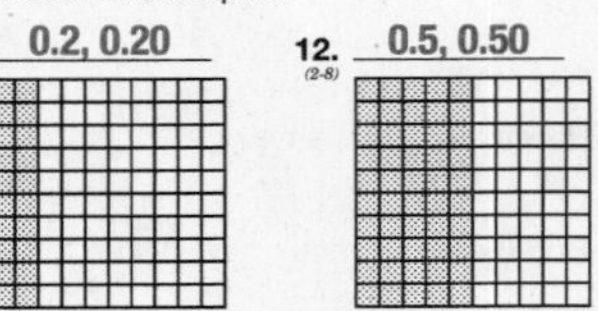

13. *(2-6)* What is the greatest number that rounds to 140,000,000 when rounded to the nearest ten million?

144,999,999

Name ______________________

Daily Review 2-14

Daily Cumulative Review

Draw a picture to solve. *(Lesson 2-13)*

1. Mike's mother agreed to give rides home to Davis, Neal, and Luis after basketball practice. From the school, she drove 3 miles east to Neal's house. Then she drove 1 mile west and 5 miles south to Davis' house. Then she drove 2 miles west to Luis' house. From there, she drove north 4 miles home.

   a. How far did Mike's mother drive? 15 miles

   b. How far is Mike's house from the school and in what direction? 1 mile south of the school

   c. How far does Luis live from Davis and in what direction? 2 miles west of Davis

Round each number to the place of the underlined digit. *(Lesson 2-12)*

2. 2.4̲61 — 2.5
3. 7.0̲36 — 7.0
4. 5.02̲7 — 5.03
5. 0.01̲3 — 0.0

Mixed Review

6. Order these numbers from least to greatest. (2-5)
   13,907,021 13,097,037 14,011,237 14,101,542
   13,097,037; 13,907,021; 14,011,237; 14,101,542

7. Make a stem-and-leaf plot for the data in the table. (1-10)

Letters in Last Name					
4	6	4	8	8	10
9	10	5	6	5	8

Stem	Leaf
0	4 4 5 5 6 6 8 8 8 9
1	0 0

8. What is the mode of the data in 7? 8 (1-10)
9. What is the median the data in 7? 7 (1-10)

Using the digits 0, 1, 3, and 9, write

10. the greatest decimal possible, in thousandths. 9 . 3 1 0 (2-9)
11. the least decimal possible, in thousandths. 0 . 1 3 9 (2-9)

Name ______________________

Daily Review 2-15

Daily Cumulative Review

Estimate each sum or difference. *(Lesson 2-14)*

1. 741 + 32 = 770
2. 497 + 812 = 1,300
3. 377 − 102 = 280
4. \$11.93 − 2.55 = \$9.00

Draw a picture or use another strategy to solve. *(Lesson 2-13)*

5. Antonio lifts weights every 5 days. He swims every 3 days. If he lifted weights and swam on October 6, what is the next date he will do both exercises?
   October 21

6. Sergio, David, Jon, and William live on the same street. William lives west of the others. Jon lives east of Sergio and west of David. In what order do the boys live from west to east?
   William, Sergio, Jon, David

Mixed Review

Round to the nearest hundred thousand.

7. 6,781,532 6,800,000 (2-6)
8. 97,499 100,000 (2-6)

9. Write in word form: 40,061,020 (2-2)
   forty million, sixty-one thousand, twenty

Write =, <, or > to complete.

10. 0.50 (=) 0.5 (2-8)
11. 2.30 (<) 23.0 (2-8)
12. 0.70 (>) 0.07 (2-8)

13. Draw place-value blocks to show the decimal 1.37. (2-7)

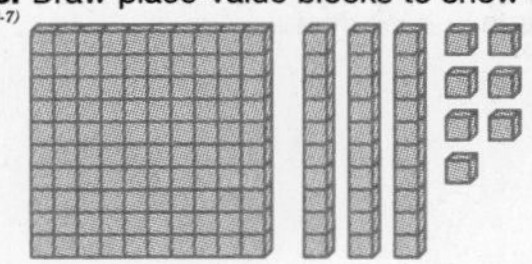

Name ______________________

Daily Review 2-16

Daily Cumulative Review

Find each sum or difference. Then estimate to check your answer. *(Lesson 2-15)*

1. 237 + 356 = 593
2. 680 + 928 = 1,608
3. 1,937 − 458 = 1,479
4. 416 − 273 = 143

Estimate. Write >, <, or = to complete. *(Lesson 2-14)*

5. 87 + 42 (>) 120
6. \$6.99 − \$3.00 (<) \$4
7. 21 + 32 + 61 (>) 110
8. \$89 − \$12 (>) \$70

Mixed Review

9. Name the number shown by each letter. (2-10)
   A 0.32 B 0.35
   C 0.37 D 0.38

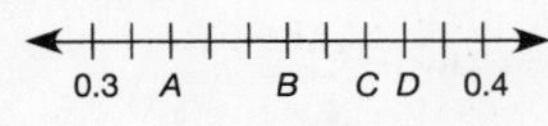

Write each number using exponents.

10. 100,000 10^5 (2-3)
11. 1,000,000 10^6 (2-3)
12. 100 10^2 (2-3)

Use the line graph to answer the questions.

13. What does this line graph show? (1-2)
    The number of blossoms on a Rose Bush each week.

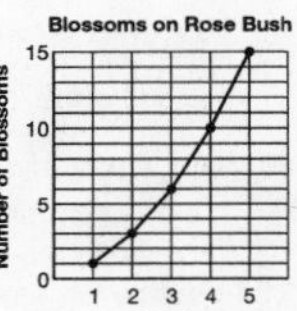

14. How many blossoms were on the plant in the 4th week? 10 (1-2)

15. What does the ordered pair (2, 3) stand for? (1-2)
    There were 3 blossoms in the 2nd week.

Name ______________________

Daily Review 2-17

Daily Cumulative Review

Use place-value blocks to add or subtract. *(Lesson 2-16)*

1. 0.37 + 0.61 = 0.98
2. 0.64 − 0.46 = 0.18

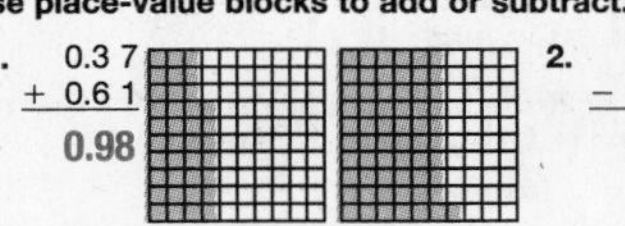

Find each sum or difference. Then estimate to check your answer. *(Lesson 2-15)*

3. 127 + 398 + 35 + 137 = 697
4. 15,261 − 4,982 = 10,279
5. 6,000 − 366 = 5,634

Mixed Review

6. Complete the table. Write its rule using a variable. (1-7)

A	1	3	5	7	9
B	5	7	9	11	13

Rule: $n + 4$

Write each number in decimal form.

7. five and thirty-six thousandths 5.036 (2-9)
8. eight and four hundredths 8.04 (2-9)
9. six and one hundred seven thousandths 6.107 (2-9)
10. In the number 59,015,576,428, give the place value of each 5. (2-4)
    ten billions; millions; hundred thousands

Use the table to answer the questions.

Sales Tax Rate at 6.135%	
Subtotal	**Tax**
\$5	0.30675
\$10	0.6135
\$15	0.92025

11. How many cents tax is there on a \$5 purchase? 31¢ (2-12)
12. What is the tax on a \$15 item? 92¢ (2-12)

Name ______________________

Daily Review 2-18

Daily Cumulative Review

Find each sum. *(Lesson 2-17)*

1. 1.83 + 0.98 = **2.81**
2. 6.07 + 2.19 = **8.26**
3. 2.16 + 7.30 = **9.46**
4. 7.29 + 1.05 = **8.34**
5. 6.00 + 2.79 = **8.79**

Complete. Use place-value blocks or drawings to help you. *(Lesson 2-16)*

6. 1.83 + **2.49** = 4.32
7. 4.21 + 3.09 = **7.30**
8. 8.20 − **4.78** = 3.42
9. 6.1 − **0.8** = 5.3

Mixed Review

Shade in the grids to show each decimal.

10. 0.36 (2-7)

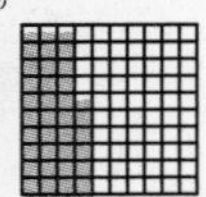

11. 1.2 (2-7)

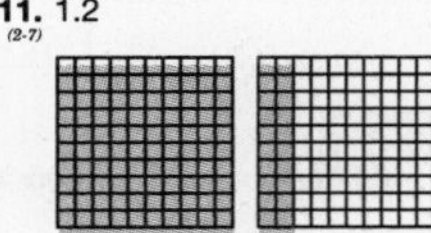

Use the stem-and-leaf plot to answer each question.

Growth of Maple Trees in Inches

Stem	Leaf
0	9
1	1 2 6 8 8
2	4 8

12. How many trees were measured? **8** (1-3)
13. A sugar maple grew the most. How much did it grow? **28 in.** (1-3)
14. Two silver maples grew the same amount. How much did they grow? **18 in.** (1-3)

What is the value in dollars of the money in each stack?

15. ten thousand \$10 bills (2-1) **\$100,000**
16. ten \$1,000 bills (2-1) **\$10,000**

Name ______________________

Daily Review 2-19

Daily Cumulative Review

Find each difference. *(Lesson 2-18)*

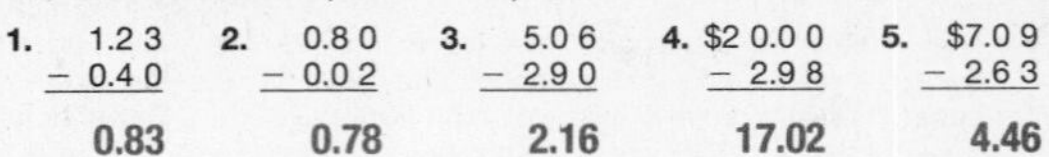

1. 1.23 − 0.40 = **0.83**
2. 0.80 − 0.02 = **0.78**
3. 5.06 − 2.90 = **2.16**
4. \$20.00 − 2.98 = **17.02**
5. \$7.09 − 2.63 = **4.46**

Find each sum. *(Lesson 2-17)*

6. 9.64 + 2.67 = **12.31**
7. 4.89 + 3.06 = **7.95**
8. 0.23 + 1.69 + 0.98 = **2.90**
9. 12.00 + 1.57 = **13.57**
10. 3.99 + 2.54 = **6.53**

Mixed Review

In each group, circle equivalent decimals.

11. 7.0 (0.7) (0.70) (2-8)
12. (0.50) 0.05 (0.5) (2-8)

13. Use logical reasoning. Martina's family has a Basset hound, a Poodle, a Siamese cat, and a parrot. A dog is the oldest pet and Mella is next in age. Duchess and Socks like to chase the cat. Popeye, the youngest pet, has feathers. The Basset hound is younger than Duchess. List the pets in order of age. (1-11)

Duchess the poodle, Mella the Siamese cat,
Socks the Basset hound, Popeye the parrot

Write <, >, or = to complete.

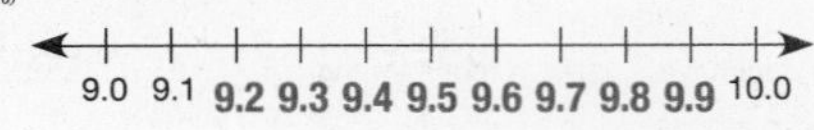

14. 62,301 (<) 503,210 (2-5)
15. 30,050 (=) thirty thousand, fifty (2-5)
16. 998,000 (>) 989,000 (2-5)
17. 6,000,000 (<) sixty million (2-5)

18. Complete the number line. (2-10)

9.0 9.1 **9.2 9.3 9.4 9.5 9.6 9.7 9.8 9.9** 10.0

Name ______________________

Daily Review 3-1

Daily Cumulative Review

Write the number sentence or sentences you would use. Then solve each problem. *(Lesson 2-19)*

1. Gena has earned a total of 267 test points. She made 92 on the first test and 86 on the second test. What score did she receive on the third test?

   92 + 86 = 178; 267 − 178 = 89. She received an 89.

2. Rich had \$2.00. He bought 3 bananas for 60¢, 2 apples for 70¢, and 1 apricot for 15¢ at a fruit stand. How much money does he have left?

   0.60 + 0.70 + 0.15 = 1.45; 2.00 − 1.45 = .55. He has 55¢.

Find each difference. *(Lesson 2-18)*

3. 7 − 3.55 = **3.45**
4. \$7.50 − \$6.78 = **\$0.72**
5. 6.5 − 2.69 = **3.81**
6. \$2.08 − \$0.68 = **\$1.40**

Mixed Review

Write >, <, or = to complete.

7. 0.337 (<) 0.373 (2-11)
8. 0.90 (=) 0.9 (2-11)

Use the data to complete **9–11**.

Cars Crossing Bridge (per day)

23	44	36	27	24	44
32	36	44	28	28	23
41	25	32	39	36	42

Stem	Leaf
2	3 3 4 5 7 8 8
3	2 2 6 6 6 9
4	1 2 4 4 4

9. Make a stem-and-leaf plot to show the Cars Crossing Bridge data. (1-10)
10. What is the mode? **36 and 44** (1-10)
11. What is the range? **21** (1-10)

Name ______________________

Daily Review 3-2

Daily Cumulative Review

Find each product. Use mental math. *(Lesson 3-1)*

1. 20 × 60 = **1,200**
2. 25 × (4 × 17) = **1,700**
3. 80 × 30 = **2,400**
4. 2 × (50 × 9) = **900**

Write the number sentence or sentences you would use. Then solve each problem. *(Lesson 2-19)*

5. Daniel wants to buy a pair of shoes that cost \$96.34 including tax. He has \$14 in his wallet and \$81.50 in his savings account. Does he have enough money to buy the shoes? If so, how much will he have left over?

   \$14.00 + \$81.50 = \$95.50; No, he does not have enough.

6. Brianna wants to buy a CD that costs \$12. Tax is \$0.76. If she pays with a twenty-dollar bill, how much change should she receive?

   \$12.00 + \$0.76 = \$12.76; \$20.00 − \$12.76 = \$7.24

Mixed Review

Write each number in decimal form.

7. four hundred six thousandths **0.406** (2-9)
8. four hundred and six thousandths **400.006** (2-9)
9. Name two decimals with digits in the tenths place that could be rounded to the ones place as 5. (2-12)

   Possible answers: 5.4, 5.3, 5.2, 5.1, 5.0, 4.9, 4.8, 4.7, 4.6, 4.5

Use the line graph to answer **10–11**.

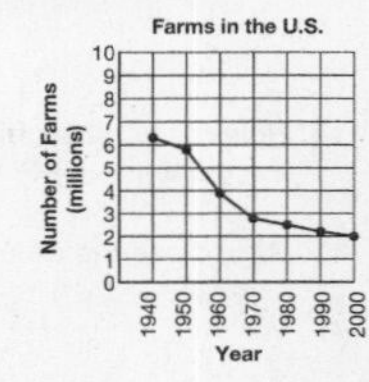

10. What is the trend in the number of farms? (1-2) **decreasing**
11. About how many farms were there in 1970? (1-2) **2.9 million**

Name ____________________

Daily Cumulative Review

Estimate each product. *(Lesson 3-2)*

1. 69 × 5 350 2. 18 × 9 180 3. 47 × 11 470

4. 73 × 51 3,500 5. 82 × 41 3,200 6. 803 × 89 72,000

Complete. *(Lesson 3-1)*

7. 30 × 70 = 2,100 8. 20 × 1,100 = 22,000

9. 60 × 800 = 48,000 10. 90 × 500 = 45,000

Mixed Review

Use place-value blocks or drawings to find each sum or difference.

11. (2-16) 2.31 − 0.71 = 1.60 12. (2-16) 6.7 − 5.8 = 0.9 13. (2-16) 2.38 + 1.80 = 4.18 14. (2-16) 1.6 + 0.9 = 2.5

15. (2-11) Compare 2.132 and 2.106. Which is greater? 2.132

Write the operation needed for each problem. Then solve.

16. (1-6) There are 8,910 books in the school library and 192,347 in the public library. How many books are there in all?

Addition; 201,257

17. (1-6) Chase earned $145 in 5 days. If he earned the same amount each day, how much did he earn in one day?

Division; $29

18. (2-6) Use the number line to help you round 1,876,650 to the nearest million.

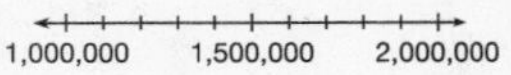

2,000,000

33

Name ____________________

Daily Review
3-4

Daily Cumulative Review

Find each product. Estimate to check. *(Lesson 3-3)*

1. 81 × 19 = 1,539 2. 37 × 59 = 2,183 3. 48 × 61 = 2,928 4. 678 × 7 = 4,746 5. 196 × 21 = 4,116

Estimate each product. *(Lesson 3-2)*

6. 36 × 24 800 7. 303 × 72 21,000 8. 85 × 38 3,600

Mixed Review

Round each number to the place of the underlined digit.

9. (2-12) 6.0̲34 6.0 10. (2-12) 1̲.578 2 11. (2-12) 0.5̲49 0.5 12. (2-12) 6.91̲8 6.92

13. (2-18) Complete. 9.12 − 4.05 = 5.07

14. (2-16) Find 2,000 − 1,603 mentally. Explain your reasoning.

397; Subtract 1,600 from 2,000 to get 400, then subtract 3 more.

15. (1-8) Amanda decided to organize the bookshelf in the den. She sorted the books according to type. Use the data to make a bar graph.

Biographies	3
Reference books	24
Science Fiction	27
Adventure	12
Romance	6
Mysteries	21

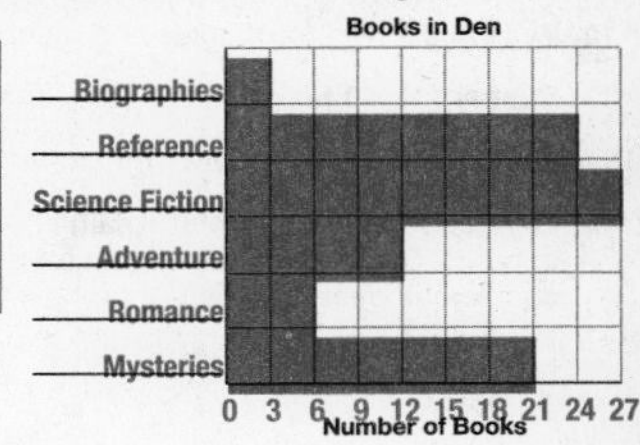

34

Name ____________________

Daily Review
3-5

Daily Cumulative Review

Use mental math to find each product. *(Lesson 3-4)*

1. 701 × 8 = 5,608 2. 71 × 3 = 213

3. 198 × 4 = 792 4. 19 × 7 = 133

Find each product. Estimate to check. *(Lesson 3-3)*

5. 28 × 7 = 196 6. 56 × 58 = 3,248 7. 44 × 80 = 3,520 8. 463 × 9 = 4,167

Mixed Review

9. (2-17) 2.06 + 3.45 + 0.37 = 5.88

10. (2-7) Write one million, one hundred, and one tenth in decimal form.

1,000,100.1

11. (2-10) Name the number shown by each letter.

A 11.1 *B* 11.3

C 11.6 *D* 11.9

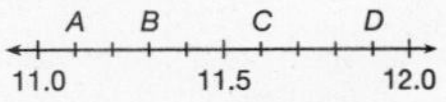

(Number line: A, B, C, D marked; 11.0, 11.5, 12.0)

12. (1-11) A class has 20 students. There are 4 more boys than girls. How many girls are there? 8

13. (1-9) Use the table to make a line graph.

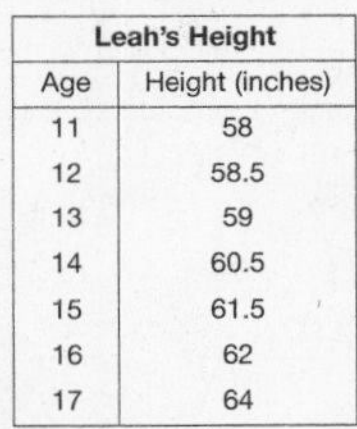

Leah's Height	
Age	Height (inches)
11	58
12	58.5
13	59
14	60.5
15	61.5
16	62
17	64

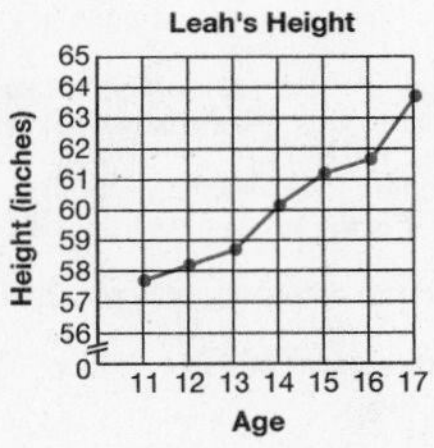

35

Name ____________________

Daily Review
3-6

Daily Cumulative Review

Choose a method. Find each product. *(Lesson 3-5)*

1. 35 × 87 = 3,045 2. 800 × 60 = 48,000 3. 741 × 29 = 21,489 4. 602 × 135 = 81,270

Use mental math to find each product. *(Lesson 3-4)*

5. 202 × 30 = 6,060 6. 99 × 6 = 594 7. 406 × 5 = 2,030 8. 198 × 3 = 594

Mixed Review

9. (2-19) Find the difference of 5 and 2.36. 2.64

10. (3-1) 90 × 600 = 54,000 11. (2-15) 409 − 97 = 312

Write >, <, or = to complete.

12. (2-14) 491 + 293 < 800 13. (2-14) 805 − 697 > 100

14. (2-8) Write which decimals are equivalent. 0.09 0.9 0.90

0.9 and 0.90

Use the pictograph to answer each question.

15. (1-1) How many vans are in the neighborhood? 3

16. (1-1) How many mid-sized cars are in the neighborhood? 6

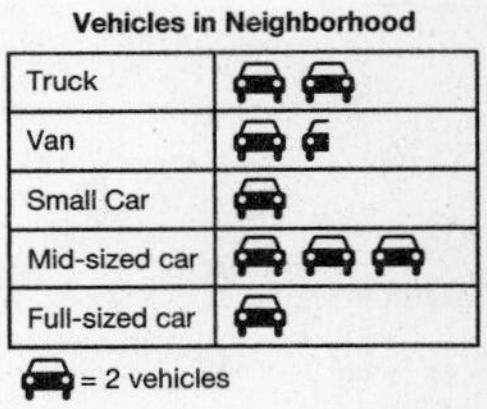

Vehicles in Neighborhood

Truck	🚗🚗
Van	🚗 half
Small Car	🚗
Mid-sized car	🚗🚗🚗
Full-sized car	🚗

🚗 = 2 vehicles

36

Name ______________________

Daily Review 3-7

Daily Cumulative Review

Find the LCM for each pair or set of numbers. *(Lesson 3-6)*

1. 2 and 7 <u>14</u> **2.** 4 and 8 <u>8</u> **3.** 12 and 8 <u>24</u>

4. 2, 8, and 20 <u>40</u> **5.** 6, 9, and 12 <u>36</u>

Find each product. *(Lesson 3-5)*

6. 49×50 = 2,450 **7.** 600×70 = 42,000 **8.** 25×43 = 1,075 **9.** 360×90 = 32,400

Mixed Review

10. (2-16) Explain how you could show $3.87 using dollars, dimes, and pennies.

Possible answer: 3 dollars, 8 dimes, 7 pennies

11. (2-13) Mountains rise high in the sky but trenches are deep in the ocean. The Mariana Trench is the lowest place on earth at 35,840 feet beneath the surface of the Pacific Ocean. The Philippine Trench is slightly deeper than the Kermadec Trench, but neither of them is as deep as the Tonga Trench. List these Pacific trenches from deepest to shallowest.

Mariana, Tonga, Phillipine, Kermadec

12. (2-9) Write in decimal form: three and eight thousandths. <u>3.008</u>

13. (2-18) Subtract 12.68 from 20. <u>7.32</u>

14. (3-2) The product of 392 and what number is about 20,000? <u>About 50</u>

15. (2-19) Emma bought 8 ounces of cream cheese. She already had 5 ounces at home. Does she have enough for a recipe that calls for 12 ounces of cream cheese? Explain.

8 + 5 = 13. She has enough and has 1 ounce left over.

Name ______________________

Daily Review 3-8

Daily Cumulative Review

Plan and solve. Make a decision. *(Lesson 3-7)*

Emma's parents have both been offered new jobs 45 miles away. They are deciding between moving and staying in their current home.

Facts and Data	
Moving	Staying
The move will cost $1,000.	Rent is $200 lower per month.
Shorter work commutes would save $100 each month in gasoline costs.	Daily commuting would take 2 hours for each parent.
Utility bills would be $30 per month lower.	A neighbor would charge $85 per month to watch Emma after school.
Emma could have a horse.	Emma stays in the same school.

1. How much rent would be saved in a year by not moving? <u>$2,400</u>

2. How much would the neighbor charge for 9 months? <u>$765</u>

3. How much would be saved in gasoline and utilities in a year if they moved? <u>$1,560</u>

4. Should they move or stay? Explain. Answers will vary. Possible answer: Move so parents would have more time at home.

Find the LCM for each pair or set of numbers. *(Lesson 3-6)*

5. 2 and 9 <u>18</u> **6.** 8, 12, and 24 <u>24</u>

Mixed Review

Write >, <, or = to complete.

7. (2-11) 5.2 (<) 5.29 **8.** (2-11) 6.07 (<) 6.7 **9.** (2-11) 4.0 (=) 4

10. (2-17) Find the sum of 3.54 and 2.9 <u>6.44</u>

Name ______________________

Daily Review 3-9

Daily Cumulative Review

Find each product *(Lesson 3-8)*

1. 6.43 × 10 <u>64.3</u> **2.** 0.571 × 100 <u>57.1</u> **3.** 4.95 × 1000 <u>4,950</u>

4. 0.003 × 10 = <u>0.03</u> **5.** 0.801 × 10 = <u>8.01</u>

0.003 × 100 = <u>0.3</u> 0.801 × 100 = <u>80.1</u>

0.003 × 1000 = <u>3</u> 0.801 × 1000 = <u>801</u>

Plan and solve. *(Lesson 3-7)*

6. You can buy a season pass for $36 for all 12 ball games or pay $4 per ticket for each game you attend. How many games would you have to attend with the season pass for it to be the better buy? Explain.

More than 9 games. $36 ÷ $4 = 9

Mixed Review

Use mental math to find each answer.

7. (3-4) 302 × 5 = <u>1,510</u> **8.** (3-4) 299 × 4 = <u>1,196</u>

9. (2-15) 5,000 − 3,999 = <u>1,001</u> **10.** (2-17) 0.42 + 1.99 = <u>2.41</u>

11. (3-5) Estimate the product of 48 and 537. Is it closer to 25,000 or 30,000? Explain.

25,000; 50 × 500 = 25,000

Complete. Use place-value blocks or drawings to help you.

12. (2-16) 5.67 − <u>4.26</u> = 1.41 **13.** (2-16) 1.56 + <u>5.31</u> = 6.87

14. (2-16) 4.8 − <u>2.16</u> = 2.64 **15.** (2-16) 4.71 + <u>3.69</u> = 8.40

16. (2-16) 1.29 − <u>0.72</u> = 0.57 **17.** (2-16) 0.18 + <u>1.14</u> = 1.32

Name ______________________

Daily Review 3-10

Daily Cumulative Review

Estimate each product. Explain what you did. *(Lesson 3-9)*

1. 36.4 × 5 <u>200; 40 × 5</u> **2.** 3.87 × 12 <u>48; 4 × 12</u>

3. 48.2 × 7 <u>350; 50 × 7</u> **4.** 92.1 × 478 <u>45,000; 90 × 500</u>

Place the decimal point in the product. Write extra zeros if necessary. *(Lesson 3-8)*

5. 0.237 × 100 = 2 3.7 **6.** 8.51 × 100 = 8 5 1.0

7. 1.089 × 100 = 1 0 8.9 **8.** 0.607 × 100 = 6 0.7

Mixed Review

Complete. For each product the factors are the same.

9. (3-1) <u>60</u> × <u>60</u> = 3,600 **10.** (3-1) <u>80</u> × <u>80</u> = 6,400

11. (2-18) <u>200</u> × <u>200</u> = 40,000 **12.** (3-1) <u>500</u> × <u>500</u> = 250,000

13. (1-6) There are 50 water balloons in one packet. How many packets must you buy to get 200 water balloons? <u>4</u>

For **14** and **15** decide if each problem needs an exact answer or an estimate. Then solve each problem.

14. (3-3) If a tree grows 4 feet every year, about how many feet does it grow in 21 years? <u>Estimate; About 80 feet</u>

15. (3-3) A bakery sold 112 combo-sacks with 4 cookies in each sack. How many cookies did they sell? <u>Exact; 448</u>

16. (2-12) Charlie owes Allison 36¢ but he only has dimes. What is the nearest amount he can give her? <u>40¢</u>

17. (2-19) Find the difference of 6 and 3.23. <u>2.77</u>

18. (2-19) Find the sum of 1.5 + 1.05 + 10.5. <u>13.05</u>

Name ______________________

Daily Review 3-11

Daily Cumulative Review

Find each product. *(Lesson 3-10)*

1. 2.3 × 7 = 16.1 **2.** 4.17 × 9 = 37.53

3. $5.65 × 3 = $16.95 **4.** $1.25 × 21 = $26.25

Is each product greater than 1,000? Write yes or no. Explain. *(Lesson 3-9)*

5. 49.2 × 19 No; 50 × 20 = 1,000

6. 149.5 × 9 Yes; 150 × 10 = 1,500

7. 10 × 9.76 No; 10 × 10 = 100

Mixed Review

Estimate. Write >, <, or = to complete.

8. (2-14) 9.82 + 4.59 (>) 14 **9.** (2-14) 216 − 109 (>) 100

Solve.

10. (2-19) 9.43 − 0.37 = 9.06 **11.** (2-17) 0.84 + 2.76 = 3.60 **12.** (3-4) 98 × 7 = 686 **13.** (3-5) 75 × 20 = 1,500

Round to the nearest hundred thousand.

14. (2-6) 90,006 100,000 **15.** (2-6) 124,899,160 124,900,000

16. (2-6) 364,749,688 364,700,000 **17.** (2-6) 1,450,099 1,500,000

18. (2-10) Use the number line to answer. Name nine numbers between 2.3 and 2.4

2.3 2.35 2.4

Possible answer: 2.31, 2.32, 2.33 2.34, 2.35, 2.36, 2.37, 2.38, 2.39

41

Name ______________________

Daily Review 3-12

Daily Cumulative Review

Solve each problem. *(Lesson 3-11)*

1. During the game against Edgarstown, Pam made 12 baskets and Bettina made 7 baskets. For each basket, 2 points were scored.

a. How many points did Pam score? 24

b. How many points did Bettina score? 14

c. How many points did the two girls score? 38

2. Maruka bought 3 pairs of earrings that cost $5.99 each. How much change would she receive from a $20 bill? $2.03

Choose the number that is closest to the actual product. *(Lesson 3-10)*

3. $3.06 × 21 B **A.** $6 **B.** $60 **C.** $600

4. $1.98 × 1000 C **A.** $2 **B.** $200 **C.** $2000

5. 6.005 × 50 B **A.** 30 **B.** 300 **C.** 3000

Mixed Review

Estimate each product.

6. (3-2) 101 × 89 9,000 **7.** (3-2) 59 × 31 1,800

8. (2-15) Find 3,998 + 6,998 mentally. Explain why it is easier to do this sum mentally than by writing it out.

10,996; Add 4,000 and 7,000 to get 11,000, then subtract 4.

9. (3-6) List the multiples of 24 and 36. What is the least common multiple of 24 and 36?

Multiples of 24: 24, 48, 72, 96, 120; Multiples of 36: 36, 72, 108, 144, 180; Least common multiple: 72

42

Name ______________________

Daily Review 3-13

Daily Cumulative Review

Use the 10 × 10 grid to show 0.4 of 0.8. *(Lesson 3-12)*

1.

a. Use horizontal stripes to shade 0.4 on the grid as 4 rows.

b. Use vertical stripes to shade 0.8 on the grid as 8 columns.

c. Count the double-striped squares. 0.4 of 0.8 is 0.32.

Solve. *(Lesson 3-11)*

2. A bookstore charges $4.95 for new paperbacks, $2.95 for used paperbacks, and $10.95 for used hardbacks.

a. Mrs. Easley bought 3 new paperbacks and 2 used paperbacks. How much did she spend? $20.75

b. Allison bought 1 used hardback and 3 used paperbacks. How much did she spend? $19.80

Mixed Review

Complete. Use place-value blocks or drawings to help you.

3. (2-16) 3.09 − 1.11 = 1.98 **4.** (2-18) 5 − 3.63 = 1.37

5. (2-19) The Rameriz family is driving 1,060 miles to their new home. They drove 328 miles the first day and 341 miles the second day. How many more miles do they have to travel? Write the number sentence or sentences you would use. Then solve the problem.

328 + 341 = 669; 1,060 − 669 = 391; 391 miles

6. (2-9) Using the digits 2, 4, 6, and 8, write the greatest decimal possible, in thousandths. 8 6 4 2

43

Name ______________________

Daily Review 3-14

Daily Cumulative Review

Find each product. Round to the nearest cent when necessary. *(Lesson 3-13)*

1. $9.35 × 0.1 = $0.94 **2.** $0.37 × 4.5 = $1.67 **3.** 640 × 0.008 = 5.12 **4.** 5.71 × 0.22 = 1.2562

Find each product. You can use 10 × 10 grids to help. *(Lesson 3-12)*

5. 0.5 of 0.4 0.20 **6.** 0.7 of 0.3 0.21 **7.** 0.8 of 0.1 0.08 **8.** 0.4 of 0.9 0.36

9. 0.1 of 0.1 0.01 **10.** 0.9 of 0.9 0.81 **11.** 0.5 of 0.5 0.25 **12.** 0.3 of 0.4 0.12

Mixed Review

Round each number to the place of the underlined digit.

13. (2-12) 4.831 4.8 **14.** (2-12) 0.286 0.29 **15.** (2-12) 3.390 3.4

Complete.

16. (3-1) 70 × 70 = 4,900 **17.** (3-1) 60 × 900 = 54,000

Use the table to answer each question.

Monthly Internet Rates	
Plan A	Plan B
10 hours: $9.95	Unlimited access: $19.95
Each additional hour: $2.00	

18. (3-7) How much would 15 hours of internet use cost using Plan A? $19.95

19. (3-7) How much would you save with plan B if you were online for 20 hours? $10

44

Name ______________________

Daily Review 3-15

Daily Cumulative Review

Between which two numbers will each product be found? *(Lesson 3-14)*

1. 4.5 × 7.2 **A**

A. 28 and 35 **B.** 35 and 40 **C.** 280 and 350

2. 31.7 × 9 **C**

A. 40 and 50 **B.** 27 and 36 **C.** 270 and 360

3. 2.91 × 6.8 **B**

A. 8 and 10 **B.** 12 and 21 **C.** 80 and 100

Find each product. Round to the nearest cent when necessary. *(Lesson 3-13)*

4. \$2.35 × 0.04 = **\$0.09**

5. 6.53 × 1.03 = **6.7259**

6. \$5.50 × 0.005 = **\$0.03**

7. \$12.60 × 6 = **\$75.60**

Mixed Review

8. (2-7) Write three and nine hundredths in decimal form. **3.09**

Write each number using exponents.

9. (2-3) 100,000 **10^5** **10.** (2-3) 100 **10^2** **11.** (2-3) 1,000,000 **10^6**

12. (3-8) If 100 people attend a dinner theater and pay \$9.75 each, how much did the theater collect? **\$975.00**

13. (3-10) One lap of a dirt track is 0.125 of a mile. How far does a car travel

a. in 3 laps? **0.375 mile** **b.** in 8 laps? **1 mile**

14. (2-17) Find the sum of 2.45 and 1.9. **4.35**

Name ______________________

Daily Review 3-16

Daily Cumulative Review

Find each product. *(Lesson 3-15)*

1. 0.05 × 0.003 = **0.00015** **2.** 0.004 × 0.07 = **0.00028**

3. 6.2 × 0.001 = **0.0062** **4.** 4.03 × 0.08 = **0.3224**

Estimate low and high. Then find each product. *(Lesson 3-14)*

5. 7.3 × 8 = **58.4** Estimate: **56–64**

6. 6.9 × 3 = **20.7** Estimate: **18–21**

7. 4.5 × 2.1 = **9.45** Estimate: **8–15**

8. 1.8 × 3.9 = **7.02** Estimate: **3–8**

Mixed Review

Estimate each product. Explain what you did.

9. (3-9) 6.8 × 5 **35; 7 × 5**

10. (3-9) 9 × 1.04 **9; 9 × 1**

11. (3-2) Give two numbers whose product is about 400.

Example: 19 × 21

12. (2-11) Order 8.27, 8.72, 8.07, 8.20 from least to greatest.

8.07; 8.20; 8.27; 8.72

13. (3-7) A plane ticket costs \$105 per person. The same trip costs \$25 for gas and \$50 for meals.

a. Write a list of reasons why flying might be the better choice.

Possible answer: Takes less time

b. Write a list of reasons why driving might be the better choice.

Possible answer: Cheaper, more than one person can travel for the same amount of money

Name ______________________

Daily Review 4-1

Daily Cumulative Review

Use the Guess and Check Strategy to solve each problem. *(Lesson 3-16)*

1. Marissa has 13 guppies and swordtails in her aquarium. She has 3 more guppies than swordtails.

a. What is a reasonable first guess for the number of guppies?

Possible answer: Anywhere from 5 to 10.

b. She has 13 fish in all. Is it possible for her to have 10 guppies and 3 swordfish?

No, the difference is not 3 fish.

c. How many of each fish does she have?

8 guppies, 5 swordtails

2. Alex mowed 6 lawns last week. He charges \$20 for medium-sized lawns and \$12 for small lawns. He earned \$104 last week. How many of each size lawn did he mow?

4 medium-sized lawns and 2 small lawns

Find each product. Write zeros where needed. *(Lesson 3-15)*

3. 4.6 × 0.03 = **0.138**

4. 0.21 × 0.15 = **0.0315**

5. 7.8 × 0.09 = **0.702**

6. 1.05 × 9.6 = **10.08**

Mixed Review

7. (2-13) Jesse is taller than Riley but shorter than Sam. Tom is the tallest of the four. Who is the shortest? **Riley**

8. (3-11) The Band Boosters sold cupcakes for 50¢ each and cookies for 10¢ each. If you bought 2 cupcakes and 3 cookies, how much did you spend? **\$1.30**

Name ______________________

Daily Review 4-2

Daily Cumulative Review

Find each quotient. *(Lesson 4-1)*

1. 42 ÷ 7 = **6** **2.** 40 ÷ 5 = **8** **3.** 54 ÷ 6 = **9**

4. 56 ÷ 8 = **7** **5.** 24 ÷ 4 = **6** **6.** 36 ÷ 9 = **4**

Use Guess and Check or any strategy to solve each problem. *(Lesson 3-16)*

7. Brenna has saved \$125. She earns \$20 each week helping her grandma in her store after school. How many weeks will it be before she has enough money to buy a saddle that costs \$245?

6 weeks

8. In Mr. Lander's class, the boys outnumber the girls by 3. There are 21 students in his class. How many girls and how many boys are there in Mr. Lander's class?

9 girls and 12 boys

Mixed Review

Complete.

9. (3-3) 87 × 45 = **3,915**

10. (2-15) 506 − 349 = **157**

11. (2-18) 3.68 − 1.47 = **2.21**

12. (2-17) 6.09 + 3.27 = **9.36**

13. (3-9) Estimate the product of 5.763 and 6.103. **36**

14. (3-11) Derrick took \$35 to the mall. He bought two shirts for \$14.26 each and spent \$4.32 on lunch. How much money did he have left?

\$2.16

15. (2-1) In 1927, Charles Lindbergh flew 3,610 miles from New York to Paris. Use your calculator to find about how many times he would have had to make the trip to fly a million miles.

About 277 trips

Name ______________________

Daily Review 4-3

Daily Cumulative Review

Use number sense and basic facts to divide mentally. *(Lesson 4-2)*

1. 35 ÷ 5 = 7
350 ÷ 5 = 70
3,500 ÷ 5 = 700
35,000 ÷ 5 = 7,000

2. 24 ÷ 2 = 12
240 ÷ 2 = 120
2,400 ÷ 2 = 1,200
24,000 ÷ 2 = 12,000

Identify each number in the equation 6 × 8 = 48 and 48 ÷ 6 = 8 as a factor, a product, a divisor, a dividend, or a quotient. *(Lesson 4-1)*

3. 6 × 8 = 48
factor, factor, product

4. 48 ÷ 6 = 8
dividend, divisor, quotient

Mixed Review

5. (3-8) A charity fund-raiser collected $100 each from 37 people. The goal was $5,000. How much more does the charity need to collect?
$1,300

6. (3-10) Connie jogs to the river and back every day, a total distance of 1.4 miles. How many miles does she jog in 4 weeks?
39.2 miles

7. (2-2) Suppose Mr. Midas buys a house for $1,573,500. He writes this amount in word form on a check. What does he write?
one million, five hundred seventy-three thousand,
five hundred

Name ______________________

Daily Review 4-4

Daily Cumulative Review

Estimate each quotient. *(Lesson 4-3)*

1. 490 ÷ 60 = 8
2. 277 ÷ 4 = 70
3. 539 ÷ 9 = 60
4. 119 ÷ 3 = 40

Use patterns and basic facts to divide mentally. *(Lesson 4-2)*

5. 3,500 ÷ 7 = 500
6. 63,000 ÷ 9 = 7,000
7. 420 ÷ 6 = 70
8. 7,200 ÷ 8 = 900

Mixed Review

Find each product.

9. (3-4) 587 × 11 = 6,457
10. (3-1) (5 × 37) × 20 = 3,700

11. (3-14) Between which two numbers will the product 9.7 × 6.3 be found?
A. 15 and 17 B. 54 and 70 C. 540 and 700
B

12. (2-19) Amber wanted to buy a computer game that costs $67.98. She saved until she had $70. When she went to buy the game, she found it on sale for $47.48. How much money did she have left?
$22.52

13. (3-7) You and a friend go to a county fair that has 6 rides. Each ride takes one ticket. You can buy 4 ride tickets for $5 or a pass with unlimited rides for $20.

a. If you go on each ride twice, how much would it cost using tickets? $15

b. How many rides would you have to go on before the pass is the better buy? More than 16

Name ______________________

Daily Review 4-5

Daily Cumulative Review

Complete. You may use play money to help. *(Lesson 4-4)*

1. 8)$17.05 = $[2].1 3 R[1]
− 1 6
[1]0
− 8
[2]5
− [2][4]
1

2. 5)$7.98 = $[1].5 9 R[3]
− [5]
[2]9
− [2][5]
[4]8
− [4][5]
[3]

Estimate each quotient. *(Lesson 4-3)*

3. 319 ÷ 8 = 40
4. 269 ÷ 4 = 70
5. 362 ÷ 6 = 60
6. 570 ÷ 7 = 80

Mixed Review

7. (3-2) Estimate the product of 195 and 97. 20,000

8. (2-14) Estimate the sum of 459 and 212. 700

9. (3-5) Lindsey and Leah each solve 307 multiplied by 386. Lindsey's answer is 118,502. Leah's answer is 95,432. Which answer is reasonable? Explain.
Lindsey's answer. 300 × 400 = 120,000

10. (2-5) Christopher's Mom is on a low-fat diet. While helping her grocery shop, he compared the grams of saturated fat in four snack foods. List the snacks in order of least to most fat.
chips, pretzels, popcorn
mixed nuts

Snack	Grams of Saturated Fat per Serving
Mixed nuts	2.5
Chips	1.5
Popcorn	2.25
Pretzels	1.75

Name ______________________

Daily Review 4-6

Daily Cumulative Review

Divide. Use multiplication to check. *(Lesson 4-5)*

1. 6)835 = 139 R1
2. 3)673 = 224 R1
3. 5)408 = 81 R3
4. 7)826 = 118

Divide. You may use play money to help. *(Lesson 4-4)*

5. 2)$5.26 = $2.63
6. 4)$1.29 = $0.32 R1
7. 3)$7.45 = $2.48 R1
8. 8)$8.96 = $1.12

Mixed Review

Complete.

9. (2-16) 2.58 − 2.14 = 0.44
10. (2-15) 900 − 466 = 434
11. (3-2) 704 × 48 = 33,792
12. (3-5) 320 × 200 = 64,000

13. (3-15) Is the product of 0.05 and 6.38 greater or less than 6.38? Explain.
Less than; multiplying by a number less than 1

14. (4-1) There are 36 paper napkins in a package. If 4 napkins are used at each meal, how many meals will one package last?
9 meals

15. (3-16) A baseball team is giving away gloves and hats to promote their team. If the gloves cost the team $15 each and the hats cost $3.00 each, how much will it cost the team for 2 gloves and 5 hats?
$45

Name ______________________

Daily Review 4-7

Daily Cumulative Review

Use any strategy to solve each problem. *(Lesson 4-6)*

1. Mrs. Bill is buying six-packs of sodas for her class of 22. Each student will get one soda. She plans to drink coffee.
   a. How many six-packs does she need to buy? **4**
   b. How many sodas will be left over? **2**
2. The science lab tables will seat 4 students each. How many tables will be needed for a class of 23? **6**

Divide *(Lesson 4-5)*

3. 6)8 0 1 — **133 R3**
4. 4)6 7 3 — **168 R1**
5. 3)4 2 9 — **143**
6. 7)9 0 0 — **128 R4**

Mixed Review

7. (3-6) Find the LCM for 4, 6, and 9. **36**

Place the decimal point in the product. Write extra zeros if necessary.

8. (3-8) 0.025 × 100 = 2.5
9. (3-8) 0.8 × 1000 = 8 0 0.

Complete.

10. (4-2) 2,400 ÷ **6** = 400
11. (4-2) 56,000 ÷ **700** = 80
12. (3-16) Jay sold a box of books at a yard sale for $51. He sold some of the books for $2 each and some for $3 each. If there were 20 books in the box, how many did he sell at each price?
    9 books for $2 and 11 books for $3

53

Name ______________________

Daily Review 4-8

Daily Cumulative Review

Divide. Check your answer. *(Lesson 4-7)*

1. 5)3 7 9 — **75 R4**
2. 7)2 4 3 — **34 R5**
3. 2)1 7 6 — **88**
4. 3)5 3 9 — **179 R2**

Use any strategy to solve each problem. *(Lesson 4-6)*

5. Hotdog buns come 8 to a package. Janice needs 36 buns for a cookout. How many packages should she buy? **5**
6. Kashan's father is going to be 38. Kashan found birthday candles that are packaged 12 to a box. How many boxes should she buy for his cake and how many candles will be left over?
   4 boxes with 10 candles left over

Mixed Review

7. (2-8) Write which decimals are equivalent.
   0.9 0.09 0.90 **0.9 and 0.90**
8. (2-10) Name the number shown by each letter.

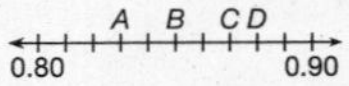

A **0.83** B **0.85** C **0.87** D **0.88**

9. (3-11) A cola sells for $0.59. A six-pack of the same cola sells for $1.59. How much would you save on 6 colas by buying the six-pack?
   $1.95

54

Name ______________________

Daily Review 4-9

Daily Cumulative Review

Divide. Multiply to check. *(Lesson 4-8)*

1. 9)9 8 7 — **109 R6**
2. 4)1 2 0 3 — **300 R3**
3. 7)7 3 4 — **104 R6**
4. 6)6 0 3 4 — **1005 R4**

Divide. Check your answer. *(Lesson 4-7)*

5. 5)2 4 7 — **49 R2**
6. 3)1 2 8 — **42 R2**
7. 8)5 7 6 — **72**
8. 2)1 7 9 — **89 R1**

Mixed Review

9. (4-3) Estimate the quotient of 549 ÷ 7. **80**
10. (3-12) Find the product of 0.5 and 0.5. **0.25**
11. (2-5) Order these numbers from least to greatest.
    6,014,000; 60,140,000; 614,000; 6,100,400
    614,000; 6,014,000; 6,100,400; 60,140,000
12. (2-9) Write three hundred and sixteen thousandths in decimal form.
    300.016
13. (2-15) Find 2000 − 998 mentally. Explain your reasoning.
    1002; Subtract 2000 − 1000 and add 2.
14. (3-14) Estimate low and high. Then find the product of 3.9 and 14.7.
    42–60; 57.33

55

Name ______________________

Daily Review 4-10

Daily Cumulative Review

Complete each sentence using a number from the number bank. *(Lesson 4-9)*

Test Scores: 76, 82, 89, 92, 92, 97

Number Bank
6
88
89
90.5
92
528

1. The mode of the test scores is **92** because it is the number that appears most.
2. To find the mean, you would divide **528** by **6** and get **88**.
3. The median is **90.5** because it is halfway between the middle numbers **89** and **92**.

Divide. Multiply to check. *(Lesson 4-8)*

4. 9)3 6 1 9 — **402 R1**
5. 2)8 0 0 5 — **4002 R1**
6. 6)7 2 3 — **120 R3**

Mixed Review

7. (3-9) Estimate the product 47.3 × 8. Explain what you did.
   400; 50 × 8
8. (3-4) Would you use the distributive property to find 730 × 2? Explain.
   Yes, (700 × 2) + (30 × 2) = 1400 + 60 = 1460
9. (4-5) The school purchased 123 boxes of paper for the 3 fifth grade teachers. If each teacher gets the same amount of paper, how many boxes would they get?
   41 boxes each

56

Name ______________________

Daily Review 4-11

Daily Cumulative Review

Match each number sentence with the property it shows. *(Lesson 4-10)*

b 1. $1 \times 99 = 99$ — a. Zero Property

d 2. $5 \times (2 \times 79) = (5 \times 2) \times 79$ — b. One Property

a 3. $6 \times 0 = 0$ — c. Commutative Property

c 4. $7 \times 33 = 33 \times 7$ — d. Associative Property

Find the mean, median, and mode for each set of data. *(Lesson 4-9)*

5. 7, 13, 13, 16, 20, 24, 26

17, 16, 13

6. 76, 80, 82, 84, 93

83, 82, no mode

Mixed Review

7. (1-7) Complete the table. Give its rule using words and a variable.

A	1	3	5	7	9	11
B	8	10	12	14	16	18

Rule: Add 7 to a number; $n + 7$

8. (2-19) Julianna must read 500 pages this summer. So far she has read a book with 151 pages and another with 209 pages. She wants to reach the goal with one more book. How many pages does it need to have? Write the number sentence or sentences you would use. Then solve the problem.

$151 + 209 = 360$; $500 - 360 = 140$. 140 pages

Name ______________________

Daily Review 4-12

Daily Cumulative Review

Find each quotient. Multiply to check. *(Lesson 4-11)*

1. 9)$6 3.0 0 — $7.00

2. 5)$1 0.5 0 — $2.10

3. 7)$2 5 5.0 8 — $36.44

Write >, <, or = to complete. *(Lesson 4-10)*

4. $56 \times 1 = n$ — a. n = 56 — b. n > 1

5. $97 \times 6 = n$ — a. n > 97 — b. n > 6

6. $48 \times n = 0$ — a. n < 48 — b. n = 0

Mixed Review

Estimate high and low. Then find each product.

7. (3-14) $21.7 \times 8 =$ 173.6 Estimate: 160–240

8. (3-14) $2.96 \times 7 =$ 20.72 Estimate: 14–21

9. (1-11) Mrs. Lotridge has 4 children, 2 boys and 2 girls. Each child has a different color hair. Joanna, the youngest, does not have brown or black hair. Stan is not the oldest and does not have red hair. Kim, the blond, is younger than Stan. Robert has the darkest hair of all. List Mrs. Lotridge's children from oldest to youngest and their hair color.

Robert-black hair, Stan-brown hair, Kim-blonde hair, Joanna-red hair

10. (4-6) Martin baked 96 cookies for a bake sale. If he puts 5 cookies per baggie, how many baggies does he need? How many cookies will be left for him to eat?

19 baggies; He will have 1 cookie left over.

Name ______________________

Daily Review 4-13

Daily Cumulative Review

Find each quotient. *(Lesson 4-12)*

1. 5)1 2.0 6 5 — 2.413

2. 3)8.1 4 8 — 2.716

3. 7)3 5.8 0 5 — 5.115

Use a calculator to divide. Write each answer to the nearest cent. *(Lesson 4-11)*

4. 4)$840.19 — $210.05

5. 6)$654.79 — $109.13

6. 8)$160.97 — $20.12

Mixed Review

Multiply.

7. (3-3) 41×68 = 2788

8. (3-10) $\$42.73 \times 9$ = $384.57

9. (3-13) 5.07×0.4 = 2.028

10. (3-5) 700×80 = 56,000

11. (2-2) Write 20,370,405 in word form.

twenty million, three hundred seventy thousand, four hundred five

12. (2-6) If 75,936,462 rounds to 75,940,000 to which place did you round?

ten thousand place

13. (3-16) Mr. Frickes bought 12 cotton tee shirts sizes large and extra large for the art club to tie dye. There were two more large shirts than extra large shirts. How many of each size did he buy?

7 large, 5 extra large

Name ______________________

Daily Review 4-14

Daily Cumulative Review

Find the factors for each number. *(Lesson 4-13)*

1. 14 — 1, 2, 7, 14

2. 35 — 1, 5, 7, 35

3. 24 — 1, 2, 3, 4, 6, 8, 12, 24

4. 48 — 1, 2, 3, 4, 6, 8, 12, 16, 24, 48

Find the length of the side of each square. *(Lesson 4-12)*

5. Perimeter = 16.492 cm — 4.123 cm

6. Perimeter = 20.32 in. — 5.08 in.

Mixed Review

7. (3-12) Find the product of 0.9 of 0.5. 0.45

8. (3-6) Find the LCM of 10 and 25. 50

9. (3-1) Which is greater, the product of $20 \times 40 \times 300$ or $200 \times 4 \times 30$?

Explain. $20 \times 40 \times 300$. There are 4 zeros in the first product and only 3 zeros in the second product.

Meg and Amelia must decide between one-day passes for $30 or two-day passes for $50 at an amusement park. The park is open 10 hours every day.

10. (3-7) If they stay the full 10 hours, what is the cost per hour for the one-day pass? $3.00

11. (3-7) If they go both days for the full time, what is the cost per hour for the two-day pass? $2.50

Name ______________________

Daily Review 4-15

Daily Cumulative Review

Use factor trees to find the prime factors of each number. *(Lesson 4-14)*

1. 18

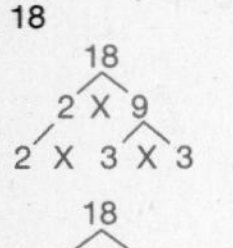

2. 50

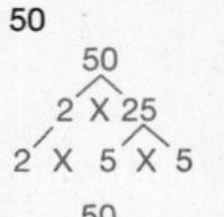

3. 27

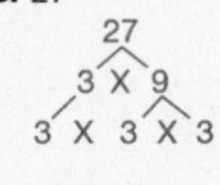

Find the factors of each number. *(Lesson 4-13)*

4. 44 1, 2, 4, 11, 22, 44 **5.** 52 1, 2, 4, 13, 26, 52

6. 70 1, 2, 5, 7, 10, 14, 35, 70 **7.** 81 1, 3, 9, 27, 81

Mixed Review

Complete.

8. *(4-7)* $574 \div 7 = 82$

9. *(3-15)* $2.7 \times 0.03 = 0.081$

10. *(3-3)* $468 \times 17 = 7956$

11. *(2-18)* $5.00 - 2.17 = 2.83$

Use the graph to answer **12** and **13**.

12. *(1-1)* How many more children does the Allen family have than the Ford family? 2

13. *(4-9)* Find the mean, median, and mode for the set of data in the bar graph. 3, 2.5, 2

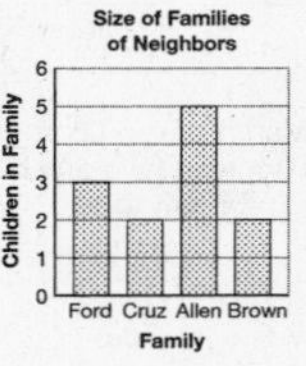

Name ______________________

Daily Review 5-1

Daily Cumulative Review

Work backward to solve the problem. *(Lesson 4-15)*

1. Jonathan went to an arcade. In the first hour he spent half his money. During the next hour, he spent 75¢. He spent half his remaining money before he left and had 50¢ left over.

a. How much did he have left? 50¢

b. What operation undoes dividing his remaining money in half? multiplying by 2

c. What operation undoes subtracting 75¢? adding 75¢

d. How much money did he have when he went to the arcade? $3.50

Write whether each number is prime or composite. *(Lesson 4-14)*

2. 23 prime **3.** 33 composite **4.** 21 composite

Mixed Review

Complete.

5. *(4-8)* $1421 \div 7 = 203$

6. *(3-3)* $366 \times 55 = 20{,}130$

7. *(2-17)* $3.09 + 1.87 + 6.1 = 11.06$

8. *(2-15)* $400 - 37 = 363$

9. *(3-9)* Estimate the product of 78.9 × 7. Explain what you did. 560; 80 × 7

10. *(2-19)* Rose and Janet want to buy a book for their mother that costs $36. Rose has $13 and Janet has $16. Do they have enough money to buy the book? If not, how much more money do they need? No, they need $7 more to buy the book.

Name ______________________

Daily Review 5-2

Daily Cumulative Review

You can use number sense and basic facts to divide with multiples of 10. *(Lesson 5-1)*

1. a. What basic fact would you use to find 240 ÷ 60? 24 ÷ 6 = 4

b. 240 ÷ 60 = 4

2. a. What basic fact would you use to find 56,000 ÷ 80? 56 ÷ 8 = 7

b. 56,000 ÷ 80 = 700

Use any strategy to solve each problem. *(Lesson 4-15)*

3. Bonnie had $1.33 left at the end of the week. She bought 2 candy bars for $0.55 each and 3 bottles of juice for $1.06 each. How much did she have at the beginning of the week? $5.61

4. Marco earns $4 an hour helping his dad. He worked 8 hours on Monday, 5 hours on Tuesday, 7 hours on Wednesday, and 2 hours on Thursday. Friday he spent 6 hours at the beach. How much money did Marco earn? $88

Mixed Review

5. *(1-1)* In a pictograph, each picture of a house stands for 20 houses. How many houses do $2\frac{1}{2}$ pictures stand for? 50

6. *(4-12)* Is 41.907 ÷ 6 = 16.1542 a reasonable answer? Explain why or why not. No; Using compatible numbers, the estimate is 42 ÷ 6 = 7.

Name ______________________

Daily Review 5-3

Daily Cumulative Review

Estimate each quotient. Give a high and low estimate. *(Lesson 5-2)*

1. 13,427 ÷ 30 500, 400 **2.** 2,316 ÷ 90 30, 20 **3.** 34,895 ÷ 80 500, 400

4. 4,563 ÷ 60 80, 70 **5.** 67,339 ÷ 80 900, 800 **6.** 5,986 ÷ 70 90, 80

Find each quotient. Use mental math. *(Lesson 5-1)*

7. 1,600 ÷ 80 = 20 **8.** 72,000 ÷ 800 = 90

9. 4,800 ÷ 60 = 80 **10.** 5,400 ÷ 900 = 6

Mixed Review

11. *(3-14)* Estimate high and low. Then find the product of 15.3 and 45.5. 1,000, 400; 696.15

12. *(2-14)* Estimate. Write >, <, or = to complete. 72 + 63 ◯ 130

13. *(2-4)* Write the place-value position for each digit in the number 47,563,128.

1 hundreds 2 tens 3 thousands

4 ten millions 5 hundred thousands 6 ten thousand

7 millions 8 ones

14. *(4-9)* Find the mean, median, and mode for the set of data. 3, 4, 4, 4, 5, 6, 7, 7, 7, 13

mean 6 median 5.5 mode(s) 4 and 7

15. *(4-7)* The divisor is 4 and the dividend is 429. Divide. 107 R1

Name ______________________

Daily Review 5-4

Daily Cumulative Review

Estimate each quotient using compatible numbers. *(Lesson 5-3)*

1. 638 ÷ 81 About 8
2. 130 ÷ 62 About 2
3. 2,671 ÷ 29 About 90
4. 19,536 ÷ 59 About 300
5. 23,932 ÷ 38 About 600
6. 123,956 ÷ 33 About 4,000

Estimate each quotient. Give a high and low estimate. *(Lesson 5-2)*

7. 2,239 ÷ 40 60, 50
8. 41,672 ÷ 60 700, 600
9. 6,637 ÷ 90 80, 70

Mixed Review

10. (4-1) In the equations 5 × 8 = 40 and 40 ÷ 8 = 5, which number is:
    a. a product? 40 b. a quotient? 5 c. a divisor? 8
11. (2-11) Write >, <, or = to complete. 0.47 (<) 0.5
12. (2-9) Write two and eighty-eight thousandths in decimal form. 2.088
13. (1-6) The average number of times Brianna visits the library each month is 5. About how many times does she visit in a year? 60
14. (4-9) Suppose you wanted to find the mean, median, and mode of your test scores 87, 88, 89, 90, 91. How could you find them mentally? Since the test scores are 5 consecutive numbers, the middle number 89 is the median and the mean. No mode.
15. (2-9) Write five hundred two thousandths in decimal form. 0.502

Name ______________________

Daily Review 5-5

Daily Cumulative Review

Complete. *(Lesson 5-4)*

1. 52)163 = 3 R 7
2. 24)99 = 4 R 3
3. 13)71 = 5 R 6

Estimate each quotient. Use compatible numbers. *(Lesson 5-3)*

4. 204 ÷ 37 About 5
5. 242 ÷ 8 About 30
6. 331 ÷ 41 About 8
7. 3,050 ÷ 49 About 60
8. 731 ÷ 80 About 9
9. 44,990 ÷ 49 About 900

Mixed Review

Complete each number sentence.

10. (3-4) 81 × 7 = 567
11. (3-13) 0.017 × 5.4 = 0.0918
12. (4-2) 21,000 ÷ 70 = 300
13. (4-5) 532 ÷ 4 = 133
14. (4-8) 35,000 ÷ 5 = 7,000
15. (2-18) \$16 − \$8.85 = \$7.15

Round each number to the place of the underlined digit.

16. (2-12) 9.387 9.4
17. (2-12) 1.961 2.0
18. (2-12) 0.39 0.0
19. (3-7) Kaylin and Clare are reading a lunch menu. They can buy a chicken dinner which serves 2 for \$13.50 or pepper steak for \$7.75 each.
    a. How much will 2 pepper steak dinners cost? \$15.50
    b. Give a reason the girls might choose the chicken dinner. Possible answers: They would save \$2.00. They like chicken more than pepper steak.

Name ______________________

Daily Review 5-6

Daily Cumulative Review

Divide. Check your answer. *(Lesson 5-5)*

1. 27)1,080 = 40
2. 51)3,723 = 73
3. 34)1,700 = 50
4. 61)1,830 = 30
5. 78)1,716 = 22
6. 49)2,989 = 61

Complete. *(Lesson 5-4)*

7. 45)437 = 9 R 32
8. 36)165 = 4 R 21
9. 74)535 = 7 R 17

Mixed Review

Write whether each equation is true or false. Explain how you know.

10. (4-10) 21 ÷ 7 = 7 ÷ 21 False; Division is not commutative.
11. (4-10) 59 × 1 = 59 True; One Property
12. (4-10) 0 × 49 = 49 False; Zero Property
13. (3-13) Find the product of \$1.24 and 26.3. Round to the nearest cent. \$32.61
14. (4-3) Estimate the quotient of 391 ÷ 9. About 40
15. (4-15) The tag shows that the price has been lowered twice. What was the original price? \$24

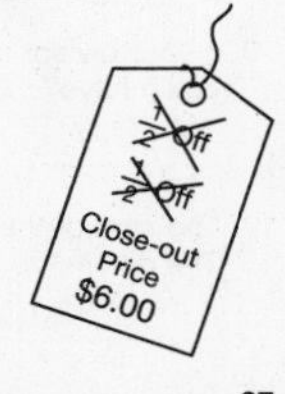

Name ______________________

Daily Review 5-7

Daily Cumulative Review

Divide and check. Explain what calculation method you used and why. *(Lesson 5-6)*

1. 60)360 = 6
2. 24)366 = 15 R6
3. 25)325 = 13
4. 20)4,400 = 220
5. 17)388 = 22 R14
6. 35)35,000 = 1,000

Estimate. Use your number sense to choose the best answer for Exercises 7 and 8. *(Lesson 5-5)*

7. 9,377 ÷ 50 is B
   A. more than 200 B. less than 200 C. exactly 200
8. 4,287 ÷ 60 is C
   A. less than 70 B. more than 80 C. between 70 and 80

Mixed Review

9. (2-7) Write four and fifty hundredths in decimal form. 4.50
10. (3-9) Estimate the quotient of 46.3 and 5.03. Explain what you did. 9; 45 ÷ 5
11. (4-11) Write the answer to the nearest cent. \$6.58 ÷ 3 = \$2.19
12. (4-5) When dividing a 4-digit number by a 2-digit number, for what divisors can you get a remainder of 24? Explain. 25–99; The remainder must be less than the divisor.

Name ______________________ **Daily Review 5-8**

Daily Cumulative Review

Divide and check. *(Lesson 5-7)*

1. $20\overline{)12{,}070}$ 603 R10
2. $40\overline{)4{,}200}$ 105
3. $33\overline{)35{,}310}$ 1,070
4. $11\overline{)2{,}222}$ 202
5. $51\overline{)15{,}555}$ 305
6. $27\overline{)27{,}164}$ 1,006 R2

Divide and check. Tell what calculation method you used and why. *(Lesson 5-6)*
Calculation methods will vary.

7. $30\overline{)6{,}352}$ 211 R22
8. $40\overline{)32{,}000}$ 8,000
9. $60\overline{)42{,}600}$ 710

Mixed Review

Complete.

10. (4-4) $4\overline{)\$12.36}$ $3.09
11. (3-15) 1.7×0.068 = 0.1156
12. (2-18) $\$20.00 - \$11.76$ = $8.24

13. (4-13) What are the factors of 54? 1, 2, 3, 6, 9, 18, 27, 54

Write whether each number is prime or composite.

14. (4-14) 13 prime
15. (4-14) 17 prime
16. (4-14) 21 composite

17. (3-11) Kiwi cost 24¢ each. Oranges cost 3 for $1.00. How much would 4 kiwi and 6 oranges cost? $2.96

Name ______________________ **Daily Review 5-9**

Daily Cumulative Review

Replace the variable with the given number and do the computation. *(Lesson 5-8)*

1. There are 4 lightbulbs in a package. How many lightbulbs are in *n* packages?
   - a. For $n = 3$
     $4 \times n = 4 \times$ 3
     = 12 lightbulbs
   - b. For $n = 8$
     $4 \times n = 4 \times$ 8
     = 32 lightbulbs

2. Mrs. Knox bought a 12-foot board. If she cuts a section *n* feet long, how much of the board does she have left?
   - a. For $n = 3$
     $12 - n = 12 -$ 3
     = 9 feet
   - b. For $n = 8$
     $12 - n = 12 -$ 8
     = 4 feet

Divide and check. *(Lesson 5-7)*

3. $3{,}355 \div 11 =$ 305
4. $12{,}060 \div 60 =$ 201
5. $48{,}073 \div 12 =$ 4,006 R1
6. $83{,}204 \div 80 =$ 1,040 R4

Mixed Review

7. (3-11) A baker can make 3 cakes from a 5-pound sack of flour. How many pounds of flour would be needed for 9 cakes?
   15 pounds

8. (3-4) Use the distributive property to find 44×5.
   $(40 \times 5) + (4 \times 5) = 200 + 20 = 220$

9. (3-8) 100 suckers cost $0.06 each. How much do they cost all together?
   $6

Name ______________________ **Daily Review 5-10**

Daily Cumulative Review

Use any strategy to solve the problem. *(Lesson 5-9)*

1. You are designing an office building with 4 stories. There will be 3 offices on each side with 2 offices in the front and back of each story. Each outside wall of each office has a window.

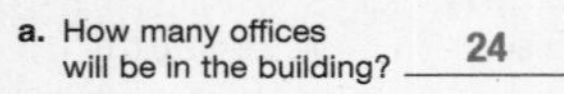

   - a. How many offices will be in the building? 24

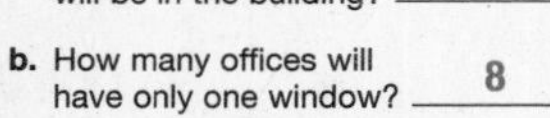

   - b. How many offices will have only one window? 8

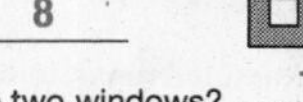

   - c. How many offices will have two windows? 16

Evaluate the expression for $n = 3$ and $n = 7$. *(Lesson 5-8)*

2. $n - 2$ 1 5
3. $42 \div n$ 14 6
4. $n + 8$ 11 15
5. $n \times 6$ 18 42

Mixed Review

6. (5-5) Divide 585 by 26. 22 R13
7. (3-13) Find the product of 4.05 and 36.02. 145.8810

Find the length of the side of each square.

8. (4-12)

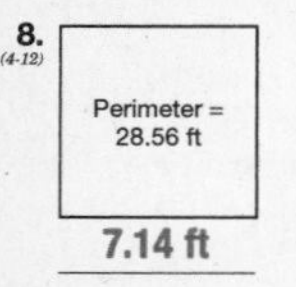

Perimeter = 28.56 ft
7.14 ft

9. (4-12) Perimeter = 6.124 yd
1.531 yd

10. (4-8) How many tables are needed for 1,208 people if each table seats 4? 302 tables

Name ______________________ **Daily Review 5-11**

Daily Cumulative Review

Estimate to decide whether each quotient in Problems 1–3 is more or less than $1.00. *(Lesson 5-10)*

1. $6\overline{)\$7.23}$ More
2. $18\overline{)\$16.98}$ Less
3. $9\overline{)\$9.36}$ More

Use any strategy to solve each problem. *(Lesson 5-9)*

4. Leslie is building a square corral for her horse. Each side of the corral needs 8 fence posts. How many posts will she need?
   28

5. Each apartment in a 5-floor apartment building needs 900 square feet of new carpet. If there are 4 apartments on each floor, how much carpet is needed?
   18,000 square feet

Mixed Review

6. (4-7) The divisor is 7 and the dividend is 878. Divide. 125 R3

7. (4-10) If you divide a number by 9 and get zero, what is the number? Explain how you know.
   0; Zero Property

8. (3-10) Circle each multiplication sentence whose product is a whole number.
   (21.2 × 5) (6 × 9.5) 7.2 × 7 (16.5 × 4)

9. (5-5) If your divisor is 29, what is the greatest possible remainder you could have?
   28

10. (3-16) The sum of the ages of Carla and her younger brother, Daniel, is 23. The difference in their ages is 5. How old are they?
    Carla 14, Daniel 9

Name ______________________

Daily Review 5-12

Daily Cumulative Review

Use the information given to answer the questions. *(Lesson 5-11)*

Science Museum
Admission
Children: \$4 Adults: \$5
Senior Citizens: \$4
Hours: 9:30 A.M.–6:00 P.M.

Show Times
Laser Light: 10:00, 12:00, 2:00, 4:00 (1 hour show)
Electricity: Every half hour starting at 9:30 (20 minute show)
Holograms: 11:00, 1:00, 3:00 (1 hour show)

1. Blythe, Baxter, their mother, and grandmother visit the science Museum. What is the cost of admission for the family? \$17

2. If it takes $1\frac{1}{2}$ hours to drive to the museum and they need to be back home by 3:00, plan a schedule so that they could see each show, visit the nature exhibit, and eat a picnic lunch. Possible answer:

Time	Activity	Time	Activity
8:00	Leave Home	11:00	Hologram Show
9:30	Arrive at museum	12:00	Picnic lunch
9:30	Electricity Show	12:30	Nature Exhibit
10:00	Laser Light Show	1:30	Leave museum
		3:00	Arrive at home

Divide and check. *(Lesson 5-10)*

3. $19\overline{)\$80.75}$ = \$4.25

4. $15\overline{)\$9.00}$ = \$0.60

5. $4\overline{)\$9.88}$ = \$2.47

Mixed Review

6. (5-3) Estimate 5,397 ÷ 52. Use compatible numbers. About 100

7. (3-6) What is the LCM for 5, 15, and 25? 75

8. (3-9) Chloe wants to buy 21 ornaments for 79¢ each. Is \$15 enough? Explain. No; 20 × \$0.80 = \$16

Name ______________________

Daily Review 6-1

Daily Cumulative Review

Complete the table. *(Lesson 5-12)*

	÷	10	100	1000
1.	3,265.4	326.54	32.654	3.2654
2.	377.1	37.71	3.771	0.3771
3.	982.56	98.256	9.8256	0.98256
4.	62.43	6.243	0.6243	0.06243
5.	7,400.5	740.05	74.005	7.4005

Use the information to answer the questions. *(Lesson 5-11)*

6. Mr. Burke plans to take his two children to dinner and a play. The play starts at 7:00 P.M. It takes 35 minutes to drive from home to the restaurant and then 25 minutes to the theater. He anticipates that they will need $1\frac{1}{2}$ hours to order, be served, and eat. He wants to be 15 minutes early to buy tickets for the play.

a. How much time will they spend driving? 1 hour

b. How much total time will they need for driving, eating, and buying tickets? 2 hours 45 minutes

c. What time do they need to leave home? 4:15 P.M.

Mixed Review

7. (4-14) Write the missing factors. 1, 2, 4, 8, 16, 32.

8. (4-13) Is 3 a factor of 651? Explain how you know.
Yes; The digits add up to 12, which is divisible by 3.

9. (5-3) Which quotient is greater, 5,732 ÷ 21 or 5,732 ÷ 23? 5,732 ÷ 21

10. (3-14) How can you use estimation to know that the product of 6.5 and 3.89 is more than 18? A low estimate is 18.

Name ______________________

Daily Review 6-2

Daily Cumulative Review

Write the name for each. *(Lesson 6-1)*

1. $\overleftrightarrow{ED}$ or $\overleftrightarrow{DE}$

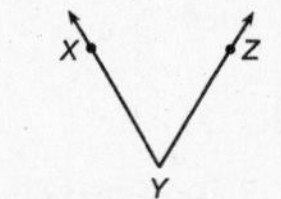

2. ∠XYZ or ∠ZYX or ∠Y

3. $\overrightarrow{BA}$

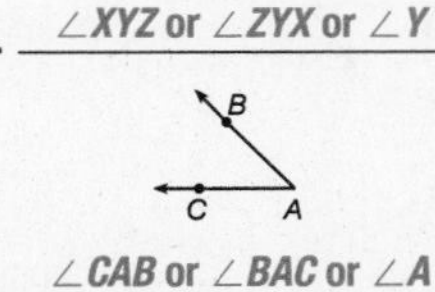

4. ∠CAB or ∠BAC or ∠A

Find each quotient. Use mental math. *(Lesson 5-12)*

5. 5.73 ÷ 10 = 0.573

6. 4.02 ÷ 100 = 0.0402

7. 42.1 ÷ 10 = 4.21

8. 5 ÷ 1,000 = 0.005

9. 759.05 ÷ 100 = 7.5905

10. 28.6 ÷ 1,000 = 0.0286

Mixed Review

Use a calculator to divide. Write each answer to the nearest cent.

11. (4-11) \$6.14 ÷ 3 = \$2.05

12. (4-11) \$76.31 ÷ 8 = \$9.54

13. (4-6) A test tube racks hold 5 tubes each. How many racks are needed to hold 28 test tubes? 6

14. (3-12) Write a number sentence that describes the shaded areas of the grid.
Possible answer: 0.5 of 0.2 = 0.10

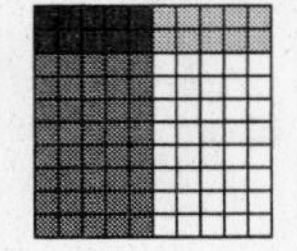

Name ______________________

Daily Review 6-3

Daily Cumulative Review

Classify each angle as acute, right, obtuse, or straight. Extend the sides of each angle and measure it with a protractor. *(Lesson 6-2)*

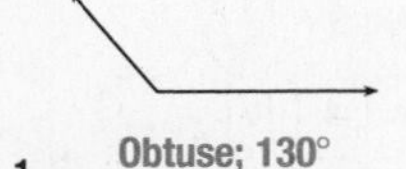

1. Obtuse; 130°

2. Right; 90°

3. Straight; 180°

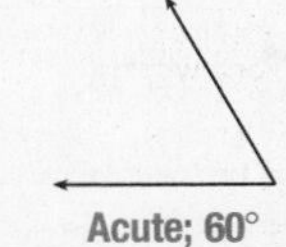

4. Acute; 60°

Name each in the figure at the right. *(Lesson 6-1)*

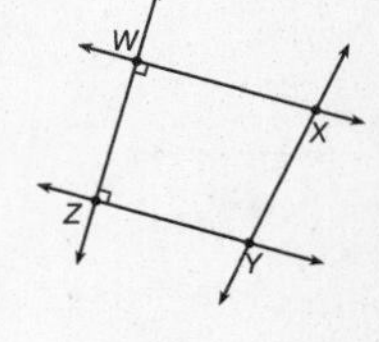

5. Perpendicular lines
$\overleftrightarrow{WZ}$ and $\overleftrightarrow{WX}$ $\overleftrightarrow{WZ}$ and $\overleftrightarrow{ZY}$

6. Parallel lines
$\overleftrightarrow{WX}$ and $\overleftrightarrow{ZY}$

Mixed Review

Multiply or divide.

7. (4-4) $5\overline{)\$7.95}$ = \$1.59

8. (4-8) $9\overline{)6{,}310}$ = 701 R1

9. (3-5) 705 × 130 = 91,650

Name ______________________

Daily Review 6-4

Daily Cumulative Review

Classify each triangle as equilateral, isosceles, or scalene. *(Lesson 6-3)*

1. Scalene
2. Isosceles
3. Equilateral

Choose the best estimate of each angle's measure. Then use a protractor to check your estimate. *(Lesson 6-2)*

4. B — A. 20° B. 60° C. 100°
5. A — A. 90° B. 120° C. 160°
6. C — A. 45° B. 90° C. 135°

Mixed Review

7. You know that 159 ÷ 4 is about 40. Find estimates for 1,590 ÷ 4 and 15,900 ÷ 4. 400, 4,000 (4-3)

Multiply or divide.

8. (5-7) $69\overline{)715}$ — 10 R 25
9. (4-12) $8\overline{)50.56}$ — 6.32
10. (3-13) 4.4×0.6 = 2.64
11. (3-5) 679×200 = 135,800

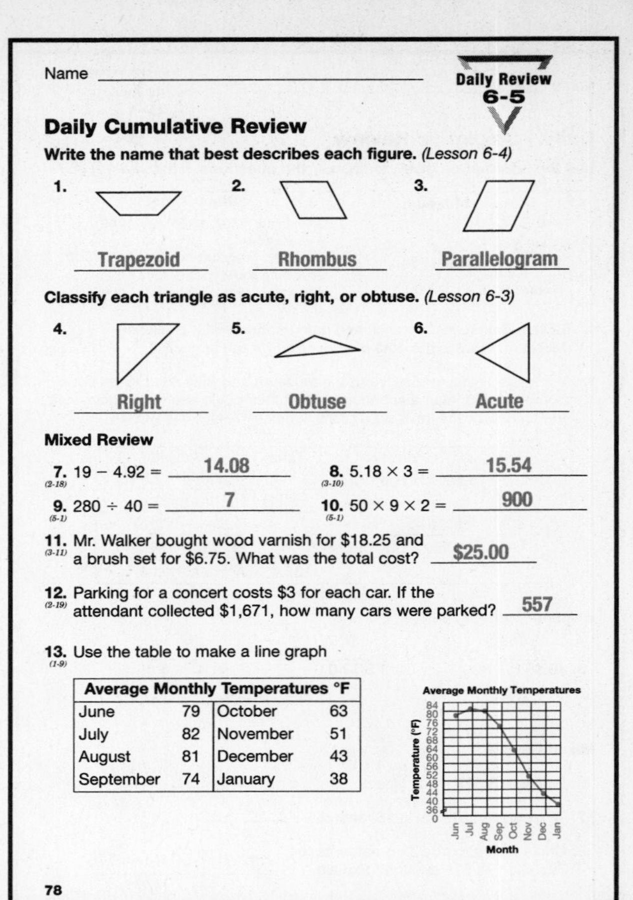

Name ______________________

Daily Review 6-5

Daily Cumulative Review

Write the name that best describes each figure. *(Lesson 6-4)*

1. Trapezoid
2. Rhombus
3. Parallelogram

Classify each triangle as acute, right, or obtuse. *(Lesson 6-3)*

4. Right
5. Obtuse
6. Acute

Mixed Review

7. (2-18) 19 − 4.92 = 14.08
8. (3-10) 5.18 × 3 = 15.54
9. (5-1) 280 ÷ 40 = 7
10. (5-1) 50 × 9 × 2 = 900
11. (3-11) Mr. Walker bought wood varnish for $18.25 and a brush set for $6.75. What was the total cost? $25.00
12. (2-19) Parking for a concert costs $3 for each car. If the attendant collected $1,671, how many cars were parked? 557
13. (1-9) Use the table to make a line graph

Average Monthly Temperatures °F			
June	79	October	63
July	82	November	51
August	81	December	43
September	74	January	38

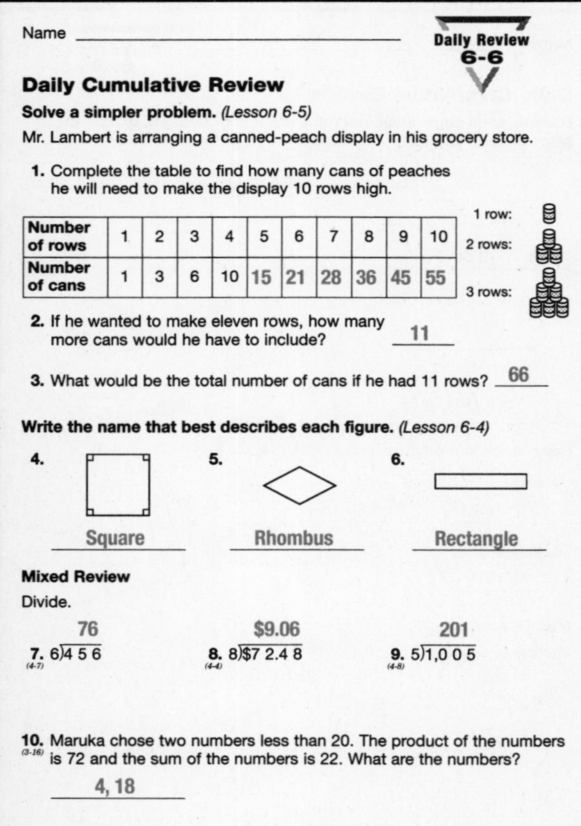

Name ______________________

Daily Review 6-6

Daily Cumulative Review

Solve a simpler problem. *(Lesson 6-5)*

Mr. Lambert is arranging a canned-peach display in his grocery store.

1. Complete the table to find how many cans of peaches he will need to make the display 10 rows high.

Number of rows	1	2	3	4	5	6	7	8	9	10
Number of cans	1	3	6	10	15	21	28	36	45	55

2. If he wanted to make eleven rows, how many more cans would he have to include? 11
3. What would be the total number of cans if he had 11 rows? 66

Write the name that best describes each figure. *(Lesson 6-4)*

4. Square
5. Rhombus
6. Rectangle

Mixed Review

Divide.

7. (4-7) $6\overline{)456}$ — 76
8. (4-4) $8\overline{)\$72.48}$ — $9.06
9. (4-8) $5\overline{)1{,}005}$ — 201
10. (3-16) Maruka chose two numbers less than 20. The product of the numbers is 72 and the sum of the numbers is 22. What are the numbers? 4, 18

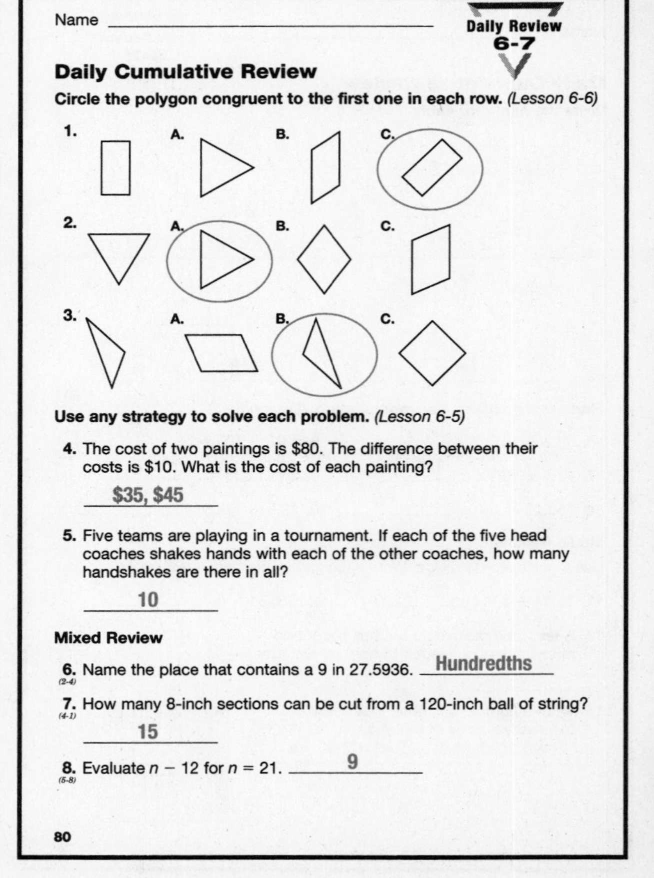

Name ______________________

Daily Review 6-7

Daily Cumulative Review

Circle the polygon congruent to the first one in each row. *(Lesson 6-6)*

1. A. B. C. (C circled)
2. A. B. C. (A circled)
3. A. B. C. (B circled)

Use any strategy to solve each problem. *(Lesson 6-5)*

4. The cost of two paintings is $80. The difference between their costs is $10. What is the cost of each painting? $35, $45
5. Five teams are playing in a tournament. If each of the five head coaches shakes hands with each of the other coaches, how many handshakes are there in all? 10

Mixed Review

6. (2-4) Name the place that contains a 9 in 27.5936. Hundredths
7. (4-1) How many 8-inch sections can be cut from a 120-inch ball of string? 15
8. (5-8) Evaluate $n - 12$ for $n = 21$. 9

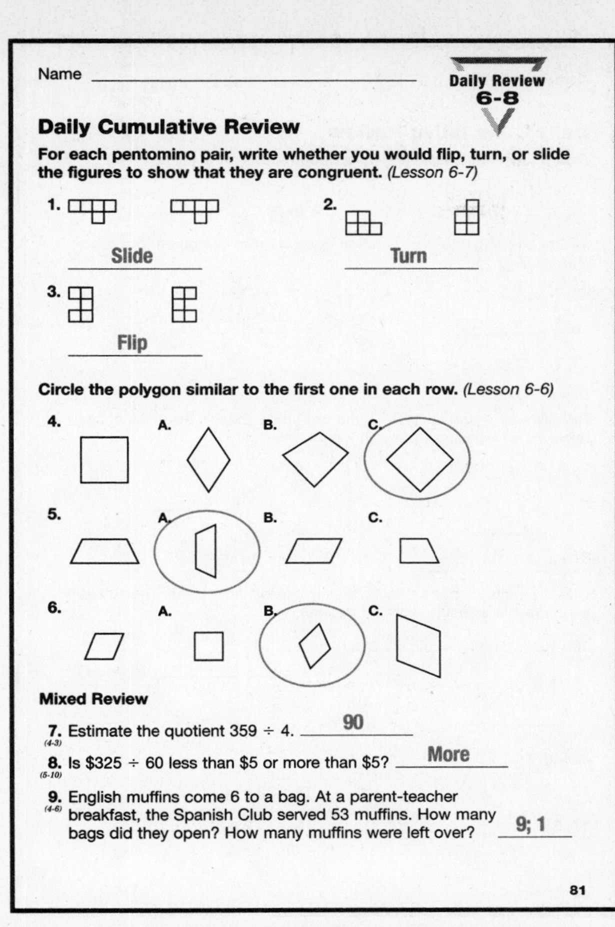

Name ______________________

Daily Review 6-8

Daily Cumulative Review

For each pentomino pair, write whether you would flip, turn, or slide the figures to show that they are congruent. *(Lesson 6-7)*

1. Slide
2. Turn
3. Flip

Circle the polygon similar to the first one in each row. *(Lesson 6-6)*

4. A. B. C.
5. A. B. C.
6. A. B. C.

Mixed Review

7. Estimate the quotient 359 ÷ 4. 90
(4-3)
8. Is $325 ÷ 60 less than $5 or more than $5? More
(5-10)
9. English muffins come 6 to a bag. At a parent-teacher breakfast, the Spanish Club served 53 muffins. How many bags did they open? How many muffins were left over? 9; 1
(4-6)

81

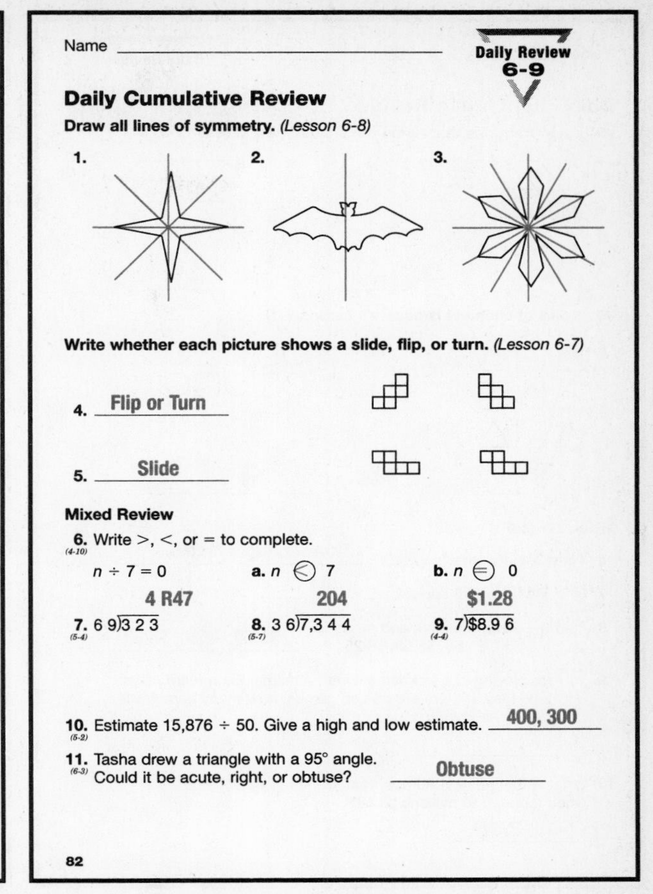

Name ______________________

Daily Review 6-9

Daily Cumulative Review

Draw all lines of symmetry. *(Lesson 6-8)*

1. 2. 3.

Write whether each picture shows a slide, flip, or turn. *(Lesson 6-7)*

4. Flip or Turn
5. Slide

Mixed Review

6. Write >, <, or = to complete.
(4-10)
$n \div 7 = 0$ a. n < 7 b. n = 0

7. $6\overline{)9\,3\,2\,3}$ 4 R47
(5-4)
8. $3\,6\overline{)7{,}3\,4\,4}$ 204
(5-7)
9. $7\overline{)\$8.9\,6}$ $1.28
(4-4)

10. Estimate 15,876 ÷ 50. Give a high and low estimate. 400, 300
(5-2)
11. Tasha drew a triangle with a 95° angle. Could it be acute, right, or obtuse? Obtuse
(6-3)

82

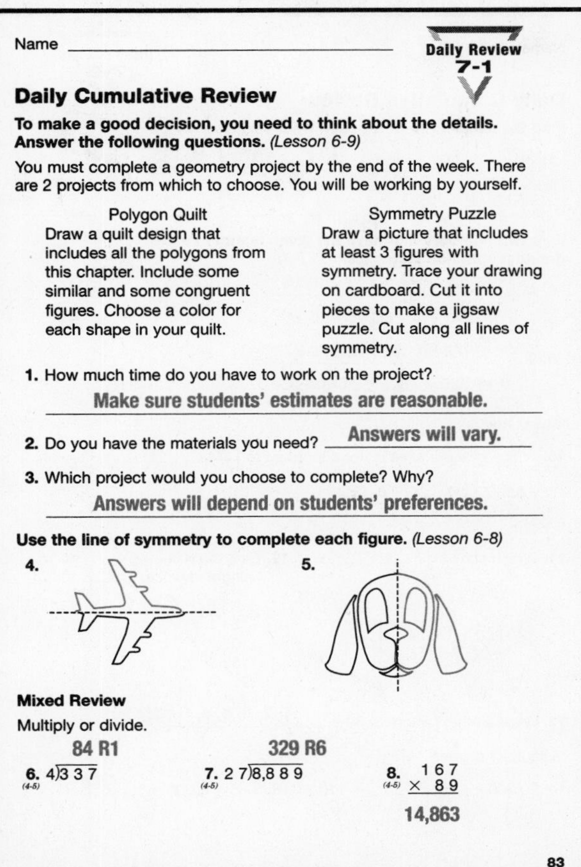

Name ______________________

Daily Review 7-1

Daily Cumulative Review

To make a good decision, you need to think about the details. Answer the following questions. *(Lesson 6-9)*

You must complete a geometry project by the end of the week. There are 2 projects from which to choose. You will be working by yourself.

Polygon Quilt	Symmetry Puzzle
Draw a quilt design that includes all the polygons from this chapter. Include some similar and some congruent figures. Choose a color for each shape in your quilt.	Draw a picture that includes at least 3 figures with symmetry. Trace your drawing on cardboard. Cut it into pieces to make a jigsaw puzzle. Cut along all lines of symmetry.

1. How much time do you have to work on the project? Make sure students' estimates are reasonable.
2. Do you have the materials you need? Answers will vary.
3. Which project would you choose to complete? Why? Answers will depend on students' preferences.

Use the line of symmetry to complete each figure. *(Lesson 6-8)*

4. 5.

Mixed Review

Multiply or divide.

6. $4\overline{)3\,3\,7}$ 84 R1
(4-5)
7. $2\,7\overline{)8{,}8\,8\,9}$ 329 R6
(4-5)
8. 167×89 14,863
(4-5)

83

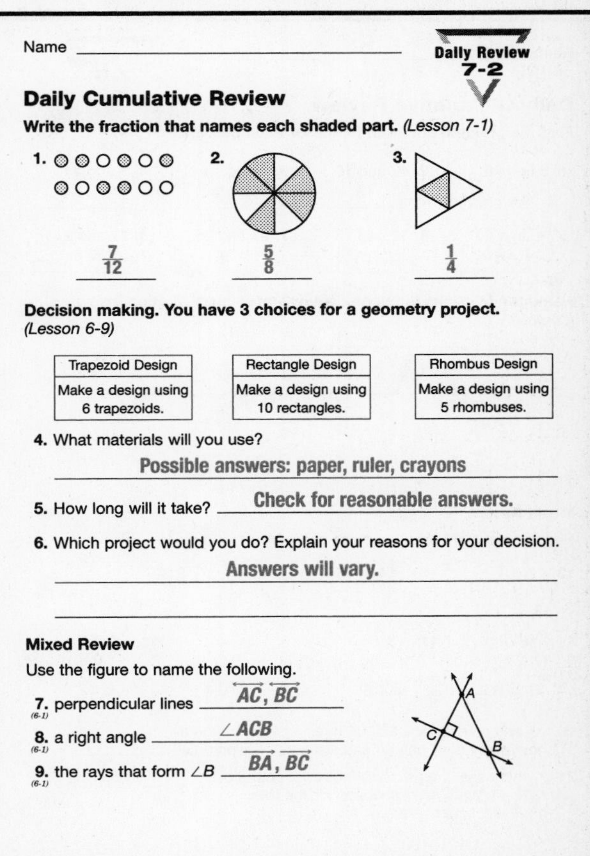

Name ______________________

Daily Review 7-2

Daily Cumulative Review

Write the fraction that names each shaded part. *(Lesson 7-1)*

1. $\frac{7}{12}$
2. $\frac{5}{8}$
3. $\frac{1}{4}$

Decision making. You have 3 choices for a geometry project. *(Lesson 6-9)*

Trapezoid Design	Rectangle Design	Rhombus Design
Make a design using 6 trapezoids.	Make a design using 10 rectangles.	Make a design using 5 rhombuses.

4. What materials will you use? Possible answers: paper, ruler, crayons
5. How long will it take? Check for reasonable answers.
6. Which project would you do? Explain your reasons for your decision. Answers will vary.

Mixed Review

Use the figure to name the following.

7. perpendicular lines $\overleftrightarrow{AC}, \overleftrightarrow{BC}$
(6-1)
8. a right angle $\angle ACB$
(6-1)
9. the rays that form $\angle B$ $\overrightarrow{BA}, \overrightarrow{BC}$
(6-1)

84

Name ____________________

Daily Cumulative Review

Write two fractions that name the shaded part. *(Lesson 7-2)*

1. 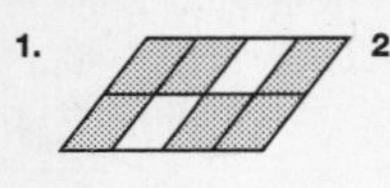 $\frac{6}{8}, \frac{3}{4}$
2. 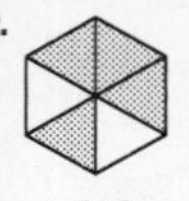 $\frac{4}{6}, \frac{2}{3}$
3. 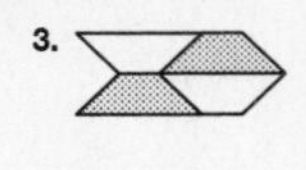 $\frac{2}{4}, \frac{1}{2}$

What part of each set is square? *(Lesson 7-1)*

4.  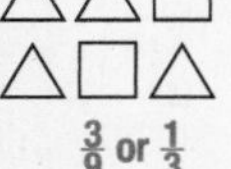 $\frac{3}{9}$ or $\frac{1}{3}$
5. 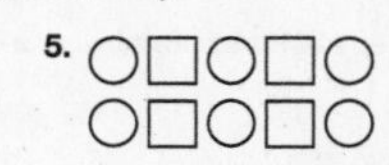 $\frac{4}{10}$ or $\frac{2}{5}$

Mixed Review

6. (2-7) Write 3.4 in words. Three and four tenths
7. (3-6) Find the LCM of 8 and 24. 24
8. (4-9) Find the mean, median, and mode for \$3.25, \$4.50, \$5.50, \$5.50, \$6.25. \$5.00, \$5.50, \$5.50
9. (6-5) You are playing in a tournament with 4 teams. Each team plays until they lose. If there are no tied games, how many games will be played? 3
10. (2-6) What is the greatest number that rounds to 41,000,000 when rounded to millions place? 41,999,999

85

Name ____________________

Daily Cumulative Review

Find equivalent fractions with a denominator of 9. *(Lesson 7-3)*

1. $\frac{3}{27}$ $\frac{1}{9}$
2. $\frac{2}{3}$ $\frac{6}{9}$
3. $\frac{12}{54}$ 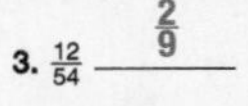 $\frac{2}{9}$
4. $\frac{6}{18}$ 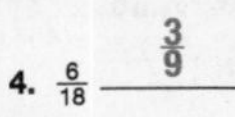 $\frac{3}{9}$

Which shading shows a fraction equivalent to the given fraction. *(Lesson 7-2)*

5. $\frac{1}{4}$ b
6. $\frac{2}{3}$ c
7. $\frac{5}{8}$ a

A.  B.  C. 

Mixed Review

Identify each angle as acute, right, or obtuse. Extend the sides of each angle. Then measure each with a protractor.

8. (6-2) Acute; 75°
9. (6-2)  Obtuse; 140°

Classify each triangle as equilateral, isosceles, or scalene. Then classify each triangle as acute, right, or obtuse.

10. (6-3) 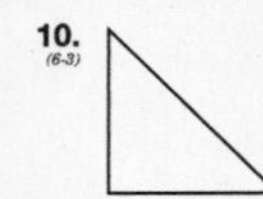 Isosceles, Right
11. (6-3) Scalene, Obtuse

Divide.

12. (4-1) 24 ÷ 3 = 8
13. (4-7) 832 ÷ 4 = 208
14. (4-11) \$37.02 ÷ 6 = \$6.17
15. (4-12) 41.12 ÷ 8 = 5.14

86

Name ____________________

Daily Cumulative Review

Find the greatest common factor for each pair. *(Lesson 7-4)*

1. 6 and 10 — 2
2. 12 and 16 — 4
3. 9 and 15 — 3
4. 8 and 24 — 8
5. 16 and 20 — 4
6. 12 and 18 — 6
7. 27 and 36 — 9
8. 14 and 21 — 7

Name the fractions in the box equivalent to each fraction below. *(Lesson 7-3)*

$\frac{5}{15}$ $\frac{6}{8}$ $\frac{7}{21}$ $\frac{8}{12}$ $\frac{4}{16}$ $\frac{12}{18}$ $\frac{9}{12}$ $\frac{3}{12}$

9. $\frac{2}{3}$ 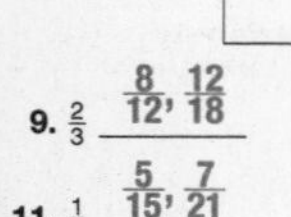 $\frac{8}{12}, \frac{12}{18}$
10. $\frac{1}{4}$ $\frac{4}{16}, \frac{3}{12}$
11. $\frac{1}{3}$ $\frac{5}{15}, \frac{7}{21}$
12. $\frac{3}{4}$ $\frac{6}{8}, \frac{9}{12}$

Mixed Review

Round each number to the place of the underlined digit.

13. (2-12) 12.49 — 12
14. (2-12) 0.051 — 0.1
15. (2-12) 6.097 — 6

Solve.

16. (2-15) 604 + 197 = 801
17. (3-3) 375 × 6 = 2,250
18. (3-13) 2.34 × 0.5 = 1.170
19. (3-16) 9.53 − 0.9 = 8.63

20. (2-1) An anteater can eat 30,000 ants in a day. In about how many days can an anteater eat 1 million ants? 33
21. (5-8) A chef uses 2 cups of olive oil and *n* cups of corn oil. Write an expression for the total number of cups used. $n + 2$

87

Name ____________________

Daily Review
7-6

Daily Cumulative Review

Find the simplest form for each fraction. *(Lesson 7-5)*

1. $\frac{3}{24}$ — $\frac{1}{8}$
2. $\frac{12}{15}$ — $\frac{4}{5}$
3. $\frac{6}{14}$ — $\frac{3}{7}$
4. $\frac{16}{20}$ — $\frac{4}{5}$
5. $\frac{28}{36}$ — $\frac{7}{9}$

Find two numbers that have the given number as the greatest common factor. *(Lesson 7-4)*

6. 4 Possible answer: 12 and 16
7. 8 Possible answer: 16 and 24
8. 9 Possible answer: 18 and 27
9. 12 Possible answer: 24 and 36

Mixed Review

10. (6-7) Which of the figures is not congruent to [figure]? B

A. B. C.

11. (7-1) Which shows $\frac{3}{5}$? A

A. 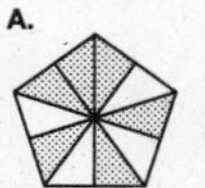 B.

12. (1-7) Give the rule using a variable. $n \div 5$

A	B
5	1
10	2
15	3
20	4

13. (4-13) What are the factors of 30? 1, 2, 3, 5, 6, 10, 15, 30

Multiply or divide.

14. (4-3) 99,000 ÷ 900 = 110
15. (3-8) 0.65 × 1,000 = 650

88

Name ____________________

Daily Review 7-7

Daily Cumulative Review

Compare each pair of fractions. You may use fraction strips or draw pictures. Write >, <, or = to complete. *(Lesson 7-6)*

1. $\frac{3}{5}$ (>) $\frac{3}{7}$ 2. $\frac{1}{8}$ (<) $\frac{1}{7}$ 3. $\frac{2}{6}$ (=) $\frac{3}{9}$ 4. $\frac{5}{9}$ (<) $\frac{7}{9}$

Write whether each fraction is in simplest form. If it is not, find the simpler form. *(Lesson 7-5)*

5. $\frac{3}{8}$ Yes   6. $\frac{9}{12}$ No; $\frac{3}{4}$ 7. $\frac{24}{36}$ No; $\frac{2}{3}$ 8. $\frac{4}{9}$ Yes

Mixed Review

Use the figure to answer questions 9–11.

9. *(6-1)* Name parallel lines. $\overleftrightarrow{AB}$ and $\overleftrightarrow{DE}$

10. *(6-3)* Classify triangle *ADE* as acute, right, or obtuse. Right

11. *(6-6)* Name a triangle congruent to triangle *ABC*. Triangle *DEC*

A B C D E

12. *(4-3)* Estimate the quotient. 297 ÷ 3 100

13. *(5-8)* Complete.

n	7	15	21	27	30	42
$n - 3$	4	12	18	24	27	39

14. *(5-9)* A kennel has for sale 18 cocker spaniels, half that many collies, and two more golden retrievers than collies. How many dogs are for sale? 38

89

Name ____________________

Daily Review 7-8

Daily Cumulative Review

Write >, <, or = to complete. *(Lesson 7-7)*

1. $\frac{3}{7}$ (<) $\frac{7}{8}$ 2. $\frac{5}{6}$ (>) $\frac{3}{4}$ 3. $\frac{3}{12}$ (=) $\frac{6}{24}$

4. $\frac{3}{4}$ (<) $\frac{4}{5}$ 5. $\frac{2}{3}$ (>) $\frac{5}{9}$ 6. $\frac{6}{10}$ (=) $\frac{9}{15}$

Order these fractions from least to greatest. Use fraction strips. *(Lesson 7-6)*

7. $\frac{1}{4}, \frac{1}{3}, \frac{1}{5}$ $\frac{1}{5}$, $\frac{1}{4}$, $\frac{1}{3}$

8. $\frac{7}{10}, \frac{3}{5}, \frac{5}{7}$ $\frac{3}{5}$, $\frac{7}{10}$, $\frac{5}{7}$

Mixed Review

Multiply or divide.

9. *(5-7)* $15\overline{)30{,}600}$ 2,040   10. *(5-7)* $16\overline{)3{,}216}$ 201   11. *(3-13)* 1.005×0.08 = 0.0804

12. *(5-1)* 40,000 ÷ 200 = 200   13. *(5-4)* 84 ÷ 14 = 6

Identify each number as prime or composite.

14. *(4-14)* 11 Prime   15. *(4-14)* 21 Composite   16. *(4-14)* 51 Composite

17. *(5-10)* If you had \$475.50 to give to 15 people, and each person gets the same amount, how much would each person get? \$31.70

18. *(6-8)* Draw a polygon that has exactly one line of symmetry.

Possible answer:

90

Name ____________________

Daily Review 7-9

Daily Cumulative Review

Make a table or use another strategy to solve each problem. *(Lesson 7-8)*

1. A brownie mix uses 2 eggs for 12 brownies. How many eggs are needed to make 48 brownies? 8

2. After running about 3 minutes, you have used about 20 calories. How many calories have you used after running for 9 minutes? About 60

3. Jennifer earns \$4.50 each afternoon babysitting for a neighbor. How much does she earn in 5 afternoons? \$22.50

Write >, <, or = to complete. *(Lesson 7-7)*

4. $\frac{5}{6}$ (>) $\frac{9}{12}$ 5. $\frac{9}{12}$ (=) $\frac{6}{8}$ 6. $\frac{2}{3}$ (<) $\frac{4}{5}$

7. $\frac{3}{15}$ (=) $\frac{4}{20}$ 8. $\frac{3}{8}$ (>) $\frac{3}{10}$ 9. $\frac{5}{9}$ (<) $\frac{2}{3}$

Mixed Review

Divide.

10. *(5-12)* 43.6 ÷ 10 = 4.36   11. *(5-4)* 215 ÷ 18 = 11 R17

12. *(6-2)* An angle's measure is more than 90° and less than 180°. How is it classified? Obtuse

Use a calculator to divide. Write each answer to the nearest cent.

13. *(4-11)* \$14.94 ÷ 7 = \$2.13   14. *(4-11)* \$32.85 ÷ 8 = \$4.11

15. *(2-3)* How many 1,000s make 100,000,000? 100,000

16. *(3-5)* Estimate the product of 42 and 328. Is it closer to 12,000 or 20,000?
12,000; 40 × 300 = 12,000

17. *(7-5)* Circle the fractions that are in simplest form.

($\frac{7}{9}$) $\frac{12}{16}$ $\frac{18}{27}$ ($\frac{13}{16}$) $\frac{2}{20}$ ($\frac{9}{11}$)

91

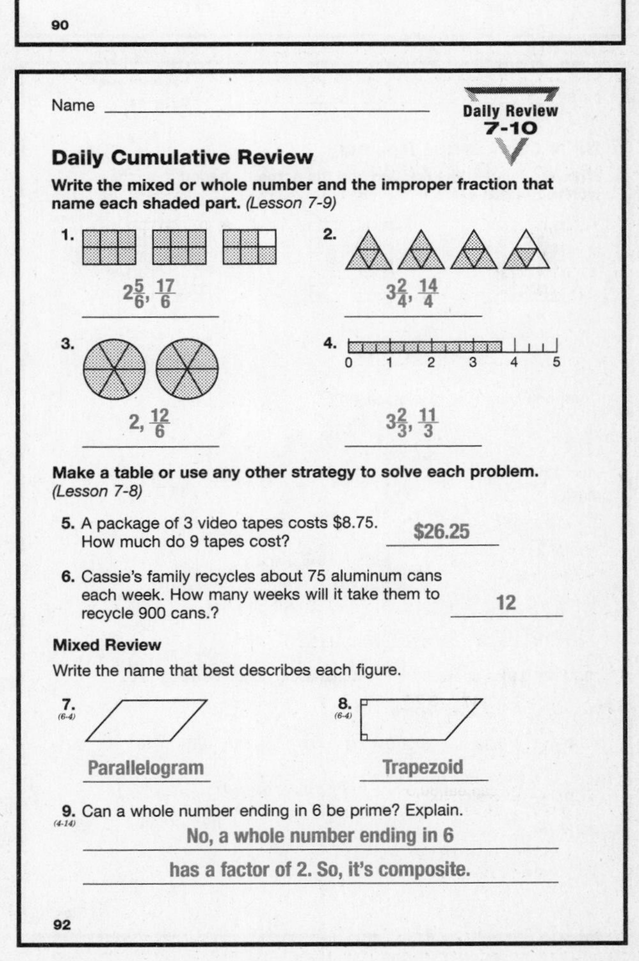

Name ____________________

Daily Review 7-10

Daily Cumulative Review

Write the mixed or whole number and the improper fraction that name each shaded part. *(Lesson 7-9)*

1. $2\frac{5}{6}$, $\frac{17}{6}$ 2. $3\frac{2}{4}$, $\frac{14}{4}$

3. 2, $\frac{12}{6}$ 4. $3\frac{2}{3}$, $\frac{11}{3}$

0 1 2 3 4 5

Make a table or use any other strategy to solve each problem. *(Lesson 7-8)*

5. A package of 3 video tapes costs \$8.75. How much do 9 tapes cost? \$26.25

6. Cassie's family recycles about 75 aluminum cans each week. How many weeks will it take them to recycle 900 cans.? 12

Mixed Review

Write the name that best describes each figure.

7. *(6-4)* Parallelogram   8. *(6-4)* Trapezoid

9. *(4-14)* Can a whole number ending in 6 be prime? Explain.
No, a whole number ending in 6 has a factor of 2. So, it's composite.

92

Name ______________________

Daily Cumulative Review

Write each improper fraction as a mixed number in simplest form or as a whole number. *(Lesson 7-10)*

1. $\frac{23}{4}$ = $5\frac{3}{4}$ 2. $\frac{14}{7}$ = 2 3. $\frac{13}{3}$ = $4\frac{1}{3}$

4. $\frac{16}{5}$ = $3\frac{1}{5}$ 5. $\frac{27}{6}$ = $4\frac{1}{2}$ 6. $\frac{43}{8}$ = $5\frac{3}{8}$

Make a drawing that shows each fraction. *(Lesson 7-9)*

7. $\frac{6}{4}$

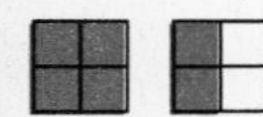

8. $\frac{7}{5}$

9. $\frac{8}{2}$

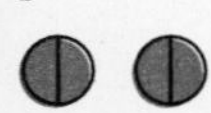

10. $\frac{4}{3}$

Mixed Review

Estimate each quotient. Give a high and low estimate.

11. 4,207 ÷ 50 (5-2) 90, 80 12. 3,729 ÷ 70 (5-2) 60, 50 13. 2,868 ÷ 30 (5-2) 100, 90

14. (4-10) Write whether the equation 3 × 405 = 405 × 3 is true or false. Explain how you knew.

True; Commutative Property

93

Name ______________________

Daily Review
7-12

Daily Cumulative Review

Give a mixed number for the shaded part of each picture. Use > or < to compare each pair of mixed numbers. *(Lesson 7-11)*

1.

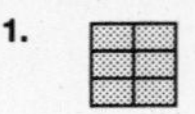

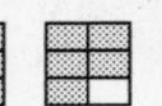

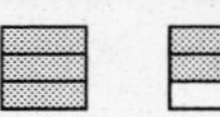

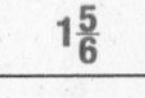

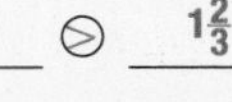

$1\frac{5}{6}$ (>) $1\frac{2}{3}$

2.

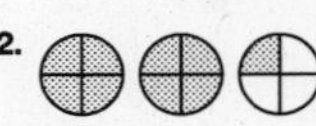

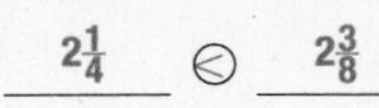

$2\frac{1}{4}$ (<) $2\frac{3}{8}$

Write each number as an improper fraction. *(Lesson 7-10)*

3. $2\frac{1}{6}$ = $\frac{13}{6}$ 4. $3\frac{2}{5}$ = $\frac{17}{5}$ 5. $4\frac{2}{3}$ = $\frac{14}{3}$

6. $1\frac{7}{8}$ = $\frac{15}{8}$ 7. $9\frac{1}{2}$ = $\frac{19}{2}$ 8. $5\frac{3}{7}$ = $\frac{38}{7}$

Mixed Review

9. (5-3) Estimate using compatible numbers.
26,897 ÷ 88 300

10. (4-12) Find the length of the side of a square with perimeter 13.88 inches.
3.47 inches

11. (3-4) Use the distributive property to find 290 × 4.
(200 × 4) + (90 × 4) = 800 + 360 = 1,160

12. (6-8) Draw a triangle that has no lines of symmetry. Check students' drawings

94

Name ______________________

Daily Cumulative Review

Write the hundredths fraction and the percent shaded in each picture. *(Lesson 7-12)*

1.

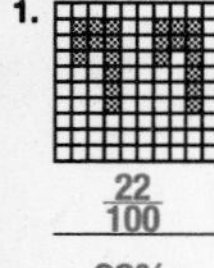

$\frac{22}{100}$
22%

2.

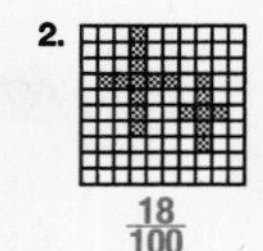

$\frac{18}{100}$
18%

3.

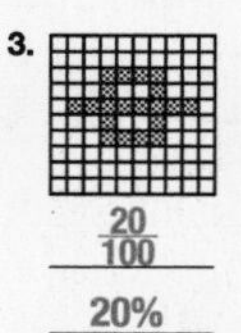

$\frac{20}{100}$
20%

Compare. Use > or <. *(Lesson 7-11)*

4. $3\frac{5}{6}$ (<) $3\frac{6}{7}$ 5. $1\frac{2}{5}$ (>) $1\frac{3}{8}$ 6. $2\frac{7}{9}$ (>) $2\frac{3}{4}$

Mixed Review

Multiply or divide.

7. (4-5) $4\overline{)423}$ 105 R3

8. (3-13) 1.5 × 1.5 = 2.25

9. (3-3) 10^3 = 10 × 10 × 10 = 1,000

10. (2-8) Write 0.9 as an equivalent decimal using hundredths. 0.90

Write >, <, or = to compare.

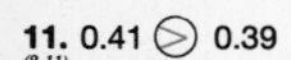

11. (2-11) 0.41 (>) 0.39 12. (2-11) 0.4 (=) 0.40 13. (2-11) 0.75 (>) 0.7

14. (4-14) Use a factor tree to find the prime factors of 70. Possible answer:

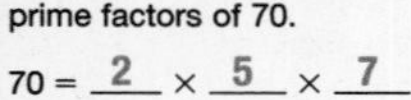

70 = 2 × 5 × 7

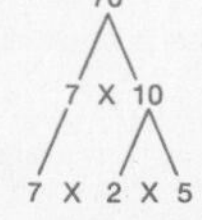

95

Name ______________________

Daily Review
7-14

Daily Cumulative Review

Write a fraction, a decimal, and a percent that names each shaded part. *(Lesson 7-13)*

1.

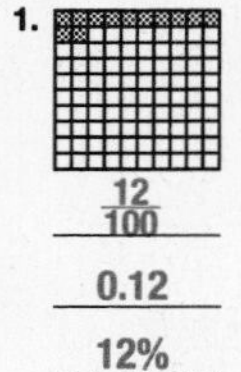

$\frac{12}{100}$
0.12
12%

2.

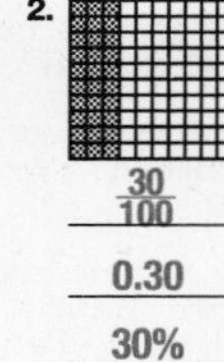

$\frac{30}{100}$
0.30
30%

3.

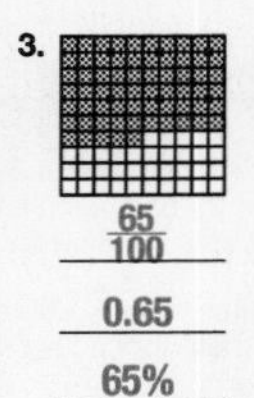

$\frac{65}{100}$
0.65
65%

For each set, decide which does *not* belong. *(Lesson 7-12)*

4. C	A. 33%	B. $\frac{33}{100}$	C. $\frac{3}{10}$	D. 33 out of 100
5. A	A. $\frac{4}{100}$	B. 40%	C. $\frac{4}{10}$	D. 40 out of 100
6. D	A. $\frac{100}{100}$	B. 100%	C. 1	D. 1 out of 100

Mixed Review

7. (4-3) Estimate the quotient of 997 ÷ 2. 500

8. (3-14) Estimate high and low and then find the product of 7.4 and 2.6.
Estimate: 24, 14 Product: 19.24

Divide.

9. (4-8) $5\overline{)3,604}$ 720 R4 10. (4-12) $8\overline{)3.288}$ 0.411 11. (5-4) $36\overline{)415}$ 11 R19

96

Name ______________________

Daily Cumulative Review

Compare survey results. *(Lesson 7-14)*

Phillipe read a survey in the newspaper about readers' favorite sports. He decided to survey 10 students in his class to see if the results would be the same. His results are shown in the table.

Favorite Sports of Readers		Votes for Favorite Sports of Students	
Basketball	35%	Basketball	4
Soccer	10%	Soccer	1
Football	40%	Football	2
Ice Skating	5%	Ice Skating	1
Baseball	10%	Baseball	2

Write fractions, decimals, and percents to describe Phillipe's survey results.

Sport	Fraction	Decimal	Percent
1. Basketball	$\frac{4}{10} = \frac{2}{5}$	0.4	40%
2. Soccer	$\frac{1}{10}$	0.1	10%
3. Football	$\frac{2}{10} = \frac{1}{5}$	0.2	20%
4. Ice skating	$\frac{1}{10}$	0.1	10%
5. Baseball	$\frac{2}{10} = \frac{1}{5}$	0.2	20%

6. Which sport has the biggest difference between the two surveys? Football

Write each as a percent. *(Lesson 7-13)*

7. 15 out of 100 — 15%
8. 0.35 — 35%
9. $\frac{11}{100}$ — 11%

Mixed Review

Find each product or quotient.

10. $427 \div 1000 =$ 0.427 *(5-12)*
11. $6 \times 0.004 =$ 0.024 *(3-15)*
12. $\$370.40 \div 20 =$ \$18.52 *(5-10)*
13. $\$9.18 \times 14 =$ \$128.52 *(3-13)*

97

Name ______________________

Daily Review
8-2

Daily Cumulative Review

Find each sum or difference. Simplify. *(Lesson 8-1)*

1. $\frac{2}{9} + \frac{4}{9}$ — $\frac{6}{9} = \frac{2}{3}$
2. $\frac{3}{10} + \frac{7}{10}$ — $\frac{10}{10} = 1$
3. $\frac{7}{8} + \frac{3}{8}$ — $\frac{10}{8} = 1\frac{1}{4}$
4. $\frac{1}{7} + \frac{3}{7}$ — $\frac{4}{7}$
5. $\frac{4}{5} - \frac{3}{5}$ — $\frac{1}{5}$
6. $\frac{5}{6} - \frac{1}{6}$ — $\frac{4}{6} = \frac{2}{3}$
7. $\frac{3}{4} - \frac{1}{4}$ — $\frac{2}{4} = \frac{1}{2}$
8. $\frac{8}{9} - \frac{5}{9}$ — $\frac{3}{9} = \frac{1}{3}$

Compare the survey results. *(Lesson 7-14)*

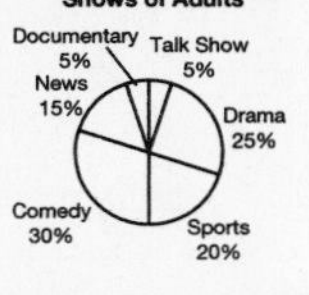

Favorite Evening Television Shows of 50 Students			
News	0	Talk show	0
Documentary	5	Drama	15
Comedy	20	Sports	10

9. How will you compare the results of the adults' survey with the results from the fifth graders. Write the results of the student survey as percents.

10. What percent of students prefer comedy shows? 40%

11. Which type of show had the same result in both surveys? Sports

Mixed Review

12. Write whether $\frac{3}{12}$ and $\frac{1}{4}$ are equivalent. Explain how you decided. *(7-3)* Yes; $3 \div 3 = 1$ and $12 \div 3 = 4$

13. What is the LCM of 4, 6, and 8? *(3-6)* 24

98

Name ______________________

Daily Cumulative Review

Find each sum. You may use fraction strips or draw pictures to help. *(Lesson 8-2)*

1. $\frac{1}{2} + \frac{1}{6}$ — $\frac{4}{6} = \frac{2}{3}$
2. $\frac{2}{5} + \frac{1}{10}$ — $\frac{5}{10} = \frac{1}{2}$
3. $\frac{1}{8} + \frac{1}{2}$ — $\frac{5}{8}$
4. $\frac{2}{3} + \frac{1}{2} + \frac{5}{6}$ — $\frac{12}{6} = 2$

Find each sum or difference. Simplify. *(Lesson 8-1)*

5. $\frac{2}{5} + \frac{3}{5}$ — $\frac{5}{5} = 1$
6. $\frac{5}{8} + \frac{7}{8}$ — $\frac{12}{8} = 1\frac{1}{2}$
7. $\frac{3}{10} + \frac{1}{10}$ — $\frac{4}{10} = \frac{2}{5}$
8. $\frac{11}{12} - \frac{3}{12}$ — $\frac{8}{12} = \frac{2}{3}$

Mixed Review

Write >, <, or = to complete.

9. $\frac{2}{9}$ ○ $\frac{3}{11}$ *(7-7)*
10. $\frac{7}{16}$ ○ $\frac{3}{8}$ *(7-7)*
11. $\frac{9}{16}$ ○ $\frac{3}{4}$ *(7-7)*

Complete.

12. $3 = \frac{12}{4}$ *(7-10)*
13. $7\frac{2}{3} = \frac{23}{3}$ *(7-10)*
14. $10^{5} = 100{,}000$ *(2-3)*

15. Estimate the fraction of the figure that is shaded. *(7-1)* B

A. $\frac{1}{2}$ B. $\frac{1}{3}$ C. $\frac{1}{4}$

16. Jadice jogs every morning to the gym. How many different routes can she take to the gym without backtracking? *(6-5)* 10

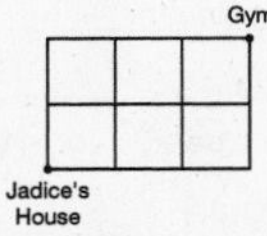

17. Todd is shorter than Mario but taller than Doug. Sam is the tallest of the four. Who is the shortest? *(2-13)* Doug

99

Name ______________________

Daily Cumulative Review

Find the LCD for each pair of fractions. *(Lesson 8-3)*

1. $\frac{11}{12}$ and $\frac{1}{5}$ — 60
2. $\frac{3}{10}$ and $\frac{1}{4}$ — 20
3. $\frac{3}{8}$ and $\frac{5}{6}$ — 24
4. $\frac{3}{12}$ and $\frac{1}{8}$ — 24

Find each sum. You may use fraction strips or draw pictures to help. *(Lesson 8-2)*

5. $\frac{3}{10} + \frac{1}{5}$ — $\frac{5}{10} = \frac{1}{2}$
6. $\frac{5}{6} + \frac{1}{9}$ — $\frac{17}{18}$
7. $\frac{5}{12} + \frac{3}{4} + \frac{1}{6}$ — $\frac{16}{12} = 1\frac{1}{3}$
8. $\frac{3}{10} + \frac{1}{4} + \frac{1}{6}$ — $\frac{43}{60}$

Mixed Review

Solve.

9. $1.44 \div 4 =$ 0.36 *(4-12)*
10. $643 \div 40 =$ 16 R3 *(5-4)*
11. $0.5 \times 9.1 =$ 4.55 *(3-13)*
12. $387 \times 24 =$ 9,288 *(3-9)*
13. 250×0.028 7 *(3-10)*
14. $1{,}003 - 345 =$ 658 *(2-15)*
15. $6.003 - 4.39 =$ 1.613 *(2-18)*
16. $9.7 - 6.8 =$ 2.9 *(2-16)*

17. Write three and twenty-eight thousandths in decimal form. *(2-5)* 3.028

18. Estimate the quotient $709 \div 8$. *(4-3)* 90

19. Javier was paid \$22.50 for working on Monday. He worked from 8 A.M. to 2 P.M. How much did he earn per hour? *(4-12)* \$3.75

20. Which of the figures is congruent to ? *(6-7)* C

A. 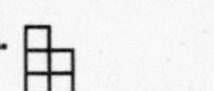
B. 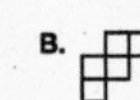
C. 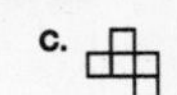
D. 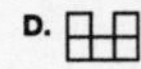

100

Name ______________________

Daily Review 8-5

Daily Cumulative Review

Find each sum. Simplify. *(Lesson 8-4)*

1. $\frac{1}{5} + \frac{1}{4}$ $\frac{9}{20}$
2. $\frac{3}{7} + \frac{2}{3}$ $\frac{23}{21} = 1\frac{2}{21}$
3. $\frac{5}{6} + \frac{2}{5}$ $\frac{37}{30} = 1\frac{7}{30}$
4. $\frac{2}{3} + \frac{4}{9}$ $\frac{10}{9} = 1\frac{1}{9}$

Find the LCD for each pair of fractions. *(Lesson 8-3)*

5. $\frac{7}{8}$ and $\frac{3}{4}$ 8
6. $\frac{11}{12}$ and $\frac{3}{8}$ 24
7. $\frac{3}{5}$ and $\frac{1}{4}$ 20
8. $\frac{5}{6}$ and $\frac{4}{5}$ 30
9. $\frac{1}{6}$ and $\frac{5}{8}$ 24
10. $\frac{5}{6}$ and $\frac{1}{2}$ 6
11. $\frac{1}{3}$ and $\frac{1}{5}$ 15
12. $\frac{1}{6}$ and $\frac{7}{9}$ 18

Mixed Review

Find the simplest form for each fraction.

13. *(7-5)* $\frac{6}{48} =$ $\frac{1}{8}$
14. *(7-5)* $\frac{6}{16} =$ $\frac{3}{8}$
15. *(7-5)* $\frac{8}{12} =$ $\frac{2}{3}$
16. $\frac{20}{35} =$ $\frac{4}{7}$

Write the name that best describes each figure.

17. *(6-4)*

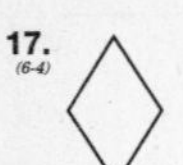

Rhombus

18. *(6-4)*

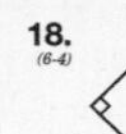

Square

19. *(6-4)*

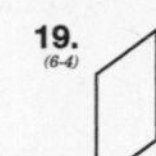

Parallelogram

20. *(6-4)*

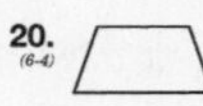

Trapezoid

Use the figures to answer questions **21** and **22**.

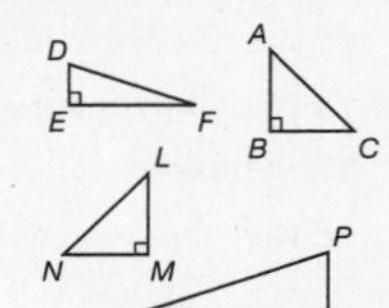

21. *(6-6)* Which triangle is congruent to triangle *ABC*? Triangle *LMN*

22. *(6-6)* Which triangle is similar to triangle *DEF*? Triangle *PQR*

Name ______________________

Daily Review 8-6

Daily Cumulative Review

Find each difference. You may use fraction strips or draw pictures to help. *(Lesson 8-5)*

1. $\frac{7}{8} - \frac{3}{4}$ $\frac{1}{8}$
2. $\frac{3}{5} - \frac{1}{2}$ $\frac{1}{10}$
3. $\frac{1}{3} - \frac{1}{5}$ $\frac{2}{15}$

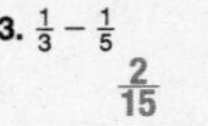

4. $\frac{1}{4} - \frac{1}{6}$ $\frac{1}{12}$

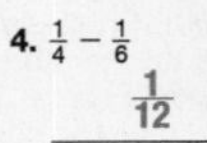

Find each sum. Simplify. *(Lesson 8-4)*

5. $\frac{2}{9} + \frac{5}{6}$ $\frac{19}{18} = 1\frac{1}{18}$
6. $\frac{4}{5} + \frac{1}{2}$ $\frac{13}{10} = 1\frac{3}{10}$
7. $\frac{5}{8} + \frac{5}{12}$ $\frac{25}{24} = 1\frac{1}{24}$
8. $\frac{3}{5} + \frac{2}{7}$ $\frac{31}{35}$

Mixed Review

Divide and check.

9. *(5-10)* 1 2)$9 8.7 6 — $8.23
10. *(5-10)* 1 5)$9 2.1 0 — $6.14
11. *(5-10)* 2 8)5,6 8 8 — 203 R4

Write >, <, or = to complete.

12. *(7-6)* $\frac{5}{8}$ (>) $\frac{7}{12}$
13. *(7-6)* $\frac{6}{9}$ (=) $\frac{2}{3}$
14. *(7-6)* $\frac{3}{5}$ (=) $\frac{6}{10}$

15. *(7-2)* What fraction of the glasses are full? $\frac{2}{6} = \frac{1}{3}$

16. *(4-15)* Pencils are sold in paackages of 12. How many packages would Mrs. Cragin need to buy if she wants to give a pencil to each of her 29 students. 3

Name ______________________

Daily Review 8-7

Daily Cumulative Review

Find each difference. Simplify. *(Lesson 8-6)*

1. $\frac{7}{12} - \frac{3}{8} =$ $\frac{5}{24}$
2. $\frac{7}{9} - \frac{2}{5} =$ $\frac{17}{45}$
3. $\frac{7}{8} - \frac{5}{6} =$ $\frac{1}{24}$
4. $\frac{3}{5} - \frac{2}{15} =$ $\frac{7}{15}$
5. $\frac{5}{6} - \frac{2}{5} =$ $\frac{13}{30}$
6. $\frac{5}{8} - \frac{1}{4} =$ $\frac{3}{8}$

Find each difference. You may use fraction strips or draw pictures to help. *(Lesson 8-5)*

7. $\frac{1}{2} - \frac{1}{3} =$ $\frac{1}{6}$
8. $\frac{3}{4} - \frac{1}{3} =$ $\frac{5}{12}$
9. $\frac{7}{8} - \frac{1}{4} =$ $\frac{5}{8}$

Mixed Review

Divide.

10. *(4-7)* 417 ÷ 4 = 104 R1
11. *(4-2)* 6,400 ÷ 8 = 800
12. *(5-1)* 40,000 ÷ 20 = 2,000
13. *(5-4)* 315 ÷ 35 = 9

Write the mixed or whole number and improper fraction that name each shaded part.

14. *(7-9)*

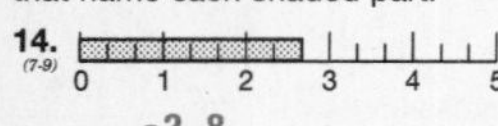

$2\frac{2}{3}, \frac{8}{3}$

15. *(7-9)*

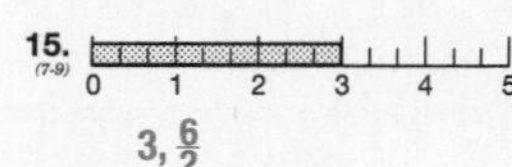

$3, \frac{6}{2}$

16. *(4-13)* What are the factors of 48? 1, 2, 3, 4, 6, 8, 12, 16, 24, 48

17. *(4-14)* Is 51 prime or composite? Composite

18. *(7-7)* Jesse ate $\frac{1}{4}$ of a medium pizza. Salla ate $\frac{1}{3}$ of the same pizza. Who ate more pizza? Salla

Name ______________________

Daily Review 8-8

Daily Cumulative Review

Write if each problem has too much or too little information. Solve, if possible, or tell what is needed to solve. *(Lesson 8-7)*

1. Mrs. Edwards bought $\frac{1}{3}$ of a case of cookies. She received $12.65 in change from the store clerk. How much does a case of cookies cost?

   Too little information; Need to know how much money she gave the clerk.

2. There are 10 windows on each floor of an office building and $\frac{1}{5}$ of the windows on each floor face east. If there are 9 floors in the building, how many windows are in the building?

   Too much information; 90 windows

Find each difference. Simplify. *(Lesson 8-6)*

3. $\frac{5}{6} - \frac{1}{12}$ $\frac{9}{12} = \frac{3}{4}$
4. $\frac{3}{4} - \frac{5}{8}$ $\frac{1}{8}$
5. $\frac{7}{8} - \frac{5}{12}$ $\frac{11}{24}$
6. $\frac{13}{14} - \frac{5}{6}$ $\frac{4}{42} = \frac{2}{21}$

Mixed Review

Solve.

7. *(5-12)* $85 ÷ 10 = $8.50
8. *(5-7)* 22,212 ÷ 18 = 1,234
9. *(2-18)* 53 − 7.89 = 45.11
10. *(2-18)* 408 − 77 = 331
11. 3.8 + 9 = 12.8
12. 4.91 × 0.66 = 3.2406

Compare. Use >, <, or = to complete.

13. *(7-11)* $3\frac{2}{5}$ (<) $3\frac{5}{8}$
14. *(2-14)* 48 + 37 (<) 90
15. *(2-11)* 0.77 (>) 0.7
16. *(2-5)* 2,002 (<) 2,020

Name ______________________

Daily Review 8-9

Daily Cumulative Review

Find each sum or difference. Use fraction strips or drawings to help. Simplify. *(Lesson 8-8)*

1. $7\frac{5}{6} + 2\frac{1}{3}$ = **$9\frac{7}{6} = 10\frac{1}{6}$**
2. $6\frac{3}{5} - \frac{1}{10}$ = **$6\frac{5}{10} = 6\frac{1}{2}$**
3. $4 - 1\frac{1}{4}$ = **$2\frac{3}{4}$**

Write if each problem has too much or too little information. Solve, if possible, or tell what is needed to solve. *(Lesson 8-7)*

4. Alana collected shells at the beach. She gave $\frac{1}{2}$ of these to Shanara who gave $\frac{1}{3}$ of what she received to Chad. How many shells did Alana collect?
Too little information; Need to know how many shells Chad received

Mixed Review

Solve.

5. 3,248 + 5,733 (2-15) **8,981**
6. 2 + 0.56 + 1.1 (2-17) **3.66**
7. $\frac{2}{6} + \frac{2}{6} + \frac{2}{6}$ (8-1) **$\frac{6}{6} = 1$**
8. 6 × 8.5 (3-10) **51**
9. 1.101 × 100 (3-8) **110.1**
10. 63 ÷ 1,000 (5-12) **0.063**
11. $8.04 – $4.66 (2-18) **$3.38**
12. 5 – 3.02 (2-18) **1.98**
13. 7,238 ÷ 9 (4-8) **804 R2**

105

Name ______________________

Daily Review 8-10

Daily Cumulative Review

Estimate each sum or difference. *(Lesson 8-9)* **Possible answers are shown.**

1. $4\frac{3}{8} + 3\frac{3}{5}$ **7–8**
2. $2\frac{1}{2} + 6\frac{4}{7}$ **8–9**
3. $5 - 3\frac{2}{3}$ **1–2**

Find each sum or difference. Use fraction strips or drawings to help. Simplify. *(Lesson 8-8)*

4. $5\frac{3}{4} - 2\frac{5}{12}$ = **$3\frac{4}{12} = 3\frac{1}{3}$**
5. $7 - 3\frac{2}{9}$ = **$3\frac{7}{9}$**
6. $2\frac{3}{16} + 1\frac{5}{8}$ = **$3\frac{13}{16}$**

Mixed Review

Complete.

7. $3 = \frac{\boxed{21}}{7}$ (7-10)
8. $5\frac{2}{3} = \frac{\boxed{17}}{3}$ (7-10)
9. **0** ÷ 99 = 0 (4-10)
10. 21,000 ÷ 300 = **70** (4-2)

11. (5-8)

n	$n \div 3$
12	**4**
21	**7**
51	**17**

12. (5-8)

n	$n - 22$
29	**7**
22	**0**
46	**24**

13. Find the length of a side of the square. (4-12)

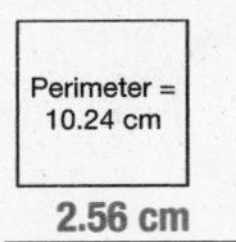

2.56 cm

14. Which of the figures shows [figure] turned? (6-7) **B**

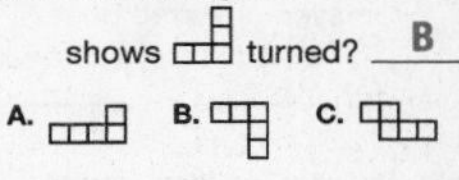

106

Name ______________________

Daily Review 8-11

Daily Cumulative Review

Find each sum or difference. Simplify. *(Lesson 8-10)*

1. $4\frac{2}{5} + 3\frac{3}{10}$ = **$7\frac{7}{10}$**
2. $10\frac{2}{3} - 7\frac{1}{5}$ = **$3\frac{7}{15}$**
3. $4\frac{5}{6} - 2\frac{5}{8}$ = **$2\frac{5}{24}$**
4. $9\frac{1}{4} + 2\frac{5}{8}$ = **$11\frac{7}{8} = 12\frac{1}{8}$**

Estimate each sum or difference. *(Lesson 8-9)* **Possible answers are shown.**

5. $4\frac{2}{9} + 5\frac{3}{7}$ **9–10**
6. $6\frac{1}{2} - 3\frac{4}{5}$ **2–3**
7. $1\frac{5}{11} + 2\frac{1}{9}$ **3–4**
8. $7\frac{1}{5} - 2$ **5–6**

Mixed Review

Find the greatest common factor for each pair.

9. 12 and 15 (7-4) **3**
10. 16 and 28 (7-4) **4**
11. 24 and 36 (7-4) **12**

Find the LCD for each pair of fractions.

12. $\frac{3}{4}$ and $\frac{3}{10}$ (8-3) **20**
13. $\frac{2}{3}$ and $\frac{4}{5}$ (8-3) **15**
14. $\frac{5}{12}$ and $\frac{9}{21}$ (8-3) **84**

Estimate the percent of each figure that is shaded.

15. (7-12)

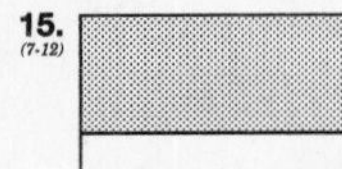

Accept 60%–80%.

16. (7-12)

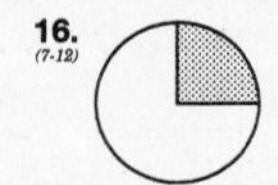

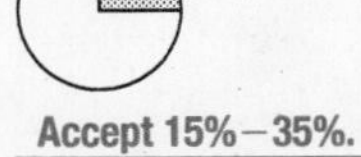

Accept 15%–35%.

107

Name ______________________

Daily Review 8-12

Daily Cumulative Review

Find each sum. Simplify. *(Lesson 8-11)*

1. $2\frac{1}{10} + 1\frac{2}{5} + 3\frac{3}{10}$ = **$6\frac{8}{10} = 6\frac{4}{5}$**
2. $1\frac{3}{4} + 2\frac{1}{3} + 4\frac{1}{6}$ = **$7\frac{15}{12} = 8\frac{3}{12} = 8\frac{1}{4}$**
3. $5\frac{2}{9} + 2\frac{1}{6} + \frac{2}{3}$ = **$7\frac{19}{18} = 8\frac{1}{18}$**
4. $5 + \frac{3}{4} + 2\frac{1}{5}$ = **$7\frac{19}{20}$**

Find each sum or difference. *(Lesson 8-10)*

5. $6 + 3\frac{7}{8}$ = **$9\frac{7}{8}$**
6. $8\frac{9}{10} - 2\frac{1}{4}$ = **$6\frac{13}{20}$**
7. $4\frac{5}{6} - 1\frac{1}{8}$ = **$3\frac{17}{24}$**
8. $21\frac{1}{2} + 7\frac{2}{7}$ = **$28\frac{11}{14}$**

Mixed Review

Divide.

9. 36)490 (5-6) **13 R22**
10. 40)$416.40 (5-10) **$10.41**
11. 0.4 ÷ 1000 = **0.0004** (5-12)

Name each triangle by its sides and by its angles.

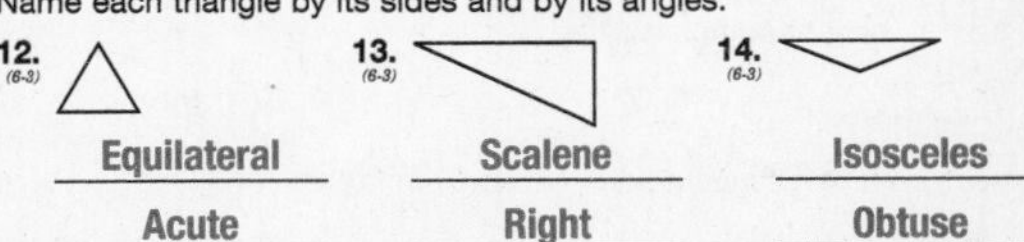

12. (6-3) **Equilateral**, **Acute**
13. (6-3) **Scalene**, **Right**
14. (6-3) **Isosceles**, **Obtuse**

For each set, decide which does **not** belong.

15. A. 50% B. $\frac{1}{2}$ C. 5 out of 1000 D. $\frac{5}{10}$ (7-12) **C**
16. A. 6% B. $\frac{60}{100}$ C. $\frac{6}{100}$ D. 6 out of 100 (7-12) **B**

108

Name ______________________

Daily Cumulative Review

Find each difference. Simplify. *(Lesson 8-12)*

1. $5\frac{5}{9} - 2\frac{8}{9}$ = $2\frac{6}{9} = 2\frac{2}{3}$
2. $7\frac{1}{10} - 5\frac{2}{10}$ = $1\frac{9}{10}$
3. $9\frac{9}{20} - 4\frac{3}{4}$ = $4\frac{14}{20} = 4\frac{7}{10}$
4. $9 - 6\frac{5}{6}$ = $2\frac{1}{6}$

Find each sum. Simplify if possible. *(Lesson 8-11)*

5. $1\frac{1}{8} + 4\frac{4}{5}$ = $5\frac{37}{40}$
6. $5\frac{3}{8} + 2\frac{1}{2}$ = $7\frac{7}{8}$
7. $3\frac{2}{5} + 6\frac{7}{10}$ = $9\frac{11}{10} = 10\frac{1}{10}$
8. $5\frac{7}{16} + 2\frac{1}{4}$ = $7\frac{11}{16}$

Mixed Review

Find equivalent fractions with a denominator of 6.

9. (7-3) $\frac{1}{2} = \frac{3}{6}$ 10. (7-3) $\frac{12}{36} = \frac{2}{6}$ 11. (7-3) $\frac{2}{3} = \frac{4}{6}$ 12. (7-3) $\frac{20}{24} = \frac{5}{6}$

Write each improper fraction as a mixed number in simplest form, or as a whole number.

13. (7-10) $\frac{52}{6}$ = $8\frac{2}{3}$ 14. (7-10) $\frac{42}{7}$ = 6   15. (7-10) $\frac{60}{8}$ = $7\frac{1}{2}$ 16. (7-10) $\frac{55}{7}$ = $7\frac{6}{7}$

Use this circle graph to answer **17** and **18**.

17. (7-12) What fractional part of those surveyed preferred dogs?

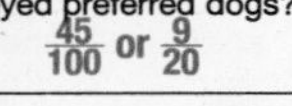

18. (7-14) Which is the least favorite pet? **Birds**

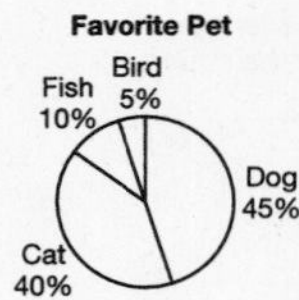

Name ______________________

Daily Review
8-14

Daily Cumulative Review

Work backward or draw a picture to solve the problem. *(Lesson 8-13)*

1. Mrs. York baked cookies and gave half to her neighbor, Mrs. Jensen. Mrs. Jensen gave $\frac{1}{3}$ of hers to Mr. Green. Mr. Green got 12 cookies. How many cookies did Mrs. York bake? **72**

2. Regina and her dad biked west $\frac{5}{8}$ mile and then turned south and biked $1\frac{1}{2}$ miles. They turned northeast and biked $1\frac{3}{8}$ miles back to their starting point. How far did they bike in all? **$3\frac{3}{4}$ miles**

Find each difference. Simplify. *(Lesson 8-12)*

3. $6 - 1\frac{7}{8}$ = $4\frac{1}{8}$
4. $4\frac{1}{4} - 2\frac{1}{3}$ = $1\frac{11}{12}$
5. $6\frac{1}{5} - 1\frac{3}{10}$ = $4\frac{9}{10}$
6. $20\frac{5}{6} - 7\frac{3}{8}$ = $13\frac{11}{24}$

Mixed Review

Find the simplest form of each fraction.

7. (7-5) $\frac{18}{24}$ = $\frac{3}{4}$ 8. (7-5) $\frac{24}{36}$ = $\frac{2}{3}$ 9. (7-5) $\frac{42}{48}$ = $\frac{7}{8}$ 10. (7-5) $\frac{20}{45}$ = $\frac{4}{9}$

Write each as a fraction and a decimal.

11. (7-13) 20% — $\frac{20}{100} = \frac{1}{5}$; 0.2
12. (7-13) 50% — $\frac{50}{100} = \frac{1}{2}$; 0.5
13. (7-13) 4% — $\frac{4}{100} = \frac{1}{25}$; 0.04
14. (7-13) 83% — $\frac{83}{100}$; 0.83

Write each rule using a variable.

15. (1-7) 6.7 less than number — $n - 6.7$
16. (1-7) Multiply a number by 11. — $n \times 11$

Name ______________________

Daily Review
8-15

Daily Cumulative Review

Find the length to the nearest $\frac{1}{4}$-inch. *(Lesson 8-14)*

1. $2\frac{3}{4}$"   2. 2"

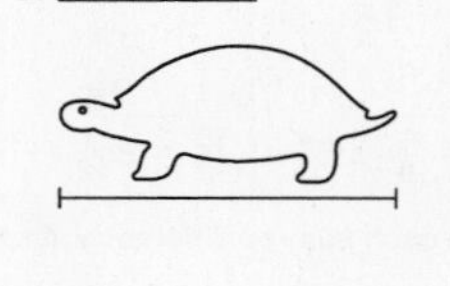

Work backward or draw a picture to solve the problem. *(Lesson 8-13)*

3. Farrad, Eli, and Sean worked on geometry projects over the weekend. Eli worked $\frac{1}{3}$ of the time that Farrad worked, and Farrad worked $\frac{3}{4}$ the time that Sean worked. Sean worked 4 hours. How long did the other boys work? **Eli – 1 hour; Farrad – 3 hours**

Mixed Review

Write >, <, or = to complete.

4. (7-7) $\frac{7}{10}$ (<) $\frac{3}{4}$ 5. (7-11) $3\frac{4}{8}$ (=) $3\frac{6}{12}$ 6. (4-10) 0 (=) 99 × 0

Shade the drawing to show each fraction.

7. (7-9) $1\frac{3}{5}$ 8. (7-9) $\frac{3}{2}$ 9. (7-9) $\frac{8}{4}$

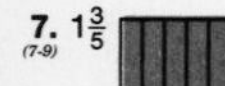

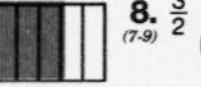

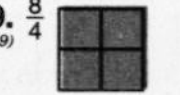

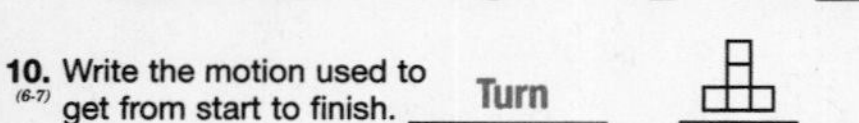

10. Write the motion used to get from start to finish. Turn

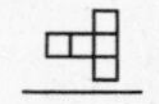

Name ______________________

Daily Review
8-16

Daily Cumulative Review

Complete. *(Lesson 8-15)*

1. 24 ft = **8** yd   2. 2 mi = **3,520** yd
3. 3 yd 2 ft = **11** ft   4. 69 in. = **5** ft **9** in.
5. 15 yd = **45** ft   6. 6 ft 3 in. = **75** in.

Find the length to the nearest $\frac{1}{4}$-inch. *(Lesson 8-14)*

7. $1\frac{3}{4}$ in.

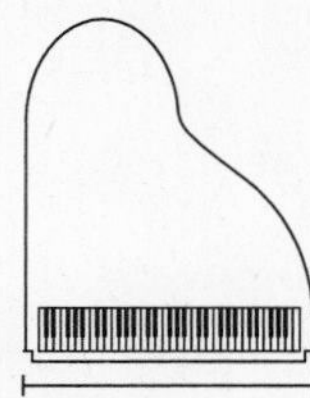

Mixed Review

Complete.

9. (7-10) $4\frac{1}{6} = \frac{25}{6}$ 10. (6-1) 900 ÷ **30** = 30
11. (2-3) **10**^{5} = 100,000   12. (2-4) 20,000,000 = twenty **million**
13. (3-8) 0.08 × 1,000 = **80**   14. (3-1) **10,000** × 60 = 600,000
15. (6-1) Lines are parallel if they **A**.
 A. never meet **B.** form a triangle **C.** intersect **D.** form angles

Name ______________________

Daily Review 9-1

Daily Cumulative Review

Decide whether you need an exact answer or estimate. Solve. *(Lesson 8-16)*

1. Jason mows lawns during the summer. He can mow Mrs. Park's lawn in $2\frac{1}{2}$ hours. He can trim with a weed-eater in about $1\frac{1}{4}$ hours. If he starts at 8:00 A.M., can he finish by noon? Explain your answer.
   Estimate; Yes, he can finish in about $3\frac{3}{4}$ hours.

2. Ryan wants to build a recycle cage for cans. He plans to cut metal rods for the frame and use wire mesh for the bottom and sides. Rods are 12 feet long and mesh comes in rolls that are 3 feet wide. Will 2 rods be enough to make a cage? Explain.
   Exact; No, he needs 12 sections of 3 feet each. He needs 3 rods.

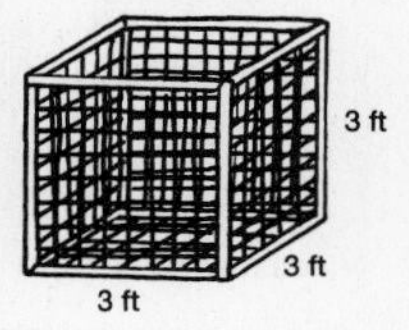

Complete. *(Lesson 8-15)*

3. a.

Number of inches	36	72	108	180	360	720
Number of yards	1	2	3	5	10	20

b. To change from inches to yards, you must divide the number of inches by 36.

c. To change from yards to inches, you must multiply the number of yards by 36.

Mixed Review

Find each sum.

4. $\frac{1}{4} + \frac{3}{8} + \frac{5}{16}$ (8-2) $\frac{15}{16}$

5. $2\frac{2}{3} + 1\frac{5}{6}$ (8-8) $3\frac{9}{6} = 4\frac{3}{6} = 4\frac{1}{2}$

6. $7.3 + 0.86 + 2$ (2-16) 10.16

Name ______________________

Daily Review 9-2

Daily Cumulative Review

Find each product. You may use counters to help. *(Lesson 9-1)*

1. $\frac{1}{4}$ of 24 6
2. $\frac{1}{3}$ of 27 9
3. $\frac{3}{4}$ of 16 12

Decide whether you need an exact answer or estimate. Solve. *(Lesson 8-16)*

4. Ashley's car holds 12 gallons of gas and gets about 25 miles to the gallon. Can she make a 500 mile trip on two tanks of gas? Explain.
   Estimate; $12 \times 25 = 300$ miles per tank. So, she can travel about 600 miles on two tanks of gas.

5. Your mom sent you to the store to get bread, milk, and eggs. Bread costs \$1.19, milk costs \$2.79, and eggs cost \$1.35. Tax is \$0.35. About how much will the total be?
   Estimate; $1 + 3 + 1 = 5$, Between \$5 and \$6.

Mixed Review

6. Find the simplest form for $\frac{18}{45}$. (7-5) $\frac{2}{5}$

Find each difference.

7. $6 - 1\frac{1}{4}$ (8-12) $4\frac{3}{4}$

8. $\frac{5}{9} - \frac{1}{3}$ (8-6) $\frac{2}{9}$

9. $\$10 - \$1.98$ (2-18) \$8.02

10. (2-18) $407 - 38$ = 369

Draw all lines of symmetry.

11. (6-8)

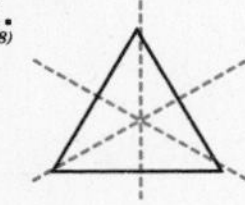

12. (6-8)

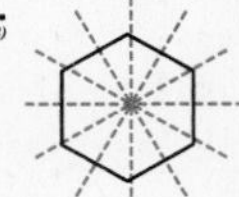

Name ______________________

Daily Review 9-3

Daily Cumulative Review

Find each product. Use mental math. *(Lesson 9-2)*

1. $\frac{1}{6}$ of 48 8
2. $\frac{1}{7}$ of 21 3
3. $\frac{1}{3}$ of 24 8
4. $\frac{3}{10}$ of 30 9
5. $\frac{5}{9}$ of 18 10
6. $\frac{7}{8}$ of 56 49

Find each product. You may use counters to help. *(Lesson 9-1)*

7. $\frac{1}{5}$ of 35 7
8. $\frac{3}{4}$ of 16 12
9. $\frac{2}{3}$ of 27 18
10. $\frac{1}{3}$ of 90 30
11. $\frac{5}{6}$ of 42 35
12. $\frac{5}{8}$ of 16 10

Mixed Review

13. Which of the figures is congruent to ▭? (6-7) C

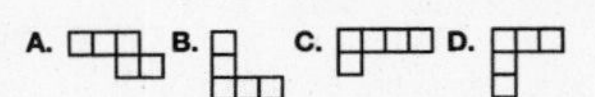

Write the name for each.

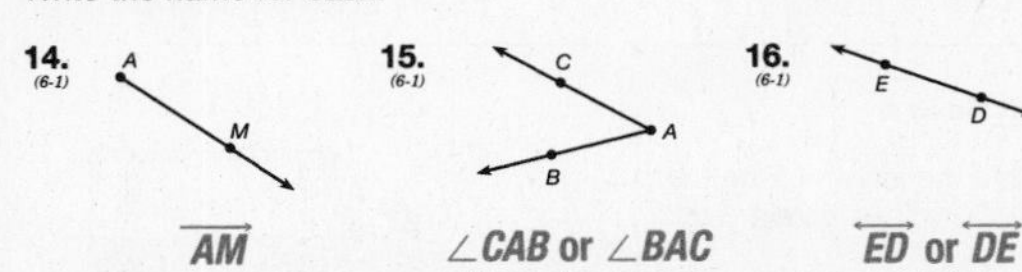

14. (6-1) $\overrightarrow{AM}$

15. (6-1) $\angle CAB$ or $\angle BAC$

16. (6-1) $\overleftrightarrow{ED}$ or $\overleftrightarrow{DE}$

17. Describe how you compare two fractions whose denominators are the same. (7-6)
    Compare the numerators.

Use any strategy to solve.

18. Andrea can make 15 cloth angels in 2 days. How many can she make in 10 days? (7-8) 75

Name ______________________

Daily Review 9-4

Daily Cumulative Review

Use rounding, benchmark, or compatible numbers to estimate each product. *(Lesson 9-3)* Possible estimates are given.

1. $\frac{7}{12} \times 8$ 4–5
2. $4\frac{5}{6} \times 7$ 28–35
3. $\frac{3}{5} \times 21$ 12
4. $\frac{11}{24} \times 12$ 5–6
5. $2\frac{1}{20} \times 9$ 18
6. $\frac{3}{4} \times 31$ 24

Complete the table. Use patterns to help you find each product. *(Lesson 9-2)*

	$\frac{1}{9}$ of 45	5
	$\frac{2}{9}$ of 45	10
7.	$\frac{3}{9}$ of 45	15

8.	$\frac{4}{9}$ of 45	20
9.	$\frac{5}{9}$ of 45	25
10.	$\frac{6}{9}$ of 45	30

11.	$\frac{7}{9}$ of 45	35
12.	$\frac{8}{9}$ of 45	40
13.	$\frac{9}{9}$ of 45	45

Mixed Review

Find each difference. Simplify.

14. $\frac{7}{8} - \frac{3}{8} =$ (8-5) $\frac{4}{8} = \frac{1}{2}$

15. $\frac{2}{3} - \frac{1}{6} =$ (8-5) $\frac{3}{6} = \frac{1}{2}$

16. $\frac{7}{10} - \frac{1}{2} =$ (8-5) $\frac{2}{10} = \frac{1}{5}$

17. Estimate the sum. $6\frac{9}{10} + 3\frac{1}{5} + 4\frac{1}{2}$. (8-9) 14–15

Use your ruler to draw a line segment for each length.

18. $1\frac{1}{2}$ in. (8-14) ______

19. $\frac{3}{4}$ in. (8-14) ______

Write each as a percent.

20. 0.04 (7-13) 4%

21. $\frac{70}{100}$ (7-13) 70%

22. 25 out of 100 (7-13) 25%

23. 0.40 (7-13) 40%

Round each answer to the nearest cent.

24. $6\overline{)\$14.07}$ (4-11) \$2.35

25. $\$1.30 \times 0.325$ (3-13) \$0.42

26. $\$0.13 \times 15$ (3-10) \$1.95

Name

Daily Review 9-5

Daily Cumulative Review

Use each drawing to help you complete each sentence. *(Lesson 9-4)*

1. $\frac{2}{3}$ is shaded. $\frac{1}{4}$ of $\frac{2}{3}$ is $\frac{2}{12} = \frac{1}{6}$

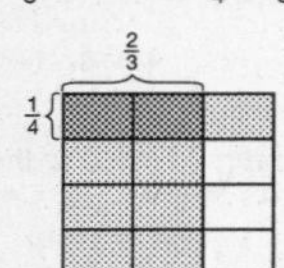

2. $\frac{1}{2}$ is shaded. $\frac{3}{5}$ of $\frac{1}{2}$ is $\frac{3}{10}$

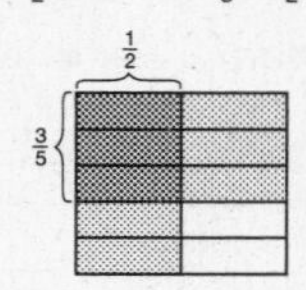

Use counting, benchmarks, or compatible numbers to estimate each product. Write the letter of the estimate that is closer to the actual product. *(Lesson 9-3)*

3. $\frac{5}{8} \times 57$ B — A. less than 35 — B. more than 35
4. $3\frac{8}{9} \times 12$ A — A. less than 48 — B. more than 48

Mixed Review

5. Vicke accidentally dropped a carton of eggs. Write four fractions that describe how many eggs were broken $\frac{1}{3}, \frac{2}{6}, \frac{3}{9}, \frac{4}{12}$

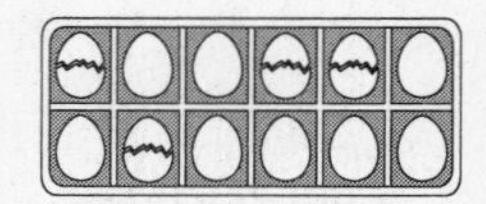

6. Find the greatest common factor of 24 and 30. 6
7. Estimate the quotient using compatible numbers. 22,000 ÷ 80 300
8. Why is the LCD of $\frac{5}{6}$ and $\frac{3}{8}$ not the product of 6 and 8? 6 and 8 share the multiple 24, so the LCD is 24
9. 153 in. = 12 ft 9 in.

117

Name

Daily Review 9-6

Daily Cumulative Review

Find each product. Simplify. *(Lesson 9-5)*

1. $\frac{5}{7} \times \frac{1}{2} = \frac{5}{14}$
2. $\frac{3}{4} \times \frac{4}{9} = \frac{1}{3}$
3. $\frac{1}{7} \times \frac{2}{9} = \frac{2}{63}$
4. $\frac{2}{3} \times \frac{7}{8} = \frac{7}{12}$
5. $\frac{5}{6} \times \frac{1}{10} = \frac{1}{12}$
6. $\frac{9}{11} \times \frac{5}{6} = \frac{15}{22}$

Use each drawing to help you complete each sentence. *(Lesson 9-4)*

7. $\frac{1}{3} \times \frac{2}{5} = \frac{2}{15}$

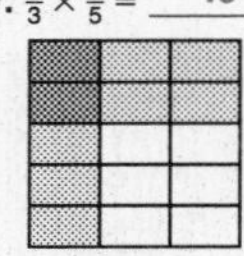

8. $\frac{5}{6} \times \frac{2}{3} = \frac{10}{18} = \frac{5}{9}$

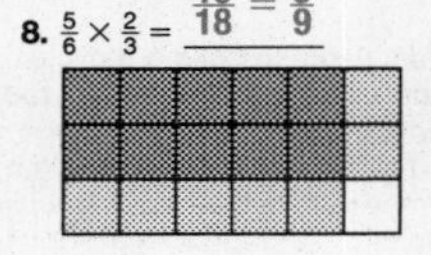

Mixed Review

9. If $\frac{3}{4}$ is subtracted from $\frac{7}{8}$, will the difference be greater or less than $\frac{1}{4}$? Explain.
Less than $\frac{1}{4}$; $\frac{3}{4} = \frac{6}{8}$, $\frac{7}{8} - \frac{6}{8} = \frac{1}{8}$ and $\frac{1}{8}$ is less than $\frac{1}{4}$.

Compare. Write >, <, or = to complete.

10. $\frac{2}{3} > \frac{2}{5}$
11. $\frac{9}{10} < \frac{11}{12}$
12. $1\frac{8}{12} = 1\frac{4}{6}$

Divide. Check your answer.

13. $3\overline{)\$7.32}$ = \$2.44
14. $38\overline{)1,634}$ = 43
15. $7\overline{)6.391}$ = 0.913

118

Name

Daily Review 9-7

Daily Cumulative Review

Overestimate or underestimate to solve the problem. *(Lesson 9-6)*

1. The art club has \$240 in its treasury. They need supplies that cost \$51.69, \$39.98, \$96.43, and \$11.24. Do they have enough to buy all of the supplies?
   a. Can the problem be solved with an estimate or does it require an exact answer? Estimate
   b. Should you overestimate or underestimate? Why? Overestimate; If the overestimate is under \$240, they have enough.
   c. Does the club have enough money? Explain. Yes; $60 + 40 + 100 + 20 = 220$. $220 < 240$, so they have enough.
   d. If they need to spend \$25 on contest entry fees, how can the club be sure it has enough? Explain. Solve the problem for the exact answer. The estimate may not tell for sure that club has enough.

Find each product. Simplify. *(Lesson 9-5)*

2. $\frac{2}{5} \times \frac{3}{16} = \frac{3}{40}$
3. $\frac{5}{6} \times \frac{8}{15} = \frac{4}{9}$
4. $\frac{3}{4} \times \frac{2}{5} = \frac{3}{10}$
5. $\frac{6}{7} \times \frac{5}{8} = \frac{15}{28}$
6. $\frac{1}{3} \times \frac{1}{3} = \frac{1}{9}$
7. $\frac{5}{7} \times \frac{2}{5} = \frac{2}{7}$

Mixed Review

Find each sum.

8. $\frac{1}{3} + \frac{4}{9} + \frac{2}{9} = \frac{9}{9} = 1$
9. $3\frac{2}{7} + \frac{11}{14} = 4\frac{1}{14}$

119

Name

Daily Review 9-8

Daily Cumulative Review

Complete. *(Lesson 9-7)*

1. $\frac{2}{5} \times 20 = \frac{40}{5} = 8$
2. $\frac{7}{8} \times 5 = \frac{35}{8} = 4\frac{3}{8}$
3. $5 \times \frac{3}{7} = \frac{15}{7} = 2\frac{1}{7}$
4. $4 \times \frac{5}{9} = \frac{20}{9} = 2\frac{2}{9}$

Estimate to solve 5–6. Write whether you overestimated or underestimated. Explain your answer. *(Lesson 9-6)*

5. Cody makes ceramic whistles to sell in his mom's booth at a craft fair. Each whistle sells for \$2.25. If 16 whistles sell, will he have enough to buy a \$30 shirt at the next booth.
Underestimate; $2 \times 16 = 32$. He has at least \$32, so he has enough to buy the \$30 shirt.
6. A recipe calls for $1\frac{3}{4}$ cups flour. Megan has $6\frac{1}{2}$ cups of flour. Does she have enough flour to triple the recipe?
Overestimate; $2 \times 3 = 6$. $6 < 6\frac{1}{2}$, so she has enough.

Mixed Review

7. Find the length of the toy truck to the nearest $\frac{1}{4}$-inch. 2 in.

8. Compare. Write $\frac{9}{11}, \frac{4}{5}, \frac{17}{22}$ in order from least to greatest. $\frac{17}{22}, \frac{4}{5}, \frac{9}{11}$
9. Make a drawing that shows the fraction $\frac{13}{5}$. Drawings may vary.

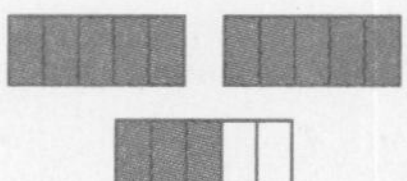

120

Name ______________________

Daily Cumulative Review

Complete. *(Lesson 9-8)*

1. $2\frac{2}{3} \times 5 = \frac{\boxed{8}}{3} \times 5 = \frac{\boxed{40}}{3} = \boxed{13}\frac{\boxed{1}}{3}$

2. $1\frac{2}{7} \times 6 = \frac{\boxed{9}}{7} \times 6 = \frac{\boxed{54}}{7} = \boxed{7}\frac{\boxed{5}}{7}$

3. $3\frac{1}{2} \times 4\frac{1}{3} = \frac{\boxed{7}}{2} \times \frac{\boxed{13}}{3} = \frac{\boxed{91}}{6} = \boxed{15}\frac{\boxed{1}}{6}$

4. $1\frac{1}{5} \times 2\frac{3}{4} = \frac{\boxed{6}}{5} \times \frac{\boxed{11}}{4} = \frac{\boxed{66}}{20} = \boxed{3}\frac{\boxed{6}}{20} = \boxed{3}\frac{\boxed{3}}{10}$

Find each product. *(Lesson 9-7)*

5. $\frac{2}{3} \times 9 =$ 6
6. $\frac{8}{9} \times 18 =$ 16
7. $\frac{4}{7} \times 21 =$ 12
8. $\frac{5}{6} \times 24 =$ 20

Mixed Review

Find each sum or difference. Simplify if possible.

9. (8-1) $\frac{7}{9} - \frac{1}{9} =$ $\frac{6}{9} = \frac{2}{3}$
10. (8-11) $6 + 1\frac{1}{2} + 2\frac{5}{8} =$ $10\frac{1}{8}$
11. (8-6) $\frac{6}{11} - \frac{2}{5} =$ $\frac{8}{55}$
12. (8-8) $3 - 1\frac{2}{3} =$ $1\frac{1}{3}$
13. (7-12) Estimate the percent of the figure that is shaded.

75%

14. (6-8) Use the line of symmetry to complete the figure.

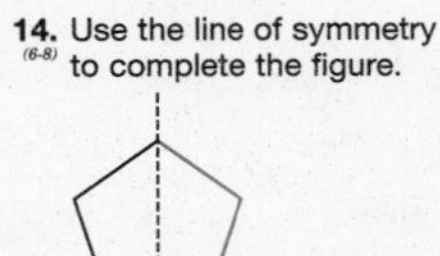

Name ______________________

Daily Review 9-10

Daily Cumulative Review

Use logical reasoning to solve the problem. *(Lesson 9-9)*

Sarah, Rachel, Halley, and Matthew won awards in math, history, reading, and science at the academic banquet. No student won an award in a subject that begins with the same letter as his or her name. Neither Sarah nor Halley won the math award. Matthew won his award for his report on the Revolutionary War. Which student won each award?

1.

	Math	History	Reading	Science
Sarah	No	No	Yes	No
Rachel	Yes	No	No	No
Halley	No	No	No	Yes
Matthew	No	Yes	No	No

2. Sarah: Reading
3. Rachel: Math
4. Halley: Science
5. Matthew: History

Find each product. Simplify. *(Lesson 9-8)*

6. $8\frac{2}{3} \times 3 =$ 26
7. $5\frac{3}{4} \times \frac{1}{2} =$ $\frac{23}{8} = 2\frac{7}{8}$

Mixed Review

8. (8-10) How do you simplify $5\frac{10}{8}$?

Possible answer: $5\frac{10}{8} = 5\frac{5}{4} = 5 + 1\frac{1}{4} = 6\frac{1}{4}$

Identify each angle as acute, right, or obtuse. Extend the sides of each angle. Then measure each with a protractor.

9. (6-2)

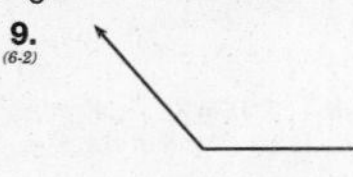

130°, obtuse

10. (6-2)

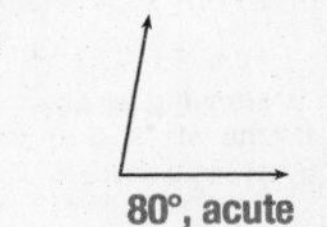

80°, acute

Name ______________________

Daily Cumulative Review

Complete the drawings to find each quotient. *(Lesson 9-10)*

1. How many $\frac{1}{2}$'s are there in 5? 10

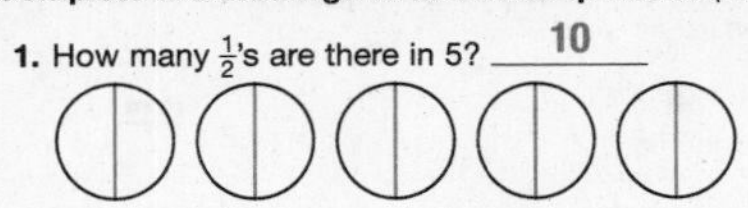

2. How many $\frac{1}{5}$'s are there in 3? 15

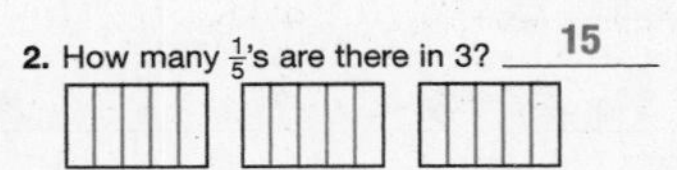

3. How many $\frac{1}{4}$'s are there in 2? 8

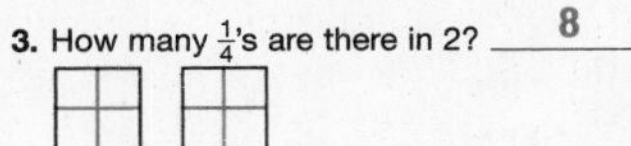

4. How many $\frac{1}{6}$'s are there in 4? 24

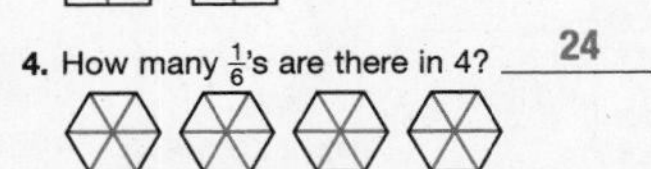

Use logical reasoning or any strategy to solve the problem. *(Lesson 9-9)*

5. A certain type of bacteria doubles in number every 24 hours in a Petri dish. At the beginning of an experiment, there are 2 bacteria in the dish. It takes 10 days for the dish to be completely covered. On what day is it half covered? What strategy did you use?

The 9th day; work backward

Mixed Review

Find each product

6. (3-13) 5.06×0.45 = 2.2770
7. (3-5) 84×62 = 5,208
8. (9-1) $\frac{2}{7} \times 21 =$ 6

Name ______________________

Daily Cumulative Review

Choose the most appropriate unit of measure to estimate the length or height of each. Write cm, dm, m, or km. *(Lesson 10-1)*

1. m

2. cm

3. cm or dm

4. km

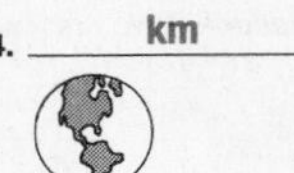

Find each quotient. *(Lesson 9-10)*

5. $6 \div \frac{1}{4} =$ 24
6. $13 \div \frac{1}{3} =$ 39
7. $5 \div \frac{1}{8} =$ 40
8. $7 \div \frac{1}{9} =$ 63

Mixed Review

You want to design an office building with 16 offices so that each office has a balcony on one wall and a window on another.

9. (5-9) How many offices will be on each floor? 4
10. (5-9) How many floors will the building have? 4

Possible answers given for 9 and 10.

11. (5-9) How many sets of curtains will you need for the windows and balcony doors? 32

Write each as a fraction and a decimal.

12. (7-13) 90% — $\frac{90}{100} = \frac{9}{10}$; 0.90
13. (7-13) 20% — $\frac{20}{100} = \frac{1}{5}$; 0.20
14. (7-13) 65% — $\frac{65}{100} = \frac{13}{20}$; 0.65

Name ______________________

Daily Review 10-3

Daily Cumulative Review

Complete. *(Lesson 10-2)*

1. 15 mm = 1.5 cm
2. 30 m = 300 dm
3. 8,000 mm = 80 dm
4. 9,000 mm = 9 m
5. 20 dm = 200 cm
6. 3,000 cm = 30 m

Choose the most appropriate unit of measure to estimate the length or height of each. Write cm, dm, m, or km. *(Lesson 10-1)*

7. km

8. cm or dm

Mixed Review

9. (7-1) What fraction of the set is square? $\frac{8}{12} = \frac{2}{3}$

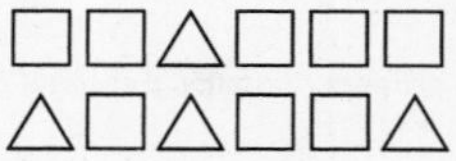

Find each quotient.

10. (9-10) $8 \div \frac{1}{4} =$ 32
11. (4-11) $5\overline{)\$50.45}$ $10.09
12. (5-10) $30\overline{)\$184.50}$ $6.15

13. (7-3) Jordan is planning an exercise schedule. He will start with 4 sit-ups. Every day, he will do 3 more sit-ups than he did the day before. On what day of his schedule will he do 40 sit-ups?

The 13th day

Name ______________________

Daily Review 10-4

Daily Cumulative Review

Complete. *(Lesson 10-3)*

1. 740 cm = 7.4 m
2. 0.12 m = 12 cm
3. 10 cm = 0.1 m
4. 90 m = 9,000 cm
5. 3.6 m = 360 cm
6. 5.1 cm = 0.051 m

Complete. *(Lesson 10-2)*

7. 900 dm = 90 m
8. 20 cm = 2 dm
9. 700 mm = 7 dm
10. 50 dm = 500 cm

Mixed Review

11. (8-14) Find the length of the bird to the nearest $\frac{1}{4}$-inch.

$1\frac{1}{4}$ in.

12. (9-4) Which of the drawings shows $\frac{1}{6} \times \frac{1}{2}$? B

A.

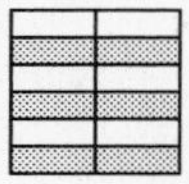

B.

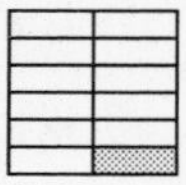

C.

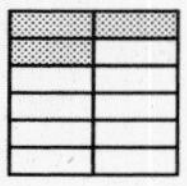

13. (7-3) Find a fraction equivalent to $\frac{5}{6}$ with a denominator of 24. $\frac{20}{24}$

Compare. Write >, <, or = to complete.

14. (7-13) 60% (=) $\frac{3}{5}$
15. (2-14) 327 + 133 (>) 400
16. (7-11) $4\frac{7}{8}$ (<) $6\frac{1}{3}$
17. (7-7) $\frac{3}{10}$ (>) $\frac{1}{4}$
18. (2-5) two million, two hundred thousand (=) 2,200,000

Name ______________________

Daily Review 10-5

Daily Cumulative Review

Complete. *(Lesson 10-4)*

1. 100 mm = 10 cm
2. 48 mm = 4.8 cm
3. 18 m = 18,000 mm
4. 538 cm = 5.38 m
5. 29 cm = 290 mm
6. 9.6 m = 9,600 mm

Write each measurement, first in centimeters only and then in meters only. *(Lesson 10-3)*

7. 4 m 26 cm 426 cm; 4.26 m
8. 5 m 9 cm 509 cm; 5.09 m
9. 7 m 83 cm 783 cm; 7.83 m

Mixed Review

Find each sum or difference. Simplify.

10. (8-1) $\frac{5}{6} + \frac{5}{6}$ $1\frac{2}{3}$
11. (8-6) $\frac{7}{10} - \frac{3}{5}$ $\frac{1}{10}$
12. (8-10) $7\frac{5}{9} - 4$ $3\frac{5}{9}$

Write if the problem has too much or too little information. Solve, if possible, or tell what is needed to solve.

13. (8-7) A tailor needs two pieces of fabric, $1\frac{2}{3}$ yards long and $1\frac{1}{2}$ yards long, and 3 spools of the thread. How much fabric should he buy?

Too much information; he needs to buy $3\frac{1}{6}$ yards of fabric

Complete.

14. (8-15) 3 ft 7 in. = 43 in.
15. 10 yd 2 ft = 32 ft
16. (7-4) Find the greatest common factor of 18 and 72. 18
17. (4-13) What are the factors of 42? 1, 2, 3, 6, 7, 14, 21, 42

Name ______________________

Daily Review 10-6

Daily Cumulative Review

Write a multiplication number sentence describing the perimeter of each polygon. *(Lesson 10-5)*

1.

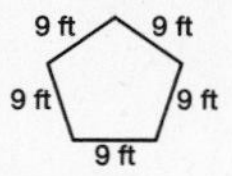
9 ft
9 ft
9 ft
9 ft
9 ft

$9\text{ ft} \times 5 = 45\text{ ft}$

2.

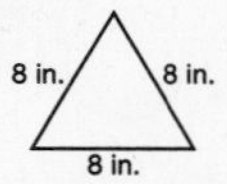
8 in.
8 in.
8 in.

$8\text{ in.} \times 3 = 24\text{ in.}$

3.

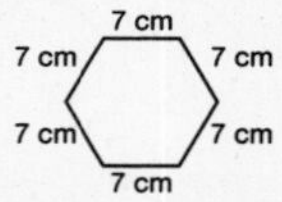
7 cm
7 cm
7 cm
7 cm
7 cm
7 cm

$7\text{ cm} \times 6 = 42\text{ cm}$

Complete. *(Lesson 10-4)*

4. Which length is the longest? C
   A. 840 mm B. 84 cm C. 8.4 m
5. Which length is the shortest? B
   A. 371 mm B. 3.71 cm C. 37.1 m
6. Which two lengths are equal? B and C
   A. 48.9 cm B. 4.89 m C. 4,890 mm

Mixed Review

Find each sum or difference. Simplify if possible.

7. (8-11) $4\frac{3}{10} + 1\frac{1}{2} + \frac{3}{5} = 6\frac{2}{5}$
8. (8-8) $6 - 3\frac{5}{6} = 2\frac{1}{6}$
9. (8-5) $\frac{5}{8} - \frac{3}{8} = \frac{1}{4}$
10. (8-4) $\frac{3}{4} + \frac{5}{6} = 1\frac{7}{12}$

11. (4-15) Work backward to solve the problem.

After doing some odd jobs during the week, Nick had $46. He cleaned Mrs. Helm's gutters for $8. He earned $5 per hour for 2 hours digging holes for Mrs. Walkers new rose bushes. He cleaned Mr. Howard's garage for 2 hours at $6 per hour.

How much did he have at the beginning of the week? $16

Name ______________________

Daily Cumulative Review

Use the formula $P = 2 \times (l + w)$ to find the perimeter of each rectangle. Fill in the missing numbers. *(Lesson 10-6)*

1.

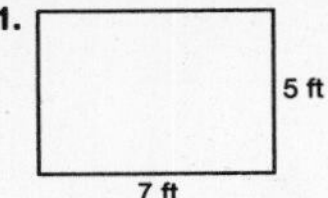

$P = 2 \times (\underline{7} + \underline{5})$

$P = 2 \times (\underline{12})$

$P = \underline{24}$ ft

2. (4 cm, 3 cm)

$P = 2 \times (\underline{3} + \underline{4})$

$P = 2 \times (\underline{7})$

$P = \underline{14}$ cm

Find each perimeter. *(Lesson 10-5)*

3.

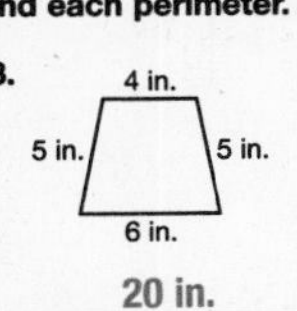

20 in.

4.

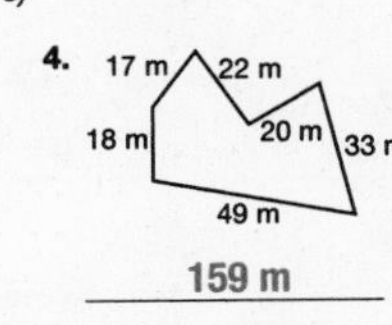

159 m

Mixed Review

Find each quotient or product.

5. (5-1) 72,000 ÷ 80 = 900

6. (5-5) 547 ÷ 24 = 22 R19

7. (3-12) 0.6 of 0.5 0.3

8. (9-2) $\frac{2}{3}$ of 24 16

9. (8-13) Use any strategy to solve the problem.

Tyler is reading a book for a book report. Monday, he read $\frac{1}{4}$ of the book. Tuesday, he read $\frac{1}{6}$. Wednesday, he read $\frac{1}{3}$. On Thursday, he read 3 chapters and finished the book.

How many chapters did the book have? 12

129

Name ______________________

Daily Review
10-8

Daily Cumulative Review

Find each sum. *(Lesson 10-7)*

1. 5 yd 1 ft + 3 yd 2 ft = 9 yd
2. 7 ft 5 in. + 4 ft 7 in. = 12 ft
3. 6 ft 10 in. + 2 ft 3 in. = 9 ft 1 in.
4. 8 yd 2 ft + 9 yd 2 ft = 18 yd 1 ft

Find the perimeter of each rectangle. *(Lesson 10-6)*

5.

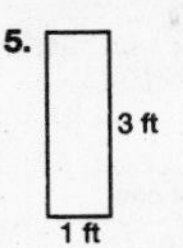

8 ft

6.

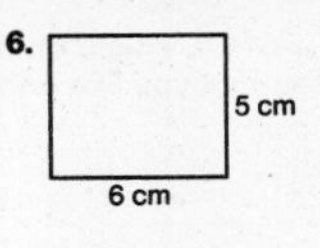

22 cm

7.

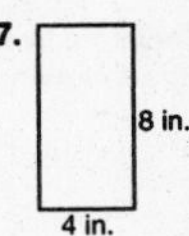

24 in.

8. l = 4 in.
w = 3 in.
P = 14 in.

9. l = 1.3 m
w = 0.7 m
P = 4 m

10. l = 171 mi
w = 48 mi
P = 438 mi

Mixed Review

Multiply.

11. (9-5) $\frac{2}{3}$ and $\frac{3}{3}$ $\frac{2}{3}$

12. (9-5) $\frac{6}{6}$ and $\frac{5}{6}$ $\frac{5}{6}$

13. (9-3) Estimate the product of $3\frac{2}{9}$ and 33.

Possible answer: 99; round $3\frac{2}{9}$ to 3.

14. (7-8) Theresa walks 7 blocks each day to school. Ryan walks 6 blocks. If Theresa has walked 56 blocks since the beginning of school, how many blocks has Ryan walked?

48

130

Name ______________________

Daily Cumulative Review

Use the formula $A = l \times w$ to find the area of each rectangle. Fill in the missing numbers. *(Lesson 10-8)*

1.

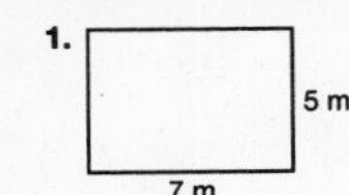

$A = \underline{7} \times \underline{5}$

$A = \underline{35}\ m^2$

2.

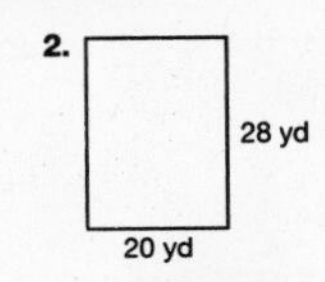

$A = \underline{20} \times \underline{28}$

$A = \underline{560}\ yd^2$

Find each product. *(Lesson 10-7)*

3. 2 × 5 ft 7 in. = 11 ft 2 in.
4. 3 × 6 ft 9 in. = 20 ft 3 in.
5. 4 × 8 yd 1 ft = 33 yd 1 ft
6. 5 × 3 yd 2 ft = 18 yd 1 ft

Mixed Review

7. (7-9) Make a drawing that shows $\frac{5}{3}$.

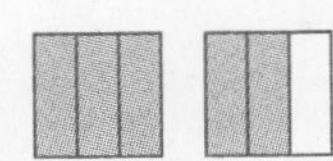

Possible answer.

Complete.

8. (7-10) $9\frac{5}{7} = \frac{\boxed{68}}{7}$

9. (9-7) $3 \times \frac{5}{6} = 2\frac{1}{2}$

10. (10-3) 5 m 2 cm = 502 cm

11. (5-8) If n = 7, what is 8 × n? 56

12. (4-9) Find the mean, median, and mode for the set of data.
$4.10, $5.60, $1.80, $1.80, $7.70

$4.20, $4.10, $1.80

131

Name ______________________

Daily Cumulative Review

Make a decision. You want to participate in music, art, and drama. The following is a list of things you might do. *(Lesson 10-9)*

Activity	Cost	Time
Piano Lessons	$12.50 a week for lessons	Lesson: Monday 4:00–4:30, Practice: $\frac{3}{4}$ hour a day except on Monday.
Art Lessons	$17 a week for lessons and supplies	Lesson: Tuesdays 4:00–6:00
Musical Play	$3 bus fare for each practice	Play practice: 6:00–7:30 Monday through Thursday for 4 weeks.

1. How much would it cost for 4 weeks for each activity?
   Piano $50; Art $68; Musical Play $48
2. How much time does each activity require in a 4-week period?
   Piano 20 hours; Art 8 hours; Musical Play 24 hours
3. Which activity would you choose? Why?
   Answers will vary. Look for answers that show an understanding of time and cost as well as interest.

Find the area of each rectangle. *(Lesson 10-8)*

4. $l = \frac{1}{2}$ ft
$w = 1\frac{1}{2}$ ft
$A = \frac{3}{4}\ ft^2$

5. l = 4.6 m
w = 2.5 m
$A = 11.5\ m^2$

6. l = 9 in.
w = 8 in.
$A = 72\ in^2$

Mixed Review

Use >, <, or = to complete.

7. (2-11) 0.3 ⊜ 0.30

8. (7-11) $\frac{8}{3}$ ⊘ $\frac{9}{4}$ (>)

9. (10-3) 8 m 5 cm ⊘ 850 cm (<)

132

Name ______________________

Daily Review **10-11**

Daily Cumulative Review

Find each area. *(Lesson 10-10)*

1. 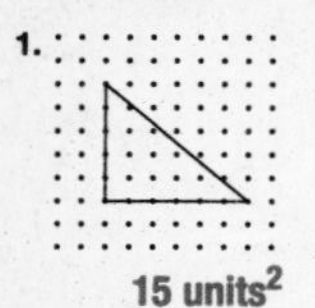

15 units^2

2. 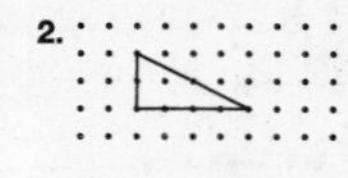

4 units^2

Make a decision. You have $75 to spend on new summer clothes. You find the following items that you like on sale. *(Lesson 10-9)*

Item	Cost	Item
Shirt A	$15	will only go with solid color shorts
Shirt B	$18	will go with any pair of shorts
Shirt C	$22	will go with any pair of shorts
Shorts A	$12	will go with only solid color shirts
Shorts B	$15	will go with any shirt
Sandals	$23	will go with casual or dress clothes
Running Shoes	$36	will go with casual clothes

3. Which items would you buy? Explain your decision.

Answers will vary. Check students' answers to make sure they haven't spent more than $75.

Mixed Review

Find each sum or difference.

4. $\frac{1}{2} + \frac{2}{5}$ (8-2) $\frac{9}{10}$

5. $7.9 - 1.3$ (2-16) 6.6

6. $6 + 1\frac{3}{4} + 2\frac{1}{7}$ (8-11) $9\frac{25}{28}$

133

Name ______________________

Daily Review **10-12**

Daily Cumulative Review

Use the formula $A = \frac{1}{2} \times (b \times h)$ to find the area of each triangle. Fill in the missing numbers. *(Lesson 10-11)*

1. 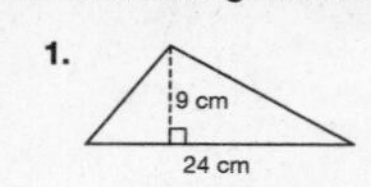

$A = \frac{1}{2} \times ($ 24 $\times$ 9 $)$

$A = \frac{1}{2} \times ($ 216 $)$

$A =$ 108 cm^2

2. 2 ft, 5 ft

$A = \frac{1}{2} \times ($ 5 $\times$ 2 $)$

$A = \frac{1}{2} \times ($ 10 $)$

$A =$ 5 ft^2

Find each area. *(Lesson 10-10)*

3. 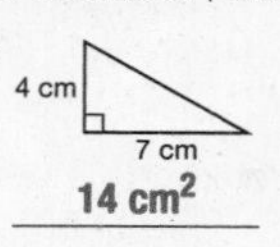

14 cm^2

4. 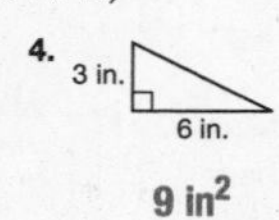

9 in^2

5. 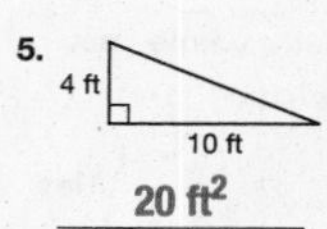

20 ft^2

Mixed Review

Estimate to solve. Tell whether you overestimated or underestimated. Explain your reasoning.

6. (9-6) Michi is making ham sandwiches for a party. If each of the 56 guests eats one sandwich that has 1 slice of ham and there are about 12 slices to a pound of ham, how many pounds of sliced ham should she buy?

Possible answer: 5 pounds; overestimate so that there is enough food for everyone.

Estimate. Then find each product.

7. $4\frac{7}{8} \times 3\frac{1}{5}$ (9-8) 15; $15\frac{3}{5}$

8. $3\frac{1}{7} \times 28$ (9-3) 90; 88

9. $6.90 × 19 (3-10) $140; $131.10

134

Name ______________________

Daily Review **10-13**

Daily Cumulative Review

Find each area. *(Lesson 10-12)*

1. 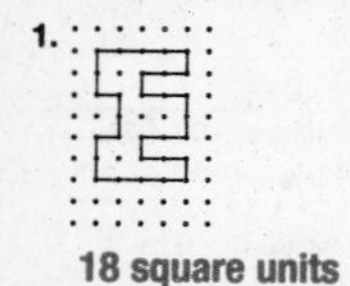

18 square units

2. 22 square units

3. 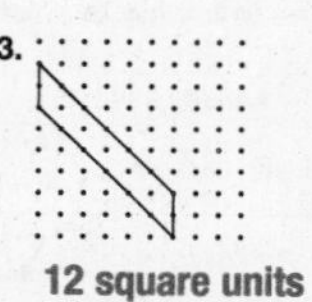

12 square units

Find each area. *(Lesson 10-11)*

4. 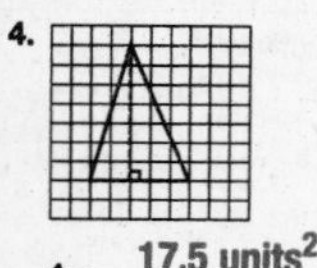

$A=$ 17.5 units^2

5. 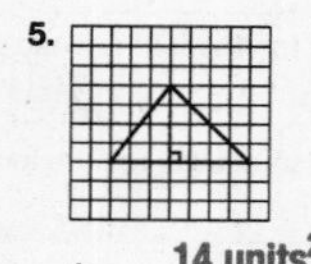

$A=$ 14 units^2

6. 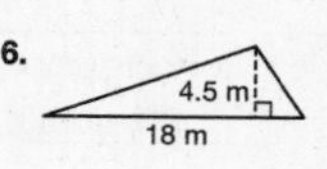

$A=$ 40.5 m^2

Mixed Review

7. (7-6) Is $\frac{1}{6}$ greater than or less than $\frac{1}{12}$? Explain.

Greater than; $\frac{1}{6} = \frac{2}{12}$

8. (7-10) Regan and her 3 friends ordered large pizzas cut into 12 pieces. Regan can eat 4 pieces. Her friends usually eat 6 pieces each. Are 2 large pizzas enough? Explain.

Yes; they eat $1\frac{10}{12}$ pizza. Two slices will be left over.

9. (9-9) Devon plans to go to bed at 9:00 P.M. He practices the piano for 45 minutes every day. He plans to work on his geometry project for 2 hours. Vacuuming the living room takes 15 minutes and dinner takes 30 minutes. He wants to watch $1\frac{1}{2}$ hours of TV. A shower takes 15 minutes. What time should he start doing all these things?

3:45

135

Name ______________________

Daily Review **10-14**

Daily Cumulative Review

Use the formula $A = b \times h$ to find the area of each parallelogram. Fill in the missing numbers. *(Lesson 10-13)*

1. 4 in., 9 in.

$A =$ 9 $\times$ 4

$A =$ 36 in^2

2. 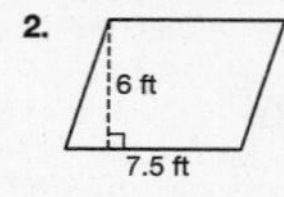

$A =$ 7.5 $\times$ 6

$A =$ 45 ft^2

On dot paper below, draw a polygon with each area. *(Lesson 10-12)*

3. 8 square units

4. 5 square units

5. $6\frac{1}{2}$ square units

Possible answers are given. Check students' drawings.

Mixed Review

6. (10-2) Kelsey's pencil is 16.5 cm long. Andrew's pencil is 135 mm long. Who has the longer pencil?

Kelsey

7. (7-12) Decide which does *not* belong to the set. C

A. 60% **B.** $\frac{6}{10}$ **C.** 0.06 **D.** 60 out of 100

Find the simplest form for each fraction.

8. $\frac{6}{40}$ (7-5) $\frac{3}{20}$

9. $\frac{9}{24}$ (7-5) $\frac{3}{8}$

10. $\frac{16}{36}$ (7-5) $\frac{4}{9}$

11. (7-2) Dawn said she would share half a bag of candy with Ian. Ian got $\frac{13}{26}$ of the bag. Did Ian get half? Explain.

Yes; $\frac{13}{26} = \frac{1}{2}$

136

Name ______________________

Daily Cumulative Review

Find the number of counters in each envelope. Fill in the missing numbers. *(Lesson 10-14)*

1. 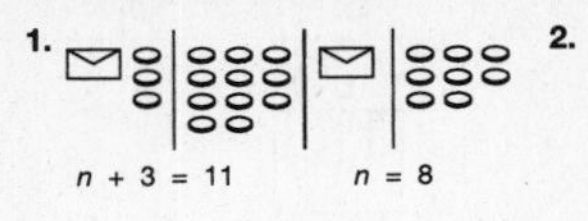

$n + 3 = 11$ $n = 8$

a. $n + 3 -$ __3__ $= 11 -$ __3__

b. $n =$ __8__

c. check __8__ $+ 3 = 11$

2. $4 \times n =$ 20 $n = 5$

a. $(4 \times n) \div$ __4__ $= 20 \div$ __4__

b. $n =$ __5__

c. check $4 \times$ __5__ $= 20$

Find each area. *(Lesson 10-13)*

3. 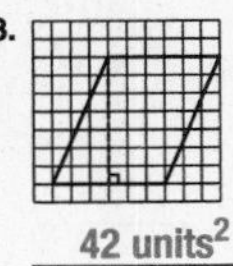

__42 units^2__

4. 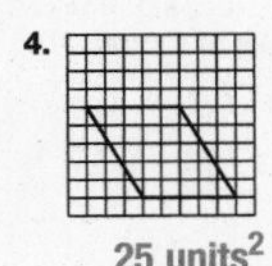

__25 units^2__

5. 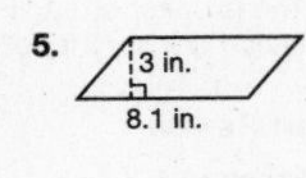

__24.3 in^2__

Mixed Review

6. Write whether you would flip, turn, or slide the figures to show they are congruent. __Slide__
(6-8)

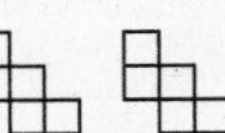

Complete.
Write acute, straight, obtuse, or right.

7. An angle with measure 180° is __Straight__.
(6-2)

8. An angle with measure 91° is __Obtuse__.
(6-2)

9. An angle with measure 90° is __Right__.
(6-2)

Name ______________________

Daily Review
10-16

Daily Cumulative Review

Look for a pattern to solve the problem. *(Lesson 10-15)*

1. During school, Jasmine wakes up at 6:30 A.M. She has been sleeping until 10:00 A.M. all summer. School starts in about a month. Jasmine plans to get up 15 minutes earlier every day until she is back on schedule for school. How many days before school starts should she begin her plan?

__At least 13 days before school starts.__

2. For an awards banquet, 2 tables will be placed at the foot of the room for the speakers. Other tables will be placed end to end as shown. How many more tables need to be added to seat a total of 52 people?

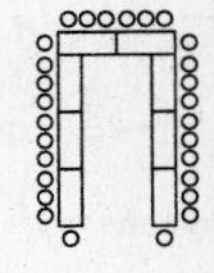

__8__

Use counters to find the number of counters in each envelope. *(Lesson 10-14)*

3. $5 + n = 9$

$n =$ __4__

4. 

$2 \times n = 16$

$n =$ __8__

Mixed Review

Estimate each product or quotient using compatible numbers.

5. $638 \div 81$ (5-4) __8__

6. $\frac{5}{6} \times 25$ (9-3) __20__

7. $4\frac{7}{9} \times 3\frac{1}{6}$ (9-8) __15__

Name ______________________

Daily Review
11-1

Daily Cumulative Review

Use the formula $C = \pi \times d$ to find the circumference of each circle. Fill in the missing numbers. *(Lesson 10-16)*

1. 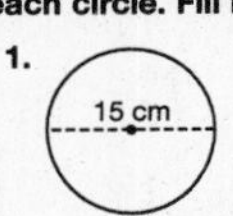

$C = 3.14 \times$ __15__

$C =$ __47.1__ cm

2. 9 in.

$C = 3.14 \times$ __2__ $\times$ __9__

$C =$ __56.52__ in.

3. 3 ft

$C = 3.14 \times$ __3__

$C =$ __9.42__ ft

Look for a pattern or use any strategy to solve each problem. *(Lesson 10-15)*

4. Stacey's mom is packing for a 6-day business trip. She packs 3 blouses (white, pink, and gray) and 2 skirts (black and white). Each blouse goes with each skirt. Will she have enough clothes to have a different outfit each day? Explain.

__Yes. Each blouse will go with 2 skirts. $3 \times 2 = 6$. She has exactly 6 different outfits.__

5. The weatherman noted that the high temperature on Monday was 1 degree cooler than on Sunday, Tuesday was 2 degrees cooler than Monday, and Wednesday was 3 degrees cooler than Tuesday. The pattern continued through Saturday. If the high temperature on Sunday was 78°F, what was the high temperature on the following Saturday? __57°F__

Mixed Review

Complete.

6. 0.08 m = __80__ mm
(10-3)

7. 6 ft 3 in. = __75__ in.
(8-15)

8. $\frac{1}{4}$ of $\frac{1}{2} =$ __$\frac{1}{8}$__
(9-4)

9. $\frac{5}{7} = \frac{15}{21} = \frac{30}{42}$
(7-3)

Name ______________________

Daily Review
11-2

Daily Cumulative Review

Write the name of the solid suggested in each drawing. *(Lesson 11-1)*

1. __Triangular prism__

2. 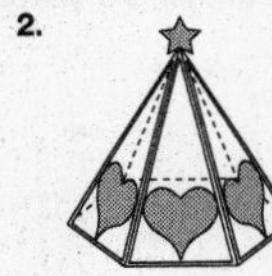

__Hexagonal pyramid__

Find each circumference. Use 3.14 for π. *(Lesson 10-16)*

3. 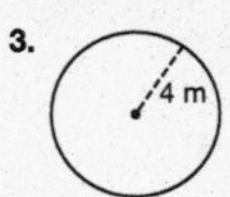

$C =$ __25.12 m__

4. 10 ft

$C =$ __31.4 ft__

Mixed Review

Find each perimeter.

5. a square with sides of 1.5 m __6 m__
(10-5)

6. a regular pentagon with sides of 3 ft __15 ft__
(10-5)

7. Choose the most appropriate unit of measure to estimate the height of a building. __C__
(10-1)

A. cm B. dm C. m D. km

Find each product.

8. $5\frac{7}{9} \times 1\frac{1}{4}$ (9-8) __$7\frac{2}{9}$__

9. 6.25×8.4 (3-13) __52.5__

10. 50×40 (3-1) __2,000__

Name ______________________

Daily Review 11-3

Daily Cumulative Review

Complete the table. *(Lesson 11-2)*

	Edges of Base	Number of Vertices	Total Number of Edges	Name of Solid
1. 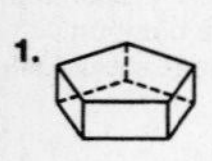	5	10	15	Pentagonal prism
2. 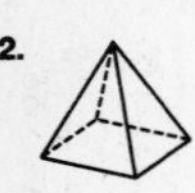	4	5	8	Rectangular pyramid

Write the name of the solid suggested in each drawing. *(Lesson 11-1)*

3. 

Triangular prism

4. 

Rectangular prism

Mixed Review

5. Which length is the shortest? C
(10-4)

A. 7,103 mm **B.** 7.103 m **C.** 71.03 cm

Use logical reasoning to solve the problem.

6. Beth, Mick, Terri, and Cathy are ages 10, 12, 14, and 16. Beth is neither the oldest nor youngest. Terri is 4 years older than Cathy. Mick is 4 years older than Beth. What are their ages?
(9-9)

	10	12	14	16
Beth	no	yes	no	no
Mick	no	no	no	yes
Terri	no	no	yes	no
Cathy	yes	no	no	no

Cathy 10, Beth 12,
Terri 14, Mick 16

Name ______________________

Daily Review 11-4

Daily Cumulative Review

Name the figure that would be formed by each net. *(Lesson 11-3)*

1. Pentagonal pyramid

2. Hexagonal prism

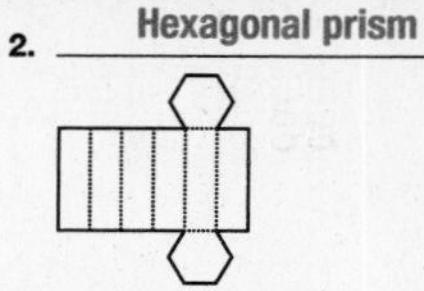

Decide if each statement is true or false. *(Lesson 11-2)*

3. A triangular prism has 9 edges. True
4. A pentagonal prism has 5 faces. False
5. A rectangular prism has 8 vertices. True
6. The number of edges of one base of a prism is half the number of vertices of the prism. True

Mixed Review

Find each area.

7. (10-13)

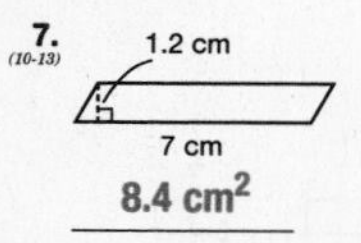

8.4 cm^2

8. (10-10) 20 ft, 15 ft

150 ft^2

9. (10-8)

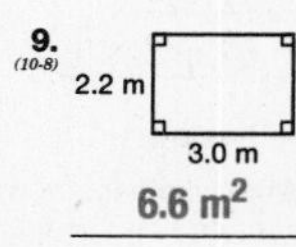

6.6 m^2

Find each quotient.

10. $4 \div \frac{1}{12}$ 48
(9-10)

11. $16\overline{)\$24.00}$ \$1.50
(5-10)

12. 60,000 ÷ 30 2,000
(5-1)

13. Write the missing factors. 1, [2], [4], [5], [10], 20
(4-14)

Name ______________________

Daily Cumulative Review

Use a calculator to find the surface area of each figure. *(Lesson 11-4)*

1. 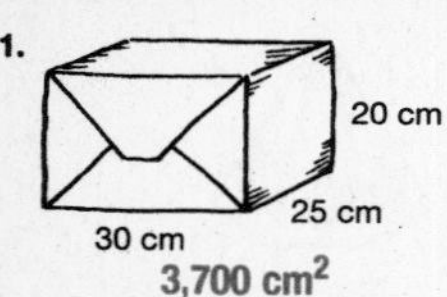

$3{,}700 \text{ cm}^2$

2. 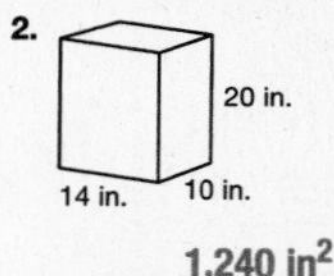

$1{,}240 \text{ in}^2$

Draw a net for the solid shown. *(Lesson 11-3)*

3. triangular prism

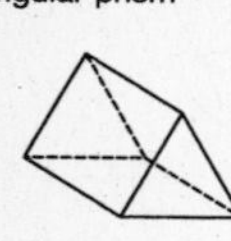

Possible Answer:

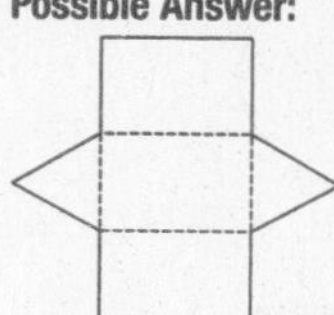

Mixed Review

Find each perimeter.

4. rectangle: $l = 2$ in. $w = 6$ in. 16 in.
(10-6)

5. equilateral triangle: side = 1.7 m 5.1 m
(10-5)

6. square: side = 3 ft 2 in. 12 ft 8 in.
(10-7)

Decide whether you need an exact answer or an estimate. Solve.

7. Your body weight is a measure of the force of gravity. Jupiter's gravitational pull is about 2.5 times that of Earth. Amy's dad weighs about 160 pounds on Earth. How much would he weigh on Jupiter?
(8-16)

Estimate; about 400 pounds

Name ______________________

Daily Review 11-6

Daily Cumulative Review

Plan and solve. *(Lesson 11-5)*

You want to build mailboxes as gifts.

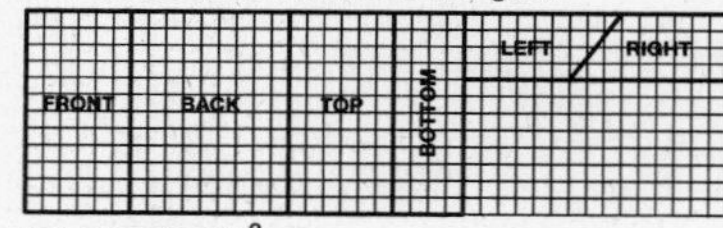

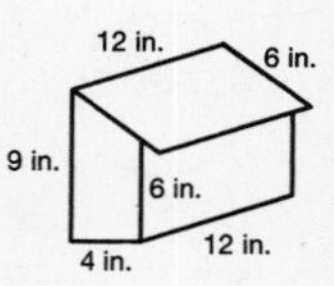

Scale: 1 square = 1 in^2

You can buy a 1-ft by 12-ft board for \$12.

1. Into what geometric figures will the board be cut? Rectangles and trapezoids

What length of board will you need for:

2. the front? 6 in.
3. the back? 9 in.
4. the top? 6 in.
5. the bottom? 4 in.
6. the left and right sides cut as shown? 15 in.
7. How many mailboxes could be made from one 12-foot board? (Hint: There is room for another pair of sides in the plan above.) 4

Use a calculator to find the surface area. Solve. *(Lesson 11-4)*

8. Kyoko's bedroom is 11 ft wide, 13 ft long, and 8 ft high. A gallon of paint covers about 400 ft². How many gallons of paint does Kyoko need for 2 coats of paint on the walls and ceiling? 3 gallons

Mixed Review

Complete.

9. 8 m = 800 cm
(10-2)

10. $\frac{4}{5} \times 3 = \frac{[12]}{5} = 2\frac{2}{5}$
(9-7)

11. 43 in. = 3 ft 7 in.
(8-15)

12. 527 ÷ 100 = 5.27
(5-12)

Name ______________________

Daily Cumulative Review

Complete. Check the reasonableness of your answer. *(Lesson 11-6)*

1. 3 lb = 48 oz
2. 4 T = 8,000 lb
3. 64 oz = 4 lb
4. 56 oz = 3 lb 8 oz
5. 6 T 500 lb = 12,500 lb
6. 9,000 lb = 4.5 T

Plan and solve. *(Lesson 11-5)*

You plan to make a toy bin from 6-in. wide boards. The bin has no top.

What is the total length of board needed to make:

7. the front? 10 ft
8. the back? 10 ft
9. the bottom? 7.5 ft
10. the left side? 6 ft
11. the right side? 6 ft
12. the entire bin? 39.5 ft
13. How many 12-ft boards should you buy? 4

Mixed Review

Find each area.

14. (10-12) **15.** (10-8)

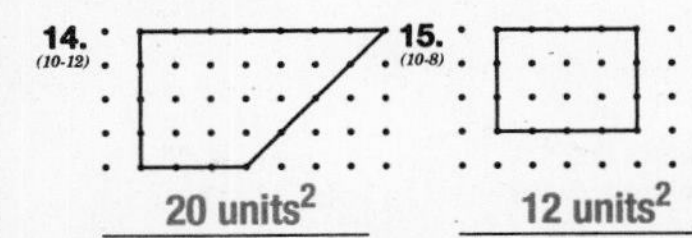

16. (10-11)

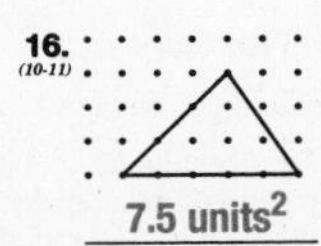

14. 20 units^2 15. 12 units^2 16. 7.5 units^2

Find each product or quotient. Simplify.

17. (9-5) $\frac{5}{9} \times \frac{9}{9} =$ $\frac{5}{9}$
18. (9-7) $\frac{2}{9} \times 45 =$ 10
19. (9-2) $\frac{4}{5}$ of 20 = 16
20. (9-10) $4 \div \frac{1}{5} =$ 20
21. (9-8) $2\frac{3}{4} \times \frac{2}{3} =$ $1\frac{5}{6}$
22. (9-10) $1 \div \frac{1}{8} =$ 8

Name ______________________

Daily Review
11-8

Daily Cumulative Review

Use mental math to change to kilograms or grams. *(Lesson 11-7)*

1. 4.7 kg = 4,700 g
2. 4,900 g = 4.9 kg
3. 0.5 kg = 500 g
4. 300 g = 0.3 kg
5. 30 g = 0.03 kg
6. 6,000 g = 6 kg

Complete. Check the reasonableness of your answer. *(Lesson 11-6)*

7. 90 oz = 5 lb 10 oz
8. 2,000,000 lb = 1,000 T
9. 17 oz = 1 lb 1 oz
10. 30 lb = 480 oz
11. 0.01 T = 20 lb
12. 5 lb = 80 oz

Mixed Review

Find the number of counters in each envelope.

13. (10-14)

$2 \times n = 14$

$n =$ 7

14. (10-14)

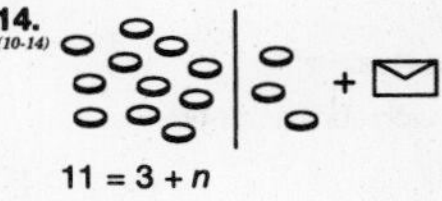

$11 = 3 + n$

$n =$ 8

Estimate to solve. Tell whether you overestimated or underestimated. Explain your reasoning.

15. (9-6) Zelda has $15 to buy school supplies. Notebooks cost $4.98 each, glue costs $1.19, pencils cost 10¢ each, and a package of 6 pens costs $1.29. Does she have enough to buy 2 notebooks, 1 bottle of glue, 10 pencils, and a package of pens?

Yes; overestimate to be sure she has enough money.
5 + 5 + 2 + 1 + 2 = 15

Name ______________________

Daily Cumulative Review

Write each temperature in Celsius and Fahrenheit. *(Lesson 11-8)*

1.

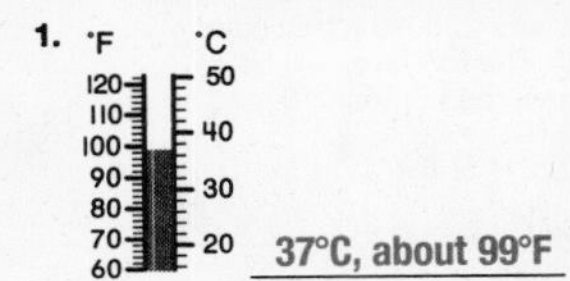

37°C, about 99°F

2.

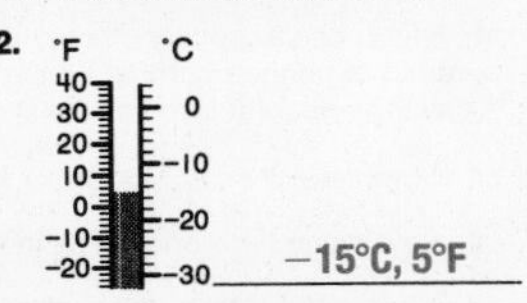

−15°C, 5°F

Use mental math to change to kilograms or grams. *(Lesson 11-7)*

3. How many kilograms?

425 g

0.425

4. How many grams?

1.81 kg

1,810

Mixed Review

Estimate each product, quotient, sum, or difference.
Possible answers are shown.

5. (9-3) $6\frac{6}{7} \times 21$ 147
6. (8-9) $4\frac{7}{8} + 9\frac{1}{10}$ 14
7. (6-2) $551 \div 90$ 6
8. (3-14) 3.9×5.12 20
9. (8-9) $16\frac{1}{8} - 8\frac{11}{12}$ 7
10. (6-10) $2.10 ÷ 40 $0.05

Write if the problem has too much or too little information. Solve if possible, or tell what is needed to solve.

11. (8-7) Chelsea finished $\frac{2}{3}$ of her math assignment in one hour. She did 4 more problems in the next 15 minutes. How many more problems does she still need to complete?

Too little information; need to know how many problems there were in all.

Name ______________________

Daily Review
11-10

Daily Cumulative Review

Find each volume. *(Lesson 11-9)*

1.

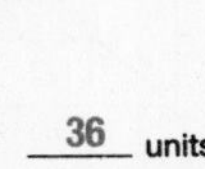

36 units^3

2.

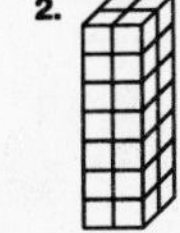

28 units^3

Write each temperature in Celsius and Fahrenheit. *(Lesson 11-8)*

3.

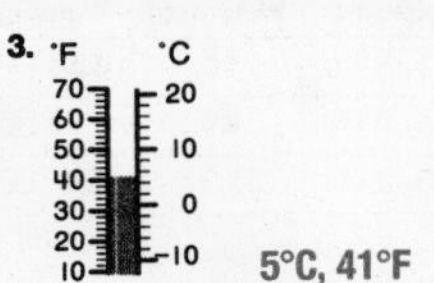

5°C, 41°F

4.

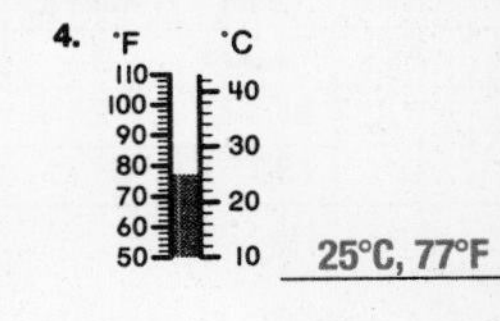

25°C, 77°F

Mixed Review

Find the diameter of each circle to the nearest hundredth. Use 3.14 for π.

5. (10-16) $C = 314$ cm, $d =$ 100 cm
6. (10-16) $C = 75$ in., $d =$ 23.89 in.
7. (10-16) $C = 4.7$ m, $d =$ 1.50 m

8. (8-14) Find the length to the nearest $\frac{1}{4}$-inch.

$1\frac{3}{4}$ inch

Find each sum or difference.

9. (8-8) $3\frac{1}{6} + 2\frac{5}{12}$ $5\frac{7}{12}$
10. (8-6) $\frac{5}{6} - \frac{2}{3}$ $\frac{1}{6}$
11. (8-1) $\frac{1}{3} + \frac{2}{3} + \frac{1}{3}$ $1\frac{1}{3}$

Name ______________________

Daily Review 11-11

Daily Cumulative Review

Complete. *(Lesson 11-10)*

1. 34 fl oz = $4\frac{1}{4}$ c
2. $\frac{1}{4}$ c = 4 tbsp
3. 1 gal = 16 c
4. $3\frac{1}{2}$ qt = 7 pt

Find each volume. *(Lesson 11-9)*

5. 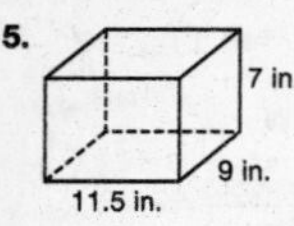

724.5 in^3

6. 10 cm, 8 cm, 2 cm

160 cm^3

7. l = 6 cm, w = 5 cm, h = 4 cm
V = 120 cm^3
8. l = 1.5 m, w = 2 m, h = 7m
V = 21 m^3

Mixed Review

Find each sum or difference.

9. (8-2) $\frac{3}{5} + \frac{7}{10}$ $\frac{13}{10} = 1\frac{3}{10}$
10. (8-5) $\frac{10}{11} - \frac{13}{22}$ $\frac{7}{22}$
11. (8-8) $9 - 3\frac{3}{7}$ $5\frac{4}{7}$
12. (7-13) Write 1% as a fraction and a decimal. $\frac{1}{100}$, 0.01
13. (7-4) Find the greatest common factor of 48 and 32. 16
14. (6-4) Jordan is drawing a sketch of a baseball diamond. There is a right angle at each base and the distances between the bases are the same.

What shape should he use? square

Name ______________________

Daily Review 11-12

Daily Cumulative Review

Complete. *(Lesson 11-11)*

1. 500 mL = 0.5 L
2. 6.25 L = 6,250 mL
3. 46 mL = 0.046 L
4. 0.01 L = 10 mL
5. 0.2 L = 200 mL
6. 20,050 mL = 20.05 L

Use the drawing to answer 7–12. *(Lesson 11-10)*

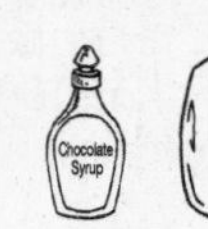

7. $\frac{1}{2}$ c of shoe polish
8. $\frac{3}{4}$ qt chocolate syrup
9. 4 qt of milk
10. 20 tbsp soy sauce
11. $1\frac{1}{2}$ c balsamic vinegar
12. 1 c baby formula

Mixed Review

Use the diagram at the right.

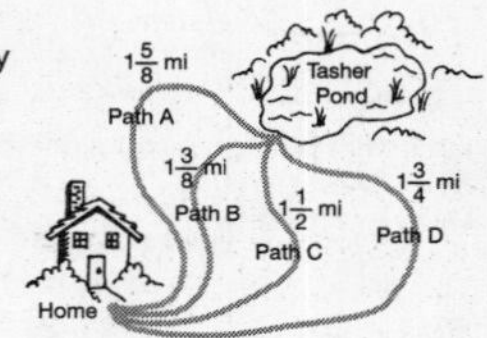

13. (6-5) For exercise, Ruthie walks to Tasher Pond and back every day. How many different routes can she take to the pond and back home again? 16
14. (7-11) List the paths from shortest to longest. B, C, A, D

Name ______________________

Daily Review 11-13

Daily Cumulative Review

Complete the table. *(Lesson 11-12)*

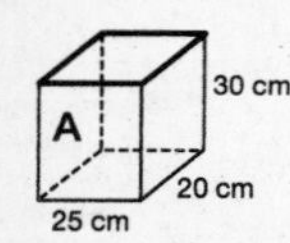

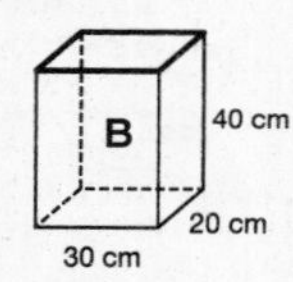

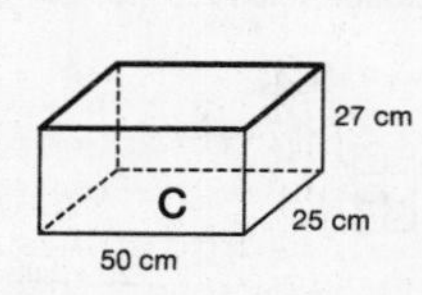

	Aquarium	Volume (cm^3)	Amount of Water (L)	Amount of Water (mL)	Mass of Water (kg)	Mass of Water (g)
1.	A	15,000	15	15,000	15	15,000
2.	B	24,000	24	24,000	24	24,000
3.	C	33,750	33.75	33,750	33.75	33,750

Complete. *(Lesson 11-11)*

4. 0.21 L = 210 mL
5. 250 mL = 0.25 L
6. 9.5 L = 9,500 mL
7. 40 mL = 0.04 L
8. 2,800 mL = 2.8 L
9. 0.005 L = 5 mL

Mixed Review

10. (6-6) Which polygon is congruent to the first one in the row? C

A. 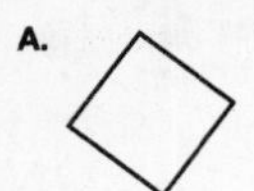
B. 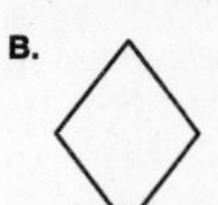
C. 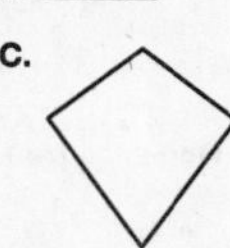

11. (6-3) What is the measure of a straight angle? 180°

Name ______________________

Daily Review 12-1

Daily Cumulative Review

Solve a simpler problem to solve the problem below. *(Lesson 11-13)*

Mr. Nemo has a grocery store. He wants to build a triangular pyramid of canned corn as a display. The top layer will be 1 can. The second layer will be 3 cans, then 6, then 10, and so on.

1. Complete. 1 + 2 = 3; 3 + 3 = 6; 6 + 4 = 10
2. How many cans should be in the 5th layer? 15
3. What is the total number of cans in a triangular pyramid with 6 layers? Explain.
56; 1 + 3 + 6 + 10 + 15 + 21 = 56

Write the number for each. *(Lesson 11-12)*

4. 3,000 mL of water would fill a 3,000 cm^3 container.
5. 1.5 kg of water would fill a 1,500 mL container.
6. 4.2 L of water would have a mass of 4.2 kg.
7. A 580 cm^3 container can hold 0.58 L.

Mixed Review

Decide if each statement is true or false. If false, write what would make the statement true.

8. (11-2) A triangular pyramid has 4 edges. False; 6 edges
9. (11-6) 6,000 lb = 3 T True
10. (11-4) The surface area of a cube with edges 2 cm is 18 cm^2.
False; 24 cm^2
11. (10-15) If the first three bells of middle school ring at 8:10, 9:00, and 9:50, the fourth bell should ring at 10:30.
False; 10:40

Name ______________________

Daily Cumulative Review

Write each ratio in three ways. Simplify. *(Lesson 12-1)*

1. butterflies to caterpillars 1 to 5 1:5 $\frac{1}{5}$

2. adult mice to baby mice 1 to 2 1:2 $\frac{1}{2}$

Use any strategy to solve. *(Lesson 11-13)*

3. Miss Eliza's quilt is made of 16 large squares. Each square is made of 4 smaller squares, and each smaller square is made of 2 colored triangles and 2 white triangles. How many white triangles are in her quilt? 128

Mixed Review

Decide if each statement is *always*, *sometimes*, or *never* true.

4. (11-1) A pyramid has two bases. Never
5. (11-3) The net for a rectangular prism consists of 6 squares Sometimes
6. (11-9) The volume of a rectangular prism with length 10 cm and width 10 cm is 100 cm^3. Sometimes
7. (6-2) The measure of an obtuse angle is between 90° and 180°. Always

Name ______________________

Daily Review 12-3

Daily Cumulative Review

Complete each ratio table. *(Lesson 12-2)*

1.

4	8	16	12	20
5	10	20	15	25

2.

5	15	20	30	50
6	18	24	36	60

3.

2	6	8	20	18
9	27	36	90	81

4.

3	9	15	12	21
7	21	35	28	49

Write each ratio in three ways. Simplify. *(Lesson 12-1)*

5. adult skunks to baby skunks

1 to 4 1:4 $\frac{1}{4}$

6. adult turtles to baby turtles

1 to 3 1:3 $\frac{1}{3}$

Mixed Review

Complete.

7. (11-6) 6 lb = 96 oz
8. (11-11) 160 mL = 0.16 L

Find each change in temperature.

9. (11-8) 72°F to 88°F 16°F
10. (11-8) 20°F to −5°F 25°F
11. (11-8) −5°C to 5°C 10°C
12. (11-8) 100°C to 37°C 63°C
13. (8-13) Daria has 10 notebooks. One fifth of them are red and $\frac{1}{2}$ of them are blue. The rest are green. How many green notebooks does she have? 3

Name ______________________

Daily Review 12-4

Daily Cumulative Review

Complete. *(Lesson 12-3)*

1. This graph shows two ordered pairs of equal ratios. Name each ratio. $\frac{3}{2}, \frac{6}{4}$

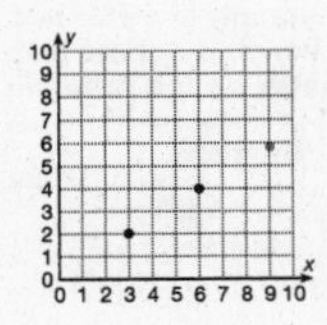

2. Plot another ratio on the graph that is equal to the others. Name the ratio. Possible answer: $\frac{9}{6}$

Complete each ratio table. *(Lesson 12-2)*

3. Jolon found his favorite ice cream on sale, 2 cartons for $5. How much would it cost to buy 4, 6, 8, or 10 cartons?

Boxes of Ice Cream	2	4	6	8	10
Price	$5	$10	$15	$20	$25

4. Each of Miss Horne's art students will need 4 brushes. How many brushes will be needed for 6, 12, 18, 20, or 22 students?

Number of Students	6	12	18	20	22
Number of Brushes	24	48	72	80	88

Mixed Review

Complete.

5. (8-15) 29 ft = 9 yd 2 ft
6. (10-4) 0.9 m = 900 mm
7. (4-2) 36,000 ÷ 400 = 90
8. (10-3) 7 m 30 cm = 7.3 m
9. (4-14) Identify 5 as prime or composite. Prime
10. (5-11) Which is cheaper: 4 for $7 or $1.70 each? $1.70 each
11. (6-8) How many lines of symmetry does a square have? 4

Name ______________________

Daily Review 12-5

Daily Cumulative Review

Solve each problem. *(Lesson 12-4)*

1. Berlin, Germany, is 4 cm from Stockholm, Sweden on a map with the scale 1 cm to 200 km. About how far apart are the cities? 800 km
2. Teona is making a scale drawing of her room. The room is 12 feet long and 10 feet wide. If her paper is $8\frac{1}{2}$ inches by 11 inches, which would be an appropriate scale to use? B

A. 1 in. to 1 ft **B.** 1 in. to 2 ft **C.** 2 in. to 1 ft

Use grid paper. Plot the ordered pairs from each ratio table on the graph and draw a straight line through each set of points. *(Lesson 12-3)*

3.

4	8	12	16	20
2	4	6	8	10

4.

3	9	12	15	18
1	3	4	5	6

5. If the lines are extended, what ordered pair represents the point where the lines cross? (0, 0)

Mixed Review

Complete.

6. (11-12) 5 kg of water would fill a 5,000 mL container.
7. (11-7) 20.4 g = 0.0204 kg
8. (10-4) 2.5 mm = 0.25 cm
9. (2-18) 4.1 − 3.2 = 0.9
10. (2-18) 6.23 − 2.15 = 4.08
11. (1-4) Find the mode, median, and range for 10,15, 25, 30, 30. 30, 25, 20

Name ______________________

Daily Cumulative Review

Complete the table. Look for patterns. *(Lesson 12-5)*

1.	Thirds			$\frac{1}{3}$		
2.	Ninths	$\frac{1}{9}$	$\frac{2}{9}$	$\frac{3}{9}$	$\frac{4}{9}$	$\frac{5}{9}$
3.	Percents	$11\frac{1}{9}\%$	$22\frac{2}{9}\%$	$33\frac{3}{9}\%$	$44\frac{4}{9}\%$	$55\frac{5}{9}\%$

Solve each problem. *(Lesson 12-4)*

4. A scale drawing of a house floor plan is 10 in. by 8 in. The real house is 75 ft by 60 ft. What does 1 in. represent in the drawing? $7\frac{1}{2}$ ft

5. A picture of a monument uses the scale 1 cm to 4 m. If the monument is actually 20 m tall, how tall is it in the picture? 5 cm

Mixed Review

6. (11-13) Chiara made a secret code where the 1st letter of the alphabet is exchanged with the 14th letter, the 2nd letter with the 15th, and so on.

What letter is exchanged with the letter G? T

7. (11-3) Name the solid formed by the net.

Hexagonal pyramid

8. (11-4) Find the surface area of the figure.

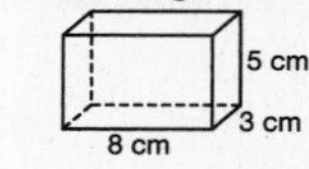

158 cm^2

9. (11-2) How many vertices does the figure in Exercise 8 have? 8

Name ______________________

Daily Review
12-7

Daily Cumulative Review

Estimate. *(Lesson 12-6)* Possible answers; estimates may vary.

1. 49% of 500 About 250

2. 24% of 200 About 50

3. 11% of 99 About 10

4. 33% of 1,200 About 400

5. 5% of 700 About 35

6. 65% of 60 About 40

Complete each pattern. *(Lesson 12-5)*

7. $\frac{1}{40} = 2\frac{1}{2}\%$

$\frac{2}{40} = 5\%$

$\frac{3}{40} = 7\frac{1}{2}\%$

$\frac{4}{40} = 10\%$

$\frac{5}{40} = 12\frac{1}{2}\%$

8. $\frac{1}{25} = 4\%$

$\frac{2}{25} = 8\%$

$\frac{3}{25} = 12\%$

$\frac{4}{25} = 16\%$

$\frac{5}{25} = 20\%$

Mixed Review

Tell which is greater. Explain.

9. (11-6) 5 lb 11 oz or 90 oz 5 lb 11 oz; 5 lb 11 oz = 91 oz

10. (11-2) the number of vertices in triangular pyramid or the number of vertices in triangular prism

Triangular prism; there are 4 vertices in a triangular pyramid and 6 in a triangular prism.

11. (10-6) the perimeter of rectangle *A* or the perimeter of rectangle *B*

Same: They both have perimeter 18 in.

Name ______________________

Daily Cumulative Review

Choose a method. Find the percent of each. *(Lesson 12-7)*

1. 12% of 30 = 3.6

2. 40% of 90 = 36

3. 62% of \$210 = \$130.20

4. 55% of \$40 = \$22

5. 8% of \$60 = \$4.80

6. 25% of \$75 = \$18.75

Estimate. *(Lesson 12-6)* Possible answers; estimates may vary.

7. 34% of 900 About 300

8. 76% of 240 About 180

9. 26% of 81 About 20

10. 49% of 66 About 33

Mixed Review

11. (10-16) Find the circumference. Use 3.14 for π.

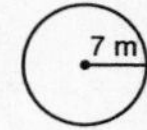

43.96 m

12. (10-14) Find the value of *n*. Use counters to help.

$n + 7 = 11$

$n = 4$

Find each product or quotient.

13. (9-8) $7\frac{2}{5} \times 3 = 22\frac{1}{5}$

14. (9-10) $11 \div \frac{1}{6} = 66$

15. (5-1) $8{,}000 \div 20 = 400$

16. (3-10) \$72.31 × 8 = \$578.48

17. (5-5) $17\overline{)105}$ 6 R3

18. (5-5) $41\overline{)12{,}560}$ 306 R14

Name ______________________

Daily Review
12-9

Daily Cumulative Review

Complete the table. Tell if the probabilities of the outcomes are equally likely or not. If the probabilities are not equal, tell which outcome is more likely. Then decide if the situation is fair or unfair. *(Lesson 12-8)*

	Situation	Probability of Outcome	Fairness
1.	Spin the spinner. Outcomes: A, B, C, or D	Not equally likely C is more likely.	Unfair
2.	Draw a marble. Outcomes: Red (R), Blue (B), or Yellow (Y)	Not equally likely Red is more likely.	Unfair
3.	Throw a number cube. Outcomes: 1, 2, 3, 4, 5, 6	Equally likely	Fair

Choose a method. Find the percent of each. *(Lesson 12-7)*

4. 48% of 7,000 = 3,360

5. 2% of \$5.00 = \$0.10

6. 15% of \$64.00 = \$9.60

7. 60% of \$82.00 = \$49.20

Mixed Review

8. (4-12) Find the length of the side of the square.

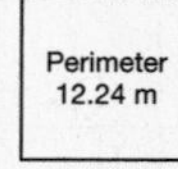

3.06 m

9. (4-15) The tag shows the price has been lowered twice. What was the original price?

\$16

10. (4-13) Find all the factors of 54. 1, 2, 3, 6, 9, 18, 27, 54

Name ______________________

Daily Review 12-10

Daily Cumulative Review

Predict from the sample. *(Lesson 12-9)*

A bag of candy-coated chocolates contains yellow, red, blue, green, brown, and orange chocolates.
How many of each color were in the samples?

Sample	Count	Color
Sample 1	4	Blue
	1	Orange
	3	Red
	2	Yellow
Sample 2	3	Blue
	1	Orange
	2	Red
	2	Yellow
	2	Brown
Sample 3	2	Blue
	2	Red
	3	Yellow
	2	Orange
	1	Green

1. blue 9 2. orange 4
3. red 7 4. yellow 7
5. brown 2 6. green 1
7. Predict the most common color candy. Blue
8. If sample 3 were the only sample, what color candy would you predict to be the most common? Yellow

Tell if the situation is fair or unfair. *(Lesson 12-8)*

9. Spin the spinner. Fair
10. Draw a number. Unfair
11. Draw card X or card Y. Fair

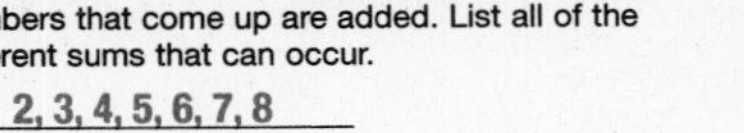

Mixed Review

Add or subtract.

12. $9 - 2\frac{1}{3} = 6\frac{2}{3}$ (8-12)
13. $3\frac{5}{6} + 1\frac{2}{3} = 5\frac{1}{2}$ (8-10)
14. 6 yd 2 ft + 7 yd 2 ft = 14 yd 1 ft (10-7)

Name ______________________

Daily Review 12-11

Daily Cumulative Review

Predict from the experiment. *(Lesson 12-10)*

If you spin the spinner 10 times, State how many times you would expect the outcome would be:

1. the letter E. 3
2. a vowel. 4
3. a consonant. 6

Predict from the samples. *(Lesson 12-9)*

You are playing a word game with a friend. You draw 6 letters at a time.

Sample	Vowels
1	3
2	3
3	4
4	1
5	1

4. How many letters were drawn in the 5 samples? 30
5. How many vowels were drawn in the 5 samples? 12
6. Predict how many vowels are in a bag of 75 tiles. 30

Mixed Review

Complete.

7. $11\frac{3}{4} = \frac{47}{4}$ (7-10)
8. $\frac{1}{3}$ of 36 = 12 (9-2)
9. $\frac{7}{20}$ = 35 % (12-5)
10. 413 g = 0.413 kg (11-7)
11. 0.07 = 7 % (7-13)
12. 5 mi = 26,400 ft (8-15)
13. $\frac{26}{6} = 4\frac{1}{3}$ (7-10)
14. 1.4 m = 140 cm (10-3)
15. $\frac{18}{27} = \frac{2}{3}$ (7-5)
16. Do you get the same sum when you use 12 rather than 6 as a common denominator for $\frac{2}{3}$ and $\frac{1}{2}$? Explain. (7-6)

Yes, $\frac{4}{6} + \frac{3}{6} = \frac{7}{6} = 1\frac{1}{6}$ and $\frac{8}{12} + \frac{6}{12} = \frac{14}{12} = 1\frac{2}{12} = 1\frac{1}{6}$

Name ______________________

Daily Review 12-12

Daily Cumulative Review

Use an organized list to solve. *(Lesson 12-11)*

1. Tony has math, science, history, and language homework to do. Make an organized list of the order in which he can do the assignment if he does:
   a. math first. MSHL, MSLH, MLSH, MLHS, MHSL, MHLS
   b. science first. SMHL, SMLH, SHML, SHLM, SLMH, SLHM
   c. history first. HMSL, HMLS, HSML, HSLM, HLMS, HLSM
   d. language first. LMSH, LMHS, LSMH, LSHM, LHMS, LHSM
   e. In how many different ways can he do his homework? 24
2. a. Angela, Brian, and Cash are going to have their picture taken together. Write a list of all the ways they can line up for the picture.
   ABC, ACB, BAC, BCA, CAB, CBA
   b. How many ways can they line up? 6

Use any strategy to solve. *(Lesson 12-10)*

3. A wooden top with 4 sides has the numbers 1, 2, 3, and 4 on the sides. The top is spun twice and the numbers that come up are added. List all of the different sums that can occur.

2, 3, 4, 5, 6, 7, 8

Mixed Review

Find the percent of each.

4. 3% of 500 15 (12-7)
5. 60% of 20 12 (12-7)
6. 15% of 20 3 (12-7)
7. Write the ratio of As to Bs in three ways. (12-1)
   A A B B B B A
   $\frac{4}{3}$ 4 to 3 4:3

Name ______________________

Daily Review 12-13

Daily Cumulative Review

Each spinner is spun once. The numbers from each spinner are added. Make tree diagrams to show possible outcomes. Give the probability of each outcome as a fraction. Simplify. *(Lesson 12-12)*

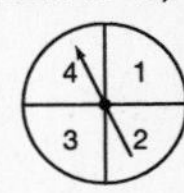

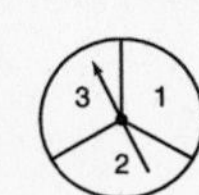

1. Sum of 1 $\frac{0}{12}$
2. Sum of 2 $\frac{1}{12}$
3. Sum of 3 $\frac{2}{12} = \frac{1}{6}$
4. Sum of 4 $\frac{3}{12} = \frac{1}{4}$
5. Sum of 5 $\frac{3}{12} = \frac{1}{4}$
6. Sum of 6 $\frac{2}{12} = \frac{1}{6}$
7. Sum of 7 $\frac{1}{12}$
8. Sum of 8 $\frac{0}{12}$

Use an organized list to solve. *(Lesson 12-11)*

9. Jarred has whole wheat and white bread, 3 kinds of meat (ham, turkey, roast beef), and 2 kinds of cheese (cheddar and Swiss). How many different sandwiches can he make with 1 bread, 1 meat, and 1 cheese? 12

Mixed Review

Complete.

10. $\frac{9}{50}$ = 18 % (12-5)
11. 900 mL = 0.9 L (11-11)
12. 13% of 40 = 5.2 (12-7)
13. 0.0001 kg = 0.1 g (11-7)
14. Circle the triangle congruent to the first one. (6-6)

15. Use a protractor to measure the angle. 60° (6-2)